KTM Enduro and Motocross
Service and Repair Manual

by Phil Mather

(4629-272)

Models covered

Europe Enduro models

250 EXC Racing	249 cc	2002 to 2006
400 EXC Racing	398 cc	2000 to 2002 and 2004 to 2007
450 EXC Racing	448 cc	2003 to 2007
520 EXC Racing	510 cc	2000 to 2002
525 EXC Racing	510 cc	2003 to 2007 (inc. MXC Desert)

US Enduro models

250 EXC RFS	249 cc	2004
400 EXC-G Racing	398 cc	2000 to 2002 and 2004 to 2007 (inc. MXC)
450 EXC-G Racing	448 cc	2003 to 2007 (inc. MXC/XC)
520 EXC-G Racing	510 cc	2000 to 2002 (inc. MXC)
525 EXC-G Racing	510 cc	2003 to 2007 (inc. MXC/XC)

Motocross models

400 SX Racing	398 cc	2000 to 2002
450 SX Racing	449 cc	2003 to 2006
520 SX Racing	510 cc	2000 to 2002
525 SX Racing	510 cc	2003 to 2006

Main features of the 450/540 SXS and Six Days models included

Supermoto models

450 SMR	449 cc	2004 to 2006
525 SMR	510 cc	2004 to 2005
560 SMR	566 cc	2006

© Haynes Publishing 2007

A book in the Haynes Service and Repair Manual Series

ABCDE
FGHIJ
KLMNO
PQRST

ISBN: 978 1 84425 629 7

British Library Cataloguing in Publication Data
A catalogue record for this book is available from the British Library.

Library of Congress Control Number 2007927678

Printed in the USA

Haynes Publishing
Sparkford, Yeovil, Somerset BA22 7JJ, England

Haynes North America, Inc
861 Lawrence Drive, Newbury Park, California 91320, USA

Haynes Publishing Nordiska AB
Box 1504, 751 45 Uppsala, Sweden

GW00771651

Contents

LIVING WITH YOUR KTM

Introduction

Pre-ride checks

MAINTENANCE

Routine maintenance and servicing

Contents

REPAIRS AND OVERHAUL

Engine, transmission and associated systems

Chassis and bodywork components

Electrical system

Wiring diagrams

REFERENCE

Index

Always ready to race

The history of the KTM Sportmotorcycle AG company goes back to 1953. The foundation for this company was the engineering shop of Hans Trunkenpolz which was establish in 1934. After WW2, and with experience from selling DKW motorcycles and repairing cars and motorcycles, Hans decided to build his own machines. Using a 98cc Sachs engine he created the KTM R100. The brand took its name from Kraftfahrzeuge Trunkenpolz Mattighofen, quite simply named after the founder's metalworking shop in the northern Austrian town of Mattighofen.

With limited production at first, the company expanded in 1955 when Ernst Kronreif came onboard. The KTM name then reflected its two principal owners, Kronreif, Trunkenpolz and of course Mattighofen. From this point full production began and a range of lightweight motorcycles was developed using engines sourced from Puch and Fichtel & Sachs. Popular models produced in the 1950s and 60s were the 125cc Tarzan, Mustang and Tourist, with success in the moped and scooter market with models such as the Pony, Mecky, Mirabell and Comet. The sports moped market was particularly buoyant towards the end of the 60s, and the KTM Comet Grand Prix RS was among the many available for the youth of that time.

Competition success was there from the very beginning, with a win in the Austrian 125 National championships in 1954 and repeat success on their off-road machines at the International Six Days events. KTM got its introduction into the US via Jack Penton who imported them under his own name from 1968. KTM later set up a US subsidiary ten years later. Development of its off-road models was of paramount importance, particularly in such a competitive market. The old air-cooled motocross engines were

Right-hand side of the EXC engine

Left-hand side of the SX engine

2003 250 EXC

2004 450 EXC

2004 450 MXC

replaced by water-cooled units in 1981 and by 1986 they had broken new ground by fitting disc brakes to their motocrossers, front and rear. Linkless rear suspension system and hydraulic clutches were two other areas in which they were ahead of the competition.

Already well-known for motocross racing, KTM soon dominated in the Paris-Dakar rally and the Atlas Rallye. Road-racing success has

been achieved in Supermoto with their SMR range of machines.

KTM hit a low point in the early 90s and filed for bankruptcy in 1991. It was rescued by Stefan Pierer who purchased the company for a figure under 4 million dollars. The new management team injected new life into the company and by 2005 its motorcycle produced had increased to 80,000 units,

helped enormously by their venture into the large-capacity road bike market with the 950 vee-twin in 2003. Known almost exclusively for its strong off-road products, the departure into other areas already well served by the Japanese and Italian brands was a brave move. The success of the 950 Adventure, then the 990 Super Duke led to a Supermoto version in 2006, and development looks set to continue with larger capacity vee twin models in the pipeline.

KTM AG consists of four divisions, Sportmotorcycles AG forms the main part of the group and is responsible for its core product motorcycle production and includes WP suspension and the Swedish Husaberg brand, these companies having been acquired in 1995. Other divisions of KTM control its bicycle production (which has roots going back to 1964), radiator production (for automotive and bikes), and its tool construction company.

A union with Polaris, the US ATV and cruiser bike manufacturer in 2005 enabled KTM to strengthen its market in the US; the benefits for Polaris were an entry into the European market, particularly through KTM's established dealer base.

With daily production around 400 units, KTM is now one of the world's leading motorcycle manufacturers, particularly of its core product off-road, rally and motocross bikes. It has many subsidiaries, notably the WP White Power suspension company and

2005 525 MXC Desert

the Husaberg brand. Strongest markets are Germany, USA, Australia, France and of course its home market Austria.

Acknowledgements

Our thanks are due to Sideways of Dorchester who supplied the main project machine featured in the illustrations throughout this manual and provided technical advice. We would also like to thank Albion Motorcycles of Exeter who supplied other models for photography, NGK Spark Plugs (UK) Ltd for supplying the colour spark plug condition photographs, the Avon Rubber Company for supplying information on tyre fitting and Draper Tools Ltd for some of the workshop tools shown.

Grateful thanks are due to KTM, and in particular the photographer H. Mitterbauer, for the model photographs on the front cover and those which accompany the introduction.

About this Manual

The aim of this manual is to help you get the best value from your motorcycle. It can do so in several ways. It can help you decide what work must be done, even if you choose to have it done by a dealer; it provides information and procedures for routine maintenance and servicing; and it offers diagnostic and repair procedures to follow when trouble occurs.

We hope you use the manual to tackle the work yourself. For many simpler jobs, doing it yourself may be quicker than arranging an appointment to get the motorcycle into a dealer and making the trips to leave it and pick it up. More importantly, a lot of money can be saved by avoiding the expense the shop must pass on to you to cover its labour and overhead costs. An added benefit is the sense of satisfaction and accomplishment that you feel after doing the job yourself.

References to the left or right side of the motorcycle assume you are sitting on the seat, facing forward.

We take great pride in the accuracy of information given in this manual, but motorcycle manufacturers make alterations and design changes during the production run of a particular motorcycle of which they do not inform us. No liability can be accepted by the authors or publishers for loss, damage or injury caused by any errors in, or omissions from, the information given.

Illegal Copying

2006 525 XC

2006 525 SX

2006 560 SMR

400 and 520 EXC Racing
400 and 520 MXC
400 and 520 SX Racing

The 400 and 520 EXC Racing, (US market designation 400 and 520 EXC-G Racing), and 400 and 520 SX Racing machines were introduced in 2000. EXC models were primarily enduro machines fitted with road-going equipment such as lights, horn and turn signals, whereas the SX models were built exclusively for off-road competition. In addition, EXC models were equipped with a battery and electric starter, whereas SX models had a kick-starter only.

All models had a single cylinder, liquid-cooled four-stroke engine, with a single overhead camshaft driven by chain from the left-hand end of the crankshaft. A balancer shaft, located in the front of the crankshaft was gear driven off the crankshaft. Two intake and two exhaust valves were fitted in the cylinder head – the exhaust valves opened into twin exhaust ports and dual pipes which were, in turn, connected to a single, high mounted silencer.

The carburettor used on all models was a twin cable-operated, flat slide type Keihin, of which two variants were used. For cold starting, a choke knob was mounted on the carburettor.

Drive was transmitted to the gearbox via a hydraulically actuated multi-plate clutch, and to the rear wheel by chain and sprockets. All EXC models had a six speed gearbox and SX models, with the exception of the 2001 and 2002 400 cc models, had a four-speed gearbox.

The chrome molybdenum steel chassis comprised a compact, twin loop tubular cradle welded to a single top tube and short front downtube. The rear sub-frame supporting the seat and mudguard assembly was made from aluminium.

Front suspension was by three-way adaptable, upside down White Power telescopic forks. The aluminium rear swingarm was controlled by a three-way adjustable White Power mono-shock with external reservoir. A variety of options were available for both front and rear suspension depending upon the intended use of the machine.

The front brake was a single disc with two piston caliper; the rear brake was a single disc with a single piston caliper.

The frame was finished in silver powder coating and the body panels were self-coloured orange and black. With minor detail changes, this scheme was retained for all machines, including the 250 EXC Racing, through to 2007.

The 400 and 520 MXC models were introduced in 2001. These were variants of the EXC, stripped of lighting equipment.

The 400 and 520 machines were discontinued at the end of 2002. The 400 EXC Racing and 400 MXC were re-introduced in 2004 – from then on, detail changes were in-line with the 450 and 525 range of machines.

450 and 525 EXC Racing
450 and 525 MXC
450 and 525 SX Racing
450 and 540 SXS

The 450 and 525 EXC Racing, (US market designation 450 and 525 EXC-G Racing), 450 and 525 MXC, and 450 and 520 SX Racing machines were introduced in 2003. As before, EXC models were primarily six-speed enduro machines fitted with road-going equipment, battery and electric starter, whereas the SX models were built exclusively for off-road competition, utilising a four-speed gearbox. MXC models were variants of the EXC, but stripped of lighting equipment, and SXS models, available between 2004 and 2006, were limited production moto-crossers – see the end of this section for full details.

Apart from minor detail changes, including gold powder coating on the frame and wheel hubs, the EXC Racing, MXC and 525 SX Racing machines for 2003 were visually similar to the earlier models. However, 450 SX Racing machines had a new one-piece rear mudguard/number plate unit, rear sub-frame, quick release air filter housing cover and two-into-one exhaust header pipe. These components were fitted to the whole of the EXC, MXC and SX range the following year.

The dimensions of the cylinder and piston fitted to the 450 SX differed from the 450 EXC and MXC models, the ports were larger and a different camshaft was used, all as an aid to increase engine rpm.

The carburettors on 450 and 525 SX models were fitted with a hot start knob and the front forks had externally adjustable spring pre-load.

The clutch on all 450 and 525 machines was retained by a nut rather than a circlip as on earlier bikes.

In 2004, the clutch master cylinder bore size was reduced and an integral rear brake master cylinder and reservoir dispensed with the remote reservoir previously located above the final drive sprocket. The brake discs were drilled for additional lightness and the swingarm was lengthened by 10 mm.

On SX models, oval section frame tubes were fitted between the rear of the top tube and the swingarm mounts, and a new, one-piece swingarm was fitted – on all the other bikes the rear axle mountings were welded on to the main tubes. The diameter of the swingarm pivot bolt was increased to 17 mm. Thinner wall tubing was used for the frame and the steering head was reinforced. These modifications were carried over to the rest of the range for 2005.

2004-on models had a throttle position sensor mounted on the carburettor.

In addition to the changes already mentioned, the bikes in the 2005 range, where appropriate, were fitted with a new shape headlight, headlight panel and turn indicators, and speedometer/multi-function display unit. All machines had a new CDI unit and the front brake master cylinder bore size was altered. The steering stem fitted to XC, EXC Sixdays and SX models allowed the fork offset to be adjusted to suit prevailing racing conditions. A new, large capacity fuel tank as fitted to the 525 MXC Desert Racing, was available for long distance enduro riding.

Apart from a stiffer crankshaft and modifications to the intake tract and, on some models, the carburettor, there were only minor detail changes on the 2006 range.

The 450 and 540 SXS models were based on the SX Racing range, utilising a number of factory competition parts to produce a super-lightweight machine for maximum performance. The increase in engine capacity from the 525 SX to the 540 SXS was achieved by enlarging the bore and stroke to 100 mm x 68 mm. The compression ratio on the 540 SXS was raised to 12:1.

All 540 SXS models had a four-speed transmission, whereas 2004 and 2005 450 SXS models had a six-speed box and 2006 models had a five speed box.

Chassis modifications on the SXS included a lightweight swingarm, White Power PDS shock with titanium spring, billet aluminium front axle clamps, fork yokes and front brake caliper. The front fork was fitted with a hole-shot device operated by a lever fitted to the front brake master cylinder. This reduced the tendency for the front wheel to lift under hard acceleration as the bike left the start line. A front fork steering damper and a carbon fibre front mudguard brace were also available.

The air filter housing had an extra intake and the exhaust system and silencer was fabricated from titanium. The right-hand engine cover featured a separate cover for the clutch and the clutch itself was a special four-spring racing unit, designed to eliminate judder. Many of the parts originally designed for the SXS could be retro-fitted to other machines in the range.

250 EXC Racing

The 250 EXC Racing was introduced in 2002. Apart from its smaller engine capacity it was identical to the larger machines in the EXC range.

Detail changes between 2002 and 2006 were, with a few exceptions, in line with the larger capacity bikes. In 2004 the chassis was modified as with the 450 and 525 SX models, utilising thinner walled chrome moly tubing and steering head gusset plates. For this year only, the longer, welded construction swingarm was fitted; this was replaced by the one-piece unit in 2005.

The 250 EXC-G (US market designation) was available in 2004 only.

The 250 EXC was discontinued at the end of 2006

450, 525 and 560 SMR

The 450 and 525 SMR models were introduced in 2004 as dedicated super-moto machines. Some American market models were equipped with lights for the first year of manufacture, but generally speaking the SMRs were based on the SX off-road competition bikes, with no lights or electric starter. The

450 and 525 SMRs shared the same cylinder dimensions and compression ratios as the 450 and 525 SXs, but all SMR machines were fitted with six-speed gearboxes.

Visually, the SMR models embodied all the updates common to the range for 2004, the notable difference being the fitment of 17 inch wheel rims and road racing tyres, and the use

of a 310 mm diameter front brake disc with radially mounted four-piston caliper.

In 2005 the SMR models were fitted with the same adjustable steering stem as the XC, Sixdays and SX models. In 2006 the engine capacity of the larger super-moto was increased to 566 cc by enlarging the cylinder bore size to 100 mm.

Bike spec

Weights and dimensions

Wheelbase . . . . 1471 to 1491 mm
Overall length . . . . 2172 mm
Overall width . . . . 810 mm
Overall height . . . . 1283 mm
Seat height . . . . 925 mm
Ground clearance . . . . 380 mm
Weight (dry)
   250 EXC . . . . 102.6 kg
   400/450/520/525 EXC and MXC/XC . . . . 113 kg
   525 MXC Desert . . . . 114.8 kg
   400/450/520/525 SX . . . . 107 kg
   450 SMR . . . . 107.5 kg
   525 SMR . . . . 109.5 kg
   560 SMR . . . . 108.5 kg

Engine

Type	Four-stroke, liquid-cooled single cylinder

Capacity (bore x stroke)

250 EXC	249.6 cc (75 x 56.5 mm)
400 EXC, MXC and SX	398 cc (89 x 64 mm)
450 EXC and MXC	448 cc (89 x 72 mm)
450 SX, SXS and SMR	449 cc (95 x 63.4 mm)
520 EXC, MXC and SX	510 cc (95 x 72 mm)
525 EXC, MXC, SX and SMR	510 cc (95 x 72 mm)
540 SXS	534 cc (100 x 68 mm)
560 SMR	566 cc (100 x 72 mm)

Compression ratio

250 EXC	12 to 1
400 EXC, MXC and SX	11 to 1
450 EXC and MXC	11 to 1
450 SX, SXS and SMR	12 to 1
520 EXC and SX	11 to 1
525 EXC, MXC and SX	11 to 1
525 and 560 SMR	11 to 1
540 SXS	12 to 1

Camshaft	Chain driven single overhead camshaft
Valves	4 valves
Fuel system	Keihin carburettor
Clutch	Wet, multi-plate, hydraulically operated

Transmission

EXC, MXC/XC and SMR models	6 speed constant mesh

SX models

400 SX (2001 and 2002)	6 speed constant mesh
400/450 SX (all other years)	4 speed constant mesh
520/525 SX	4 speed constant mesh
450 SXS (2004 and 2005)	6 speed constant mesh
450 SXS (2006)	5 speed constant mesh
540 SXS	4 speed constant mesh
Final drive	Chain (5/8 x 1/4 in)

Chassis

Type	Tubular steel cradle frame, aluminium sub-frame and swingarm
Rake and trail	63.5°, 112 mm

Front suspension

Type	White Power USD telescopic fork

Travel

250 EXC	300 mm
400 and 520 EXC, MXC and SX	295 mm
450 and 525 EXC, MXC/XC and SX	300 mm
450 and 540 SXS	300 mm
450, 525 and 560 SMR	285 mm
Adjustment	Spring preload, compression and rebound damping

Rear suspension

Type	Swingarm with White Power shock

Travel

250 EXC	335 mm
400 and 520 EXC, MXC and SX	320 mm
450 and 525 EXC, MXC/XC and SX	335 mm
450 and 540 SXS	335 mm
450, 525 and 560 SMR	310 mm
Adjustment	Spring preload, compression and rebound damping

Tyre sizes

	Front	Rear
Europe 250, 400, 450, 520 and 525 EXC, MXC Desert	90/90 – 21	140/80 – 18
US 400, 450, 520 and 525 EXC, MXC/XC	80/100 – 21	110/100 – 18
All SX and SXS models	80/100 – 21	110/90 – 19
All SMR models	120/75 – 17	165/55 – 17

Front brake

SMR models	Single 310 mm disc with four-piston radially mounted caliper
All other models	Single 260 mm disc with two-piston sliding caliper
Rear brake	Single 220 mm disc with single-piston sliding caliper

Buying spare parts

When ordering replacement parts, it is essential to identify exactly the machine for which the parts are required. While in some cases it is sufficient to identify the machine by its title e.g. '250 EXC', any modifications made to components mean that it is usually essential to identify the machine by its KTM **production year** e.g. '2004 250 EXC', and sometimes by its engine and/or frame number as well.

Note that the production year is not necessarily the same as the year of registration or manufacture. The production year starts at the end of the previous calendar year. Therefore a 2005 machine was **produced** at some time between late 2004 and late 2005.

To be absolutely certain of receiving the correct part, not only is it essential to have the machine's identifying title and engine and frame numbers, but it is also useful to take the old part for comparison (where possible). Note that where a modified component has superseded the original, a careful check must be made that there are no related parts which have also been modified and must be used to enable the replacement to be correctly refitted; where such a situation is found, purchase all the necessary parts and fit them, even if this means replacing apparently unworn items.

Always purchase replacement parts from an authorised KTM dealer who will either have the parts in stock or can order them quickly from the importer, and always use genuine parts to ensure the machine's performance and reliability. Pattern parts are available for certain components (ie. disc brake pads, oil and air filters); if used, ensure these are of recognised quality brands which will perform as well as the original.

Expendable items such as lubricants, spark plugs, some electrical components, bearings, bulbs and tyres can usually be obtained at lower prices from accessory shops, motor factors or from specialists advertising in the national motorcycle press.

Frame and engine numbers

The engine number is stamped into the crankcase on the left-hand side below the final drive (gearbox) sprocket **(see illustration)**. The frame serial number is stamped into the steering head on the right-hand side **(see illustration)**. Both of these numbers should be recorded and kept in a safe place so they

can be furnished to law enforcement officials in the event of a theft. The manufacturer's vehicle identification plate is located on the front of the steering head.

The frame serial number and engine number should be kept in a handy place so they are always available when purchasing or ordering parts for your machine.

The procedures in this manual identify the bikes by model code and, if necessary, also by production year. The model code (e.g. 250 EXC) is used by itself if the information applies to all bikes produced over the life of the model. The production year is added where the information applies only to bikes produced in certain years of the model's life, usually when a component has been

changed or upgraded. Note that the production year can be established from the frame number – the number immediately before the letter M in the frame number denotes the year, e.g. 7 denoting 2007 in the photograph.

Production year codes
2000 – Y
2001 – 1
2002 – 2
2003 – 3
2004 – 4
2005 – 5
2006 – 6
2007 – 7

The frame number is stamped into the steering head – production year code arrowed

The engine number is stamped into the crankcase below the final drive sprocket

Professional mechanics are trained in safe working procedures. However enthusiastic you may be about getting on with the job at hand, take the time to ensure that your safety is not put at risk. A moment's lack of attention can result in an accident, as can failure to observe simple precautions.

There will always be new ways of having accidents, and the following is not a comprehensive list of all dangers; it is intended rather to make you aware of the risks and to encourage a safe approach to all work you carry out on your bike.

Asbestos

● Certain friction, insulating, sealing and other products - such as brake pads, clutch linings, gaskets, etc. - contain asbestos. Extreme care must be taken to avoid inhalation of dust from such products since it is hazardous to health. If in doubt, assume that they do contain asbestos.

Fire

● Remember at all times that petrol is highly flammable. Never smoke or have any kind of naked flame around, when working on the vehicle. But the risk does not end there - a spark caused by an electrical short-circuit, by two metal surfaces contacting each other, by careless use of tools, or even by static electricity built up in your body under certain conditions, can ignite petrol vapour, which in a confined space is highly explosive. Never use petrol as a cleaning solvent. Use an approved safety solvent.

● Always disconnect the battery earth terminal before working on any part of the fuel or electrical system, and never risk spilling fuel on to a hot engine or exhaust.

● It is recommended that a fire extinguisher of a type suitable for fuel and electrical fires is kept handy in the garage or workplace at all times. Never try to extinguish a fuel or electrical fire with water.

Fumes

● Certain fumes are highly toxic and can quickly cause unconsciousness and even death if inhaled to any extent. Petrol vapour comes into this category, as do the vapours from certain solvents such as trichloro-ethylene. Any draining or pouring of such volatile fluids should be done in a well ventilated area.

● When using cleaning fluids and solvents, read the instructions carefully. Never use materials from unmarked containers - they may give off poisonous vapours.

● Never run the engine of a motor vehicle in an enclosed space such as a garage. Exhaust fumes contain carbon monoxide which is extremely poisonous; if you need to run the engine, always do so in the open air or at least have the rear of the vehicle outside the workplace.

The battery

● Never cause a spark, or allow a naked light near the vehicle's battery. It will normally be giving off a certain amount of hydrogen gas, which is highly explosive.

● Always disconnect the battery ground (earth) terminal before working on the fuel or electrical systems (except where noted).

Electricity

● When using an electric power tool, inspection light etc., always ensure that the appliance is correctly connected to its plug and that, where necessary, it is properly grounded (earthed). Do not use such appliances in damp conditions and, again, beware of creating a spark or applying excessive heat in the vicinity of fuel or fuel vapour. Also ensure that the appliances meet national safety standards.

● A severe electric shock can result from touching certain parts of the electrical system, such as the spark plug wires (HT leads), when the engine is running or being cranked, particularly if components are damp or the insulation is defective. Where an electronic ignition system is used, the secondary (HT) voltage is much higher and could prove fatal.

Remember...

✗ **Don't** start the engine without first ascertaining that the transmission is in neutral.

✗ **Don't** suddenly remove the pressure cap from a hot cooling system - cover it with a cloth and release the pressure gradually first, or you may get scalded by escaping coolant.

✗ **Don't** attempt to drain oil until you are sure it has cooled sufficiently to avoid scalding you.

✗ **Don't** grasp any part of the engine or exhaust system without first ascertaining that it is cool enough not to burn you.

✗ **Don't** allow brake fluid or antifreeze to contact the machine's paintwork or plastic components.

✗ **Don't** siphon toxic liquids such as fuel, hydraulic fluid or antifreeze by mouth, or allow them to remain on your skin.

✗ **Don't** inhale dust - it may be injurious to health (see Asbestos heading).

✗ **Don't** allow any spilled oil or grease to remain on the floor - wipe it up right away, before someone slips on it.

✗ **Don't** use ill-fitting spanners or other tools which may slip and cause injury.

✗ **Don't** lift a heavy component which may be beyond your capability - get assistance.

✗ **Don't** rush to finish a job or take unverified short cuts.

✗ **Don't** allow children or animals in or around an unattended vehicle.

✗ **Don't** inflate a tyre above the recommended pressure. Apart from overstressing the carcass, in extreme cases the tyre may blow off forcibly.

✔ **Do** ensure that the machine is supported securely at all times. This is especially important when the machine is blocked up to aid wheel or fork removal.

✔ **Do** take care when attempting to loosen a stubborn nut or bolt. It is generally better to pull on a spanner, rather than push, so that if you slip, you fall away from the machine rather than onto it.

✔ **Do** wear eye protection when using power tools such as drill, sander, bench grinder etc.

✔ **Do** use a barrier cream on your hands prior to undertaking dirty jobs - it will protect your skin from infection as well as making the dirt easier to remove afterwards; but make sure your hands aren't left slippery. Note that long-term contact with used engine oil can be a health hazard.

✔ **Do** keep loose clothing (cuffs, ties etc. and long hair) well out of the way of moving mechanical parts.

✔ **Do** remove rings, wristwatch etc., before working on the vehicle - especially the electrical system.

✔ **Do** keep your work area tidy - it is only too easy to fall over articles left lying around.

✔ **Do** exercise caution when compressing springs for removal or installation. Ensure that the tension is applied and released in a controlled manner, using suitable tools which preclude the possibility of the spring escaping violently.

✔ **Do** ensure that any lifting tackle used has a safe working load rating adequate for the job.

✔ **Do** get someone to check periodically that all is well, when working alone on the vehicle.

✔ **Do** carry out work in a logical sequence and check that everything is correctly assembled and tightened afterwards.

✔ **Do** remember that your vehicle's safety affects that of yourself and others. If in doubt on any point, get professional advice.

● If in spite of following these precautions, you are unfortunate enough to injure yourself, seek medical attention as soon as possible.

Note : *The Pre-ride checks detailed below cover those items which should be inspected before every ride. However, if the bike is being used in competition, the full pre-race maintenance schedule shown in Chapter 1 should be undertaken.*

Engine oil level

Before you start

✔ Support the motorcycle in an upright position on level ground.
✔ The oil level can be checked either with the engine warm or cold – note that the oil level varies with engine temperature.
✔ Take extreme care when topping-up the oil if the engine has been running – the hot exhaust pipes can cause severe burns.

Bike care

● If you have to add oil frequently, you should check whether there are any oil leaks. If there is no sign of oil leakage from the joints and gaskets, the engine could be burning oil (see *Fault Finding*).
● Never run the engine with the oil level below the bottom of the window, and do not fill it above the top of the window.

The correct oil

● Modern, high-revving engines place great demands on their oil. It is very important that the correct oil for your bike is used.
● Always top up with a good quality fully synthetic motorcycle oil of the specified viscosity and do not overfill the engine. KTM recommend using Motorex Power Synt 4T. Do not use motor oils designed for use in car engines.

Oil type	API grade SG minimum, JASO MA
Oil viscosity	SAE 10W/50

1 Check the oil level through the inspection window in the right-hand side of the engine. If necessary, wipe the window so that it is clean.

2 If the engine is cold, the oil should be level with the lower edge of the window. If the engine is warm, the oil should be level with the upper edge of the window.

3 If the level is low, remove the filler cap from the front of the clutch cover. Note that on early models the filler cap incorporates a dipstick.

4 Top the engine up with the recommended type and grade of oil (see accompanying table). Take care not to over-fill the engine. If a dipstick is fitted to the filler cap, wipe the dipstick before inserting it fully in the clutch cover, then withdraw it – the oil should be near the upper end of the hatched area if the engine is warm.

5 On completion, fit the filler cap, making sure it is secure. If there are any signs of oil leakage from around the cap, renew the sealing O-ring.

Coolant level

> ⚠️ **Warning: DO NOT remove the radiator pressure cap when the engine is hot – wait for it to cool. DO NOT leave open containers of coolant about, as it is poisonous.**

Before you start

✔ Make sure you have a supply of coolant available (a mixture of 50% distilled water and 50% corrosion inhibited ethylene glycol anti-freeze is needed).
✔ Support the motorcycle in an upright position on level ground.
✔ If possible, always check the coolant level when the engine is cold.

Bike care

● Use only the specified coolant mixture. It is important that anti-freeze is used in the system all year round, and not just in the winter. Do not top the system up using only water, as the system will become too diluted.
● Do not overfill the radiators. If necessary, surplus coolant should be siphoned or drained off to prevent the possibility of it being expelled out of the overflow hose.
● If the coolant level falls steadily, check the system for leaks (see Chapter 1). If no leaks are found and the level continues to fall, it is recommended that the machine is taken to a KTM dealer for a pressure test.

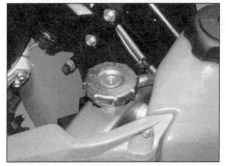

1 The pressure cap is located on the left-hand radiator. Remove the cap carefully – if the radiator is warm, cover the cap with a cloth to avoid scalding.

3 If the level is low, top the coolant up with the recommended mixture, using a funnel to avoid spillage.

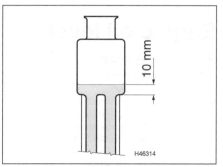

2 With the motorcycle held upright, the coolant level should be 10 mm above the top of the radiator fins when the engine is cold.

4 On completion, fit the pressure cap, making sure it is secure.

Clutch fluid level

Before you start

✔ When checking the fluid level, position the handlebars so that the top of the master cylinder reservoir is as level as possible.
✔ Make sure you have the correct clutch fluid – KTM specify Shell Naturelle HF-E15 or Magura Blood biohydraulic oil, depending upon year of manufacture – do not use brake/clutch hydraulic fluid.

Bike care

● If the reservoir requires repeated topping-up this is an indication of a fluid leak somewhere in the system, which should be investigated immediately.
● Check for signs of fluid leakage from the clutch hose and components – if found, rectify immediately.

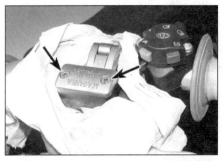

1 Undo the two cover screws and lift off the cover and the diaphragm.

3 If the level is low, top-up with new fluid of the correct specification. Do not overfill.

2 The level should be 4 mm below the top edge of the reservoir.

4 Ensure that the diaphragm is correctly seated, then tighten the cover screws securely.

Brake fluid levels

> ⚠️ **Warning: Brake hydraulic fluid can harm your eyes and damage painted surfaces, so use extreme caution when handling and pouring it and cover surrounding surfaces with rag. Do not use fluid that has been standing open for some time, as it absorbs moisture from the air which can cause a dangerous loss of braking effectiveness.**

Before you start

✔ When checking the front brake fluid level, position the handlebars so that the top of the master cylinder is as level as possible.

✔ When checking the rear brake fluid level, hold the machine upright. The fluid level is visible through the reservoir body.

✔ Make sure you have the correct brake fluid – KTM specify Shell Advance Brake DOT 5.1 or Motorex DOT 5.1, depending upon year of manufacture. Do not use DOT 5.0 – it is not compatible. Wrap a rag around the reservoir being worked on to ensure that any spillage does not come into contact with painted surfaces.

Bike care

● The fluid level in the front and rear brake master cylinder reservoirs will drop slightly as the brake pads wear down.

● If either reservoir requires repeated topping-up this is an indication of a fluid leak somewhere in the system, which should be investigated immediately.

● Check for signs of fluid leakage from the brake hoses and components – if found, rectify immediately.

● Check the operation of both brakes before riding the machine. If there is evidence of air in the system (spongy feel to lever or pedal), the system must be bled as described in Chapter 7.

FRONT

1 The fluid level is visible through the sightglass in the reservoir body – do not allow it to drop below the middle of the glass.

3 Top-up with new DOT 5.1 brake fluid until the level is 5 mm below the top edge of the reservoir. Do not overfill and take care to avoid spills (see **Warning** above).

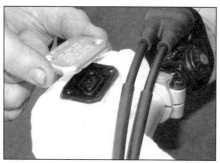

2 If the level is low, undo the two cover screws and lift off the cover and the diaphragm.

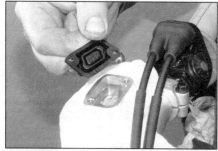

4 Ensure that the diaphragm is correctly seated, then fit the cover and tighten its screws.

REAR

Note: *The following photos show the integral fluid reservoir and master cylinder fitted to 2004-on models. Earlier models have a separate reservoir mounted above the oil filters on the left side of the engine.*

1 The level is visible through the sightglass in the reservoir body – do not allow it to drop below the top of the glass.

2 If the level is low, unscrew the cap.

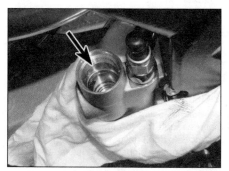

3 Top-up with new DOT 5.1 brake fluid until the level reaches the level line inside the reservoir.

4 Do not overfill and take care to avoid spills (see **Warning** above).

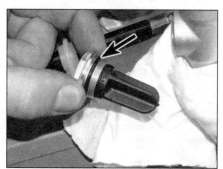

5 If there are any signs of fluid leakage from around the cap, renew the sealing O-ring, then tighten the cap securely.

Tyres

The correct pressures
● The tyres must be checked when **cold**, not immediately after riding.
● Use an accurate pressure gauge. Many garage forecourt gauges are wildly inaccurate – if you buy your own, spend as much as you can on a quality gauge.
● Note that for road use, low tyre pressures may cause the tyre to slip on the rim. High tyre pressures will cause abnormal tread wear.
● Correct air pressure will increase tyre life and provide maximum stability, handling capability and rider comfort.

Tyre care
● Check the tyres carefully for cuts, tears, embedded nails or other sharp objects and excessive wear. Operation of the motorcycle with excessively worn tyres is extremely hazardous, as traction and handling are directly affected.
● Check the condition of the tyre valve and ensure the dust cap is in place.
● Pick out any stones or nails which may have become embedded in the tyre tread. If left, they will eventually penetrate through the casing and puncture the inner tube.

● If tyre damage is apparent, or unexplained loss of pressure is experienced, remove the tyre for further examination (see Chapter 7).

Tyre tread depth
● At the time of writing UK law requires that tread depth for road use must be at least 1 mm over 3/4 of the tread breadth all the way around the tyre, with no bald patches. KTM specify an absolute minimum of 2 mm, although many riders would renew tyres before this point is reached.
● Many tyres now incorporate wear indicators in the tread. Identify the arrow, triangular pointer or TWI marking on the tyre sidewall to locate the indicator bars and replace the tyre if the tread has worn down level with the bars.

Recommended pressures	Front	Rear
Road use – EXC	21 psi (1.5 Bar)	28 psi (2.0 Bar)
Road use – SMR	21 psi (1.5 Bar)	23 psi (1.6 Bar)
Off-road use	14 psi (1.0 Bar)	14 psi (1.0 Bar)

1 Check the pressures when the tyres are cold and keep them properly inflated.

2 Measure tread depth at the centre of the tyre using a tread depth gauge.

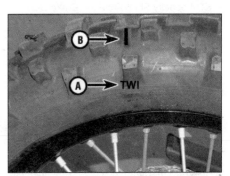

3 Tyre tread wear indicator bar (B) and its location marking (A) – usually either an arrow, a triangle or the letters TWI on the sidewall.

Suspension, steering and chain

Suspension and steering
● Check that the front and rear suspension operates smoothly without binding.
● Check that there are no fluid leaks from the front fork seals or the rear shock.

● Check that the suspension is adjusted as required.
● Check that the steering moves smoothly from lock-to-lock.

Final drive
● Check that the chain slack isn't excessive and adjust it if necessary (see Chapter 1).
● If the chain looks dry, lubricate it (see Chapter 1).

Legal and safety checks

Lighting and signalling
● On models with lights, take a minute to check that the headlight, tail light, brake light, instrument lights and turn signals all work correctly.
● Check that the horn sounds when the switch is operated.
● A working speedometer is a statutory requirement in the UK.

Safety
● Check that the throttle grip rotates smoothly and snaps shut when released, in all steering positions.
● Check that the engine shuts off when the kill switch is operated.
● Check that the sidestand return springs hold the stand securely up when retracted.

Fuel
● This may seem obvious, but check that you have enough fuel to complete your journey – SX models don't have a reserve setting.
● If you notice signs of fuel leakage – rectify the cause immediately.
● Ensure you use the correct grade unleaded fuel (see Chapter 4).

Chapter 1
Routine maintenance and Servicing

Contents

Degrees of difficulty

Easy, suitable for novice with little experience	**Fairly easy,** suitable for beginner with some experience	**Fairly difficult,** suitable for competent DIY mechanic	**Difficult,** suitable for experienced DIY mechanic	**Very difficult,** suitable for expert DIY or professional

Specifications

Engine
Spark plug
  2000 to 2002 – 400 EXC and SX, 520 EXC and SX
    Type . . . . NGK CR8EK
    Gap . . . . 0.6 mm
  All other models
    Type . . . . NGK DCPR8E
    Gap . . . . 0.6 mm
Spark plug cap resistance . . . . 5 K-ohms
Engine idle speed. . . . . 1400 to 1500 rpm
Valve clearances (COLD engine – intake and exhaust) . . . . 0.12 mm (0.10 to 0.15 mm range)

Cycle parts

Front brake lever freeplay	3 mm
Rear brake pedal freeplay	3 to 5 mm
Brake pad minimum thickness	1 mm
Brake disc minimum thickness	
Front	2.5 mm
Rear	3.5 mm
Drive chain slack	8 to 10 mm between chain and swingarm (see text)
Drive chain stretch (service limit)	272 mm over 18 pins
Throttle cable freeplay	3 to 5 mm
Decompressor cable freeplay	10 mm
Tyre pressures	see *Pre-ride checks*

Torque settings

Crankshaft position screw	25 Nm
Engine oil drain plug	20 Nm
Short oil strainer plug	10 Nm
Long oil strainer plug	15 Nm
Oil filter cover bolts	6 Nm
Brake disc mounting bolts	14 Nm
Rear brake fluid reservoir mounting bolt	8 Nm
Camshaft oil feed unions	10 Nm
Rear axle	80 Nm
Rocker adjuster locknuts	11 Nm
Rocker cover bolts	10 Nm
Wheel spoke	5 Nm
Fuel tank support bolts	25 Nm

Lubricants and fluids

Engine oil	
Type	API grade SG or SH (minimum)
Viscosity	
Consistently below 0°C (32°F)	SAE 10W 40 or SAE 10W 50
Consistently above 0°C (32°F)	SAE 15W 40 or SAE 15W 50
Capacity	1.25 litres approx
Brake fluid	DOT 5.1
Clutch fluid	Shell Naturelle HF-E15 or Magura Blood biohydraulic oil
Coolant	
Type	50% distilled water, 50% corrosion inhibited ethylene glycol anti-freeze
Capacity	1 litre approx
Swingarm pivot bearings	Medium weight, lithium-based multi-purpose grease
Cables	Aerosol lube for nylon-lined cables, e.g. Putoline Super Cable Guard Spray
Stand, lever and footrest pivots	Dry film lubricant
Throttle twistgrip	Dry film lubricant

Note 1: *The pre-ride checks detailed at the beginning of this manual cover those items which should be inspected before every ride. However, if the bike is being used in competition, the full pre-race maintenance schedule shown below should be undertaken.*
Note 2: *Always carry-out the pre-ride checks at every maintenance interval (in addition to the procedures listed). The intervals listed below are the intervals recommended by KTM for the models covered in this manual.*
Note 3: *This maintenance schedule was developed for off-road competition and motocross and is based on hours of running time or equivalent fuel consumption.*

After the initial 3 hours running time/20 litres fuel

Note: *This check is usually performed by a KTM dealer after the first 3 hours running time (20 litres fuel) from new. Thereafter, maintenance is carried out according to the following intervals of the schedule.*

Pre-race

Note: *If the bike is being used in competition, carry-out the 15 hours/100 litres checks after each race.*

- [ ] Carry out the *Pre-ride checks* at the beginning of this manual.
- [ ] Check/adjust and lubricate the drive chain (see Section 1)
- [ ] Check the cooling system for leaks (see Section 2)
- [ ] Check the brake pads for wear (see Section 3)
- [ ] Check the suspension for proper operation and adjustment (see Section 4)
- [ ] Check the tyres, wheels and wheel bearings (see Section 5)
- [ ] Check the throttle and decompressor cables (see Section 6)
- [ ] Check the ignition system (see Section 7)
- [ ] Check the handlebar switches and headlight aim (see Section 8)
- [ ] Check the security of all fasteners (see Section 9)

Post race – after washing

Note: *Avoid using a high pressure water jet – this can penetrate components, such as the carburettor, exhaust and electrical system, and cause running problems. It will also wash lubricating grease out of bearings.*

- [ ] Drain and clean the carburettor float bowl (see Section 10)
- [ ] Clean the air filter element and housing (see Section 11)
- [ ] Lubricate the drive chain (see Section 1)
- [ ] Release excess pressure in the front forks (see Section 4)
- [ ] Clean the front fork sliders (see Section 4)
- [ ] Lubricate the throttle and decompressor cables (see Section 6)
- [ ] Lubricate the stand and lever pivots (see Section 12)
- [ ] Clean and check the operation of the switchgear (see Section 8)

Every 15 hours running time/ 100 litres fuel

Note : *Carry-out the pre-ride and pre-race checks plus the following.*

☐ Change the engine oil and filters (see Section 13)
☐ Check/adjust the valve clearances (see Section 14)
☐ Check the rocker oil feed (see Section 15)
☐ Check the brake and clutch hoses (see Section 16)
☐ Check the engine, fuel tank and carburettor breather hoses (see Section 17)
☐ Check the exhaust system for leaks and check the tightness of the fasteners (Section 18)
☐ Check/adjust the idle speed (see Section 19)
☐ Check the brake discs (see Section 20)
☐ Check the suspension for proper operation and fluid leaks (see Section 4)
☐ Check/adjust the steering head bearings (see Section 21)
☐ Check the electrical system and components (see Section 22)

Additional maintenance item for:
2005 250/400/450/525 EXC and SX racing machines
☐ Check the clutch plates (see Section 23)

2006-on 250/400/450/525 EXC and SX racing machines
☐ Check the clutch plates (see Section 23)
☐ Renew the packing in the silencer – SX models (see Chapter 4)
☐ Renew the rear brake master cylinder seals – SX models (see Chapter 7)

Every 30 hours running time/200 litres fuel

Note : *Carry-out the 15 hours/100 litres checks plus the following.*
☐ Change the spark plug (see Section 24)
☐ Drain and clean the carburettor float bowl (see Section 10)
☐ Renew the packing in the silencer (see Chapter 4)
☐ Clean the spark arrestor – US models (see Chapter 4)

Additional maintenance items for:
2000 to 2002 400/520 EXC and SX racing machines
2003 250/450/525 EXC and SX racing machines
2004 and 2005 250/400/450/525 EXC and SX racing machines
☐ Check the clutch plates and springs (see Section 23)
☐ Check the cam chain tensioner blade (see Chapter 2)

Every 30 hours running time/200 litres fuel (continued)

2004 and 2005 250/400/450/525 EXC hobby and recreational machines
☐ Check the clutch plates (see Section 23)

2006-on 250/400/450/525 EXC and SX racing machines
☐ Check the clutch springs (see Section 23)
☐ Check the cam chain tensioner blade (see Chapter 2)
☐ Renew the rear brake master cylinder seals (see Chapter 7)

2006-on 250/400/450/525 EXC and SX hobby and recreational machines
☐ Check the clutch plates (see Section 23)
☐ Renew the rear brake master cylinder seals – SX models (see Chapter 7)

Every 45 hours running time/300 litres fuel

2000 to 2002 400/520 EXC and SX racing machines
☐ Check the camshaft, cam chain and tensioner blade (see Chapter 2)
☐ Check the rocker arms (see Chapter 2)
☐ Check the valves, springs and guides (see Chapter 2)
☐ Check the piston and cylinder (see Chapter 2)
☐ Check the clutch plates (see Chapter 2)
☐ Check clutch fit on transmission output shaft (see Chapter 2)
☐ Check the con-rod bearings (see Chapter 2)
☐ Check the crankshaft and crankshaft bearings (see Chapter 2)
☐ Check the balancer shaft bearings (see Chapter 2)
☐ Check the transmission (see Chapter 2)

2003 250/450/525 EXC and SX racing machines
2004 and 2005 250/400/450/525 EXC and SX racing machines
2006-on 250/400/450/525 EXC and SX racing machines
☐ Check the clutch plates and springs (see Chapter 2)
☐ Check the camshaft, cam chain and tensioner blade (see Chapter 2)
☐ Renew the camshaft bearings (see Chapter 2)
☐ Check the rocker arms (see Chapter 2)
☐ Check the valves, springs and guides (see Chapter 2)
☐ Check the piston and cylinder (see Chapter 2)
☐ Renew the con-rod bearings (see Chapter 2)
☐ Renew the crankshaft bearings (see Chapter 2)
☐ Renew the balancer shaft bearings (see Chapter 2)
☐ Check the transmission (see Chapter 2)

Every 60 hours running time/400 litres fuel

2003 250/450/525 EXC hobby and recreational machines
2004 and 2005 250/400/450/525 EXC hobby and recreational machines

☐ Check the clutch plates and springs (see Section 23
☐ Check the cam chain tensioner blade (see Chapter 2)

2006-on 250/400/450/525 EXC and SX hobby and recreational machines

☐ Check the clutch springs (see Section 23)
☐ Check the cam chain tensioner blade (see Chapter 2)
☐ Renew the rear brake master cylinder seals – EXC models (see Chapter 7)

Every 90 hours running time/600 litres fuel

2003 250/450/525 EXC hobby and recreational machines
2004 and 2005 250/400/450/525 EXC hobby and recreational machines
2006-on 250/400/450/525 EXC and SX hobby and recreational machines

☐ Check the clutch plates and springs (see Chapter 2)
☐ Check the camshaft, cam chain and tensioner blade (see Chapter 2)
☐ Renew the camshaft bearings (see Chapter 2)
☐ Check the rocker arms (see Chapter 2)
☐ Check the valves, springs and guides (see Chapter 2)
☐ Check the piston and cylinder (see Chapter 2)
☐ Renew the con-rod bearings (see Chapter 2)
☐ Renew the crankshaft bearings (see Chapter 2)
☐ Renew the balancer shaft bearings (see Chapter 2)
☐ Check the transmission (see Chapter 2)

Every 200 hours running time

2006-on 250/400/450/525 EXC and SX – all models

☐ Renew the carburettor throttle slide, needle and needle jet (see Chapter 4)

At least every 12 months

Note: *Whether or not the appropriate running time has been reached, carry-out the following.*

☐ Change the engine oil and filters (see Section 13)
☐ Check the carburettor for wear (see Chapter 4)
☐ Clean the air filter element and housing (see Section 11)
☐ Check the coolant/anti-freeze (see Section 2)
☐ Check the exhaust system for leaks and check the tightness of the fasteners (Section 18)
☐ Clean the spark arrestor – US models (see Chapter 4)
☐ Change the brake fluid (see Chapter 7)
☐ Change the clutch fluid (see Chapter 2)
☐ Change the front fork oil (see Chapter 6)
☐ Check the front forks for wear (see Chapter 6)
☐ Check the rear shock for wear (see Chapter 6)
☐ Check and lubricate the steering head bearings (see Chapter 6)
☐ Check and lubricate the swingarm bearings (see Chapter 6)
☐ Check the tyres (see Chapter 7)
☐ Check/lubricate the throttle and decompressor cables (see Section 6)

Component locations on right side

1 Silencer packing
2 Rear brake fluid reservoir
3 Battery
4 Throttle cable adjuster
5 Front brake fluid reservoir

6 Steering head bearings
7 Spark plug
8 Front fork oil seals
9 Coolant drain plug
10 Engine oil filler cap/dipstick

11 Engine oil level window
12 Rear brake pedal stop bolt
13 Rear brake pedal freeplay adjuster
14 Drive chain adjuster

Component location on left side

1 Decompressor cable adjuster
2 Clutch fluid reservoir
3 Radiator pressure cap
4 Mixture screw

5 Engine oil filters
6 Air filter
7 Drive chain adjuster

8 Oil drain plug
9 Long oil screen
10 Short oil screen

1 This Chapter is designed to help the home mechanic maintain his/her motorcycle for safety, economy, long life and peak performance.

2 If the machine has been maintained according to the warranty standards, you may want to pick up routine maintenance as it coincides with the next service interval. If you have no knowledge of the machine's history or maintenance record, you are advised to combine all the checks into one large initial service and then settle into the maintenance schedule prescribed.

3 Before beginning any maintenance or repair, the machine should be cleaned thoroughly. Cleaning will help ensure that dirt does not contaminate the engine and will allow you to detect wear and damage that could otherwise easily go unnoticed.

4 Maintenance information is sometimes printed on decals attached to the motorcycle. If any information on the decals differs from that included here, use the information on the decal.

Read the *Safety first!* section of this manual carefully before starting work.

Maintenance procedures

1   Drive chain and sprockets

Check

1 As the chain stretches with wear, regular maintenance is essential. A neglected drive chain won't last long and can quickly damage the sprockets. Routine chain adjustment and lubrication isn't difficult and will ensure maximum chain and sprocket life.

2 To check the chain, position a support underneath the crankcase so that the bike is upright with the rear wheel off the ground **(see illustration)**. Ensure that the transmission is in neutral.

3 Check the tension by pushing up on the bottom run of the chain just behind the chain slider on the swingarm and measure the distance between the top of the chain and the swingarm **(see illustration)**. Compare the result with the specification at the beginning of this Chapter.

4 Since the chain will rarely wear evenly, rotate the rear wheel so that another section of chain can be checked. Do this several times to check the entire length of the chain. Any adjustment should be based upon the measurement taken at the tightest point (see Steps 11 to 16).

5 Check the chain stretch using a spring balance attached to the upper chain run. Apply a pull of 15 kilograms (33 lbs) and measure the distance between 18 pins on the lower run **(see illustration)**. Compare the result with the specification at the beginning of this Chapter.

6 Check the entire length of the chain for damaged or missing rollers, loose links and pins, and missing O-rings.

7 In some cases, where lubrication has been neglected, corrosion may cause the links to bind and kink, which effectively shortens the chain's length. Any such links should be thoroughly cleaned and worked free. If the chain is tight between the sprockets, rusty or kinked, it is time to replace it with a new one. If you find a tight area, mark it with paint, and repeat the check after the bike has been ridden. If the chain is still tight in the same area, it may be damaged. Because a tight or kinked chain can damage the transmission output shaft bearing, it should be renewed.

8 If the chain has stretched to the service limit or is damaged, fit a new one (see Chapter 7). **Note:** *Never install a new chain on old sprockets, and never use the old chain if you install new sprockets – renew the chain and sprockets as a set.*

9 Check the teeth on the front and rear final drive sprockets for wear **(see illustration)**. If either sprocket is worn, renew the chain and sprockets as a set (see Chapter 7).

10 Inspect the drive chain slider on the swingarm and the chain roller on the upper

1.2 Supporting the bike upright makes routine checks easier

1.3 Checking the chain tension on the bottom run behind the slider (arrowed)

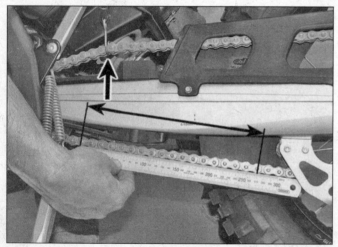

1.5 Checking chain stretch with a spring balance (arrowed) and ruler

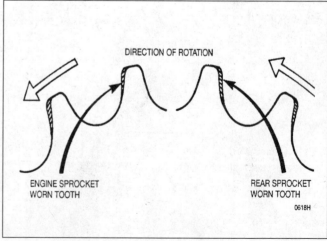

1.9 Check the sprockets in the areas indicated to see if they are worn excessively

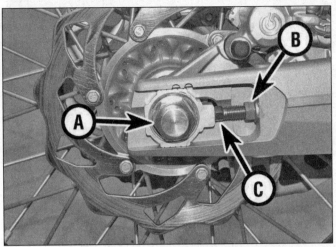
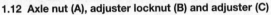

1.12 Axle nut (A), adjuster locknut (B) and adjuster (C)

1.14 Check the alignment of the grooves and cut-outs (arrowed)

run behind the front sprocket for excessive wear. Renew either components if they are worn (see Chapter 6).

Adjustment

11 Ensure that the bike is supported securely upright with the rear wheel off the ground. Position the chain with the tightest point in the bottom run below the chain slider.

12 Loosen the axle nut **(see illustration)**.

13 Loosen the adjuster locknuts on both sides of the swingarm, then turn the adjusters evenly, a small amount at a time, until the specified chain tension is obtained **(see illustration 1.12)**. If the chain has reached the end of its adjustment, it has stretched beyond its service limit and must be replaced with a new one (see Chapter 7).

14 Following chain adjustment, check that the grooves on the top edge of both adjuster plates are in the same position in relation to the cut-outs on the swingarm **(see illustration)**. It is important that each plate aligns with the same cut-out; if not, the rear wheel will be out of alignment with the front.

> **HAYNES HiNT** *Refer to Chapter 7, Section 11, for information on checking wheel alignment.*

15 If there is a discrepancy in the position of the plates, correct it with the adjusters and then check the chain tension as described above. Also check that there is no clearance between the adjusters and the front of the adjuster plates – push the wheel forwards to eliminate any clearance.

16 Tighten the axle nut to the torque setting specified at the beginning of this Chapter. Recheck the chain adjustment, then tighten the adjuster locknuts securely.

Lubrication

17 If required, wash the chain in paraffin (kerosene) or use a dedicated chain cleaner, then wipe it off and allow it to dry. If the chain is excessively dirty, remove it for cleaning (see Chapter 7).

Caution: Don't use petrol (gasoline), solvent or other cleaning fluids which might damage the internal sealing properties of the chain. Don't use high-pressure water. The entire process shouldn't take longer than five minutes – if it does, the O-rings in the chain rollers could be damaged.

18 The best time to lubricate the chain is after the motorcycle has been ridden. When the chain is warm, the lubricant will penetrate the joints between the side plates better than when cold. **Note:** *An O-ring or X-ring chain*

is fitted as standard, depending upon year of manufacture. Some lubricants contain solvents that could damage the seals. KTM specifies Motorex Chainlube 622 spray chain lube.

19 Apply the lubricant to the area where the side plates overlap – not the middle of the rollers – and protect the tyre and rear brake disc from overspray with a rag or piece of cardboard **(see illustration)**.

> **HAYNES HiNT** *Apply the lubricant to the top of the lower chain run, so centrifugal force will work it into the chain when the bike is moving. After applying the lubricant, let it soak in a few minutes before wiping off any excess.*

2 Cooling system

> ⚠ *Warning: The engine must be cool before beginning this procedure.*

1 Check the coolant level (see *Pre-ride checks*).

2 The entire cooling system should be checked for evidence of leaks and damage. Remove the fuel tank (see Chapter 4). Remove the radiator panels and, if fitted, the cooling fan assembly (see Chapter 3).

3 Check the radiator fins for mud, dirt and insects, which may impede the flow of air through the radiator. If the fins are dirty, clean the radiator using water or low pressure compressed air directed through the fins from the back of the radiator **(see illustration)**. If the fins are bent or distorted, straighten them carefully with a screwdriver. Bent or damaged fins will restrict airflow and impair the efficiency of the radiator causing the engine to overheat.

1.19 Protect the tyre and brake disc from chain lube overspray

2.3 Clean the radiators from the back to the front

2.5a Examine the coolant hoses (arrowed) . . .

2.5b . . . for splits and abrasions (arrowed)

Where there is substantial damage to the radiator's surface area, renew the radiator.

4 Check the radiators for leaks. Leaks leave tell-tale scale deposits or coolant stains on the outside of the core below the leak. If leaks are noted, remove the radiator (see Chapter 3) and have it repaired by a specialist.

Caution: Do not use a liquid leak stopping compound to try to repair leaks.

2.8a Location of the water pump

5 Examine each coolant hose along its entire length **(see illustrations)**. Look for splits, abrasions and other signs of deterioration. Squeeze each hose at various points. They should feel firm, yet pliable, and return to their original shape when released. If they are cracked or hard, replace them with new ones (see Chapter 3).

6 Check for evidence of leaks at each cooling system joint. If necessary, tighten the hose clips carefully to prevent future leaks.

7 Check the thermostat housing joint for evidence of leaks (see Chapter 3). If the joint is leaking, renew the O-ring (see Chapter 3).

8 The water pump is located on the left-hand side of the cylinder head **(see illustration)**. To prevent leakage of water from the cooling system to the lubrication system and vice versa, two seals are fitted in the pump. If either seal fails, a drain hole below the pump allows the leaking coolant or oil to escape **(see illustration)**. If there are signs of leakage, either water or oil, or both if the leakage is white with the texture of emulsion, remove the

pump and replace both seals with new ones (see Chapter 3).

9 Check the condition of the coolant in the system. If it is discoloured or accumulations of scale are visible, drain, flush and refill the system with new coolant (see Chapter 3).

10 Check the antifreeze content of the coolant with an antifreeze hydrometer **(see illustration)**. A mixture with less than 40% antifreeze (40/60 antifreeze to distilled water) will not provide proper corrosion protection. Sometimes coolant looks like it's in good condition, but might be too weak to offer adequate protection. If the hydrometer indicates a weak mixture, drain, flush and refill the system (see Chapter 3). A higher than specified concentration of antifreeze decreases the performance of the cooling system and should only be used in extremely cold conditions when additional protection against freezing is needed.

11 If fitted, check the operation of the cooling fan. If there is a fault, refer to Chapter 3 and check the fan motor and switch.

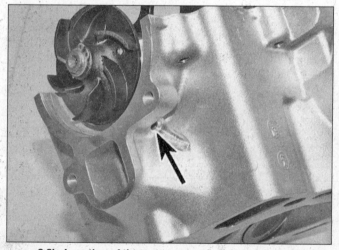

2.8b Location of the water pump drain hole (arrowed)

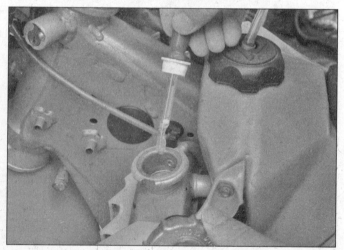

2.10 Using an antifreeze hydrometer

3.1a Wear indicator grooves (arrowed) on the front brake pads

3.1b Check the rear brake pads (arrowed) from the rear of the caliper

12 If the engine overheats, it is possible that the thermostat is faulty. Refer to Chapter 3 for test details.

13 If the coolant level is consistently low, and no evidence of leaks can be found, have the system pressure-checked by a KTM dealer.

3 Brake pads, lever and pedal

⚠ **Warning: The dust created by the brake system may contain asbestos, which is harmful to your health. Never blow it out with compressed air and don't inhale any of it. An approved filtering mask should be worn when working on the brakes.**

Brake pads

1 Pad wear can be determined without removing them from the calipers. On the front brake, the friction material has wear indicator grooves which are visible on the front edge of each pad **(see illustration)**. On the rear brake, the thickness of the friction material can be checked visually at the back of the caliper **(see illustration)**.

2 If the pads are dirty or if you are in doubt as to the amount of friction material remaining, remove them for inspection (see Chapter 7). If required, measure the amount of friction material remaining and compare the result with the Specifications at the beginning of this Chapter **(see illustration)**. If the pads are worn to the limit, new ones must be installed. Always renew both pads in the caliper at the same time.

Caution: Do not allow the pads to wear to the extent that the backing plates contact the disc itself, as the disc will be damaged.

3 Inspect the surface of the pads for contamination. If a pad is fouled with oil or grease, or is heavily scored or damaged by dirt and debris, both pads must be renewed as a set. Note that it is not possible to degrease the friction material; if the pads are contaminated in any way, new ones must be fitted. **Note:** *If the pads are contaminated with brake fluid check for leaks at the brake hose banjo union and at the caliper bleed valve. Check for leaks from behind the caliper piston seals (see Chapter 7).*

4 Check that each pad has the same amount of wear as the other. If uneven wear is evident, either a caliper piston or the caliper slider pins are probably sticking, in which case the caliper must be overhauled (see Chapter 7).

5 If the pads are in good condition, clean them carefully using a fine wire brush which is completely free of oil and grease, to remove all traces of dirt and corrosion. Using a pointed instrument, dig out any embedded particles of foreign matter. Any areas of glazing may be removed using a fine file.

6 Spray the inside of the caliper with a dedicated brake cleaner to remove any dust. Check that the pad spring is correctly secured inside the caliper **(see illustration)**.

7 Remove any traces of corrosion from the pad pin which might cause sticking of the

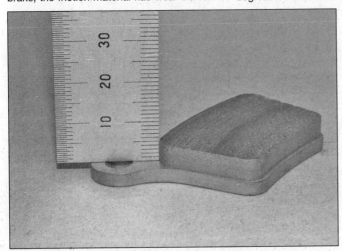
3.2 If required, the friction material can be measured

3.6 The pad spring must be securely located inside the caliper – rear brake shown

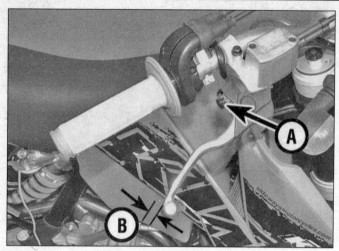

3.9 Brake lever adjuster (A) should allow at least 3 mm free travel at (B)

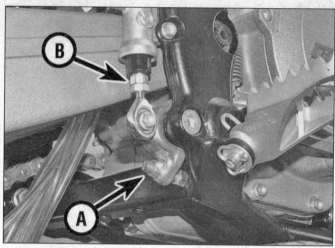

3.10 Rear brake pedal stop bolt (A) and pushrod locknut (B)

caliper/pad operation. Renew the pin R-clips if they are corroded or sprained.

8 Follow the procedure in Chapter 7 to install the brake pads.

Front brake lever

9 The front brake lever has a span adjuster which alters the distance of the lever from the handlebar (see illustration). Turn the adjuster until the setting which best suits the rider is obtained. When making adjustment, ensure that there is at least 3 mm free travel in the lever before the lever pushrod contacts the master cylinder piston.

Rear brake pedal

10 The position of the rear brake pedal can be adjusted by turning the stop bolt (see illustration). Loosen the locknut and turn the bolt until the setting which best suits the rider is obtained, then tighten the locknut. When making adjustment, ensure that there is between 3 to 5 mm free travel in the pedal

before the master cylinder pushrod contacts the piston inside the cylinder. If necessary, loosen the locknut on the pushrod and adjust the freeplay, then tighten the locknut.

4 Suspension

1 The suspension components must be maintained in top operating condition to ensure rider safety. Loose, worn, damaged or badly adjusted suspension will decrease the motorcycle's stability and control.

Front suspension

Note: *If the machine is ridden in competition, loosen the air bleed screws in the fork top bolts after five hours use to release excess pressure (see Step 8). Pressure build-up can cause oil leaks even when the seals are good – always release the pressure and test ride the bike before condemning the fork oil seals.*

2 While standing alongside the motorcycle, apply the front brake and push on the handlebars to compress the forks several times. See if they move up and down smoothly without binding. If binding is felt, the forks should be disassembled and inspected (see Chapter 6).

3 Undo the screws securing the fork protectors and remove them (see illustration). Ensure that the fork sliders are clean – if not, wash them with warm soapy water to avoid scratching the surface. Carefully lever off the dust seals using a flat-bladed screwdriver and inspect the area around the seals (see illustration).

4 If the dust seals are worn, water and dirt will be trapped behind them – note that fine dust will accumulate behind the seals even if they are good. If the oil seals are worn, oil will leak from the forks. In both cases, new seals must be fitted (see Chapter 6). Note that pressure build-up inside the fork legs can cause oil to leak even when the seals are good (see Step 8).

4.3a Remove the fork protectors

4.3b Lever the dust seals off carefully

4.5 Check for scratches, corrosion and pitting on the inner tubes (arrowed)

4.8 Location of the front fork air bleed screws (arrowed)

5 Inspect the fork inner tubes for scratches, corrosion and pitting **(see illustration)**. Any damage to the surface of the tubes will cause premature seal failure (see Step 4). Use chrome polish to remove minor surface imperfections. If the damage is excessive, new inner tubes should be installed (see Chapter 6).

6 Before installing the dust seals ensure they are clean and that no dirt is trapped in the seal seats in the bottom of the fork outer tubes. Lubricate the seals with dry film lubricant or a smear of engine oil, then push them into position by hand.

7 Check the tightness of all suspension nuts and bolts to be sure none have worked loose, referring to the torque settings specified at the beginning of Chapter 6.

8 Support the motorcycle using an auxiliary stand so that the front wheel is off the ground **(see illustration 1.2)**. Loosen the air bleed screws in the fork top bolts to release any excess pressure that has built-up inside the fork legs during use **(see illustration)**. Note

that on some models an air bleed valve is fitted. Under certain circumstances, pressure can force oil past the fork seals even thought the seals are in good condition – always release the pressure and test ride the bike before condemning the fork oil seals.

9 The front suspension is adjustable for spring pre-load, compression and rebound damping. See Chapter 6 for details. **Note:** *It is essential that both fork legs are adjusted equally.*

10 The front fork oil should be changed at the specified service interval (see Chapter 6, Section 7). Note that it is not necessary to disassemble the fork legs completely the change the oil.

Rear suspension

Note: *If the machine is ridden in competition, White Power Suspension recommend that the shock is serviced after 20 to 25 hours use. Servicing should only be carried out by a KTM dealer or White Power Suspension specialist.*

11 Inspect the rear shock for fluid leaks and tightness of its mountings. If leakage is

found, a new shock should be installed (see Chapter 6).

12 With the aid of an assistant to support the bike, compress the rear suspension several times. It should move up and down freely without binding. If any binding is felt, the worn or faulty component must be identified and renewed. The problem could be caused by a damaged shock absorber or swingarm.

13 Support the motorcycle using an auxiliary stand so that the rear wheel is off the ground **(see illustration 1.2)**. Grab the swingarm and rock it from side to side – there should be no discernible movement at the rear **(see illustration)**. If there is a little movement or a slight clicking can be heard, check that all the rear suspension mounting bolts are tight, referring to the torque settings specified at the beginning of Chapter 6, and re-check for movement.

14 Next, grasp the top of the rear wheel and pull it upwards – there should be no discernible freeplay before the shock absorber begins to compress **(see illustration)**. Any freeplay felt

4.13 Checking for play in the swingarm

4.14 Checking for play in the rear suspension

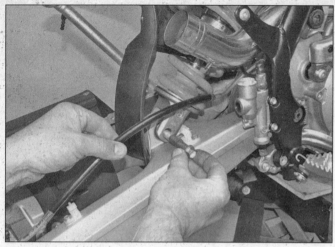

4.15 Remove the lower shock mounting bolt

5.2 Check that the rim lock nut (arrowed) is tight

in either check indicates worn bearings in the swingarm, or worn shock absorber mountings. The worn components must be renewed (see Chapter 6).

15 To make a more accurate assessment of the swingarm bearings, first remove the rear wheel (see Chapter 7). Next, remove the bolt securing the lower end of the shock absorber to the swingarm **(see illustration)**. Support the shock with a cable-tie to the rear sub-frame so that it is clear of the mounting on the swingarm.

16 Grasp the rear of the swingarm with one hand and place your other hand at the junction of the swingarm and the frame. Try to move the rear of the swingarm from side to side. Any wear (play) in the bearings should be felt as movement between the swingarm and the frame at the front. If there is any play, the swingarm will be felt to move forward and backward at the front (not from side-to-side).

17 Next, move the swingarm up and down through its full travel. It should move freely, without any binding or rough spots. If any play

in the swingarm is noted or if the swingarm does not move freely, it must be removed for inspection (see Chapter 6).

18 The rear shock is adjustable for spring pre-load, compression and rebound damping. See Chapter 6 for details.

5 Tyres, wheels and wheel bearings

Tyres

1 Check the tyre condition, pressures and tread depth thoroughly – see *Pre-ride checks*.
2 Check that the rim locknut is tightened securely **(see illustration)**. When the bike is ridden off-road with the appropriate low tyre pressures, the rim lock prevents the tyre slipping on the rim and pulling the valve out of the inner tube.
3 Check the valve stem for signs of damage and renew the inner tube if necessary (see

Chapter 7). Also, make sure the valve cap is in place and tight. Check that the wheel balance weights, if fitted, are fixed firmly to the wheel rim. If the weights have fallen off, have the wheel rebalanced by a motorcycle tyre specialist.

Wheels

4 Support the motorcycle using an auxiliary stand so that the wheels are free to rotate **(see illustration 1.2)**. Check each spoke for looseness by tapping it gently with a small spanner or screwdriver and listening to the sound **(see illustration)**. The 'tone' of each spoke should sound the same.
5 If a spoke sounds dull or rattles, try to pull it backwards and forwards to confirm that it is loose.
6 A loose spoke can be tightened with a torque wrench once the tyre has been removed. Tighten the spoke carefully to the torque setting specified at the beginning of this Chapter. Alternatively, tighten the spoke using a spoke key **(see illustration)**.

5.4 Tap each spoke to check for looseness

5.6 Spokes can be tightened with a spoke key

7 If several spokes are loose, note their positions, then tighten them evenly, a little at a time in a criss-cross pattern to avoid pulling the wheel out of true. Check the wheel's radial and axial runout (see Chapter 7). If necessary, take the wheel to a wheel building expert for correction.

8 If a spoke is bent it must be replaced with a new one. First check the wheel runout (see Chapter 7). If the wheel is true, remove the tyre and rim tape (see Chapter 7), then undo the spoke nipple and draw the damaged spoke out from the hub, noting its alignment with adjacent spokes. Insert the new spoke through the hub and screw it into the nipple in the rim, then tighten the spoke to the specified torque setting. If the wheel is out of true, take it to a KTM dealer or wheel building expert for correction.

9 If a spoke is damaged, inspect the wheel rim for cracks, flat spots and other damage. Look very closely for dents in the area where the tyre bead contacts the rim. Dents in this area may prevent the tyre seating against the rim, which leads to vibration and uneven wear of the tyre over a period of time. If damage is evident, or if runout in either direction is excessive, the wheel will have to be replaced with a new one.

Wheel bearings

10 Wheel bearings will wear over a period of time and result in handling problems.

11 Support the motorcycle upright using an auxiliary stand so that the wheel being checked is off the ground – have an assistant hold the bike to ensure that it is secure. Check for any play in the bearings by pushing and pulling the wheel against the hub (see illustrations). Also rotate the wheel and check that it rotates smoothly.

12 If any play is detected in the hub, or if the wheel does not rotate smoothly (and this is not

5.11a Checking for play in the front . . .

5.11b . . . and rear wheel bearings

due to brake or transmission drag), the wheel must be removed and the bearings inspected for wear or damage (see Chapter 7).

6 Cables

> **Warning: Petrol (gasoline) is extremely flammable, so take extra precautions when you work on any part of the fuel system. Don't smoke or allow open flames or bare light bulbs near the work area, and don't work in a garage where a natural gas-type appliance is present. If you spill any fuel on your skin, rinse it off immediately with soap and water. When you perform any kind of work on the fuel system, wear safety glasses and have a fire extinguisher suitable for a Class B type fire (flammable liquids) on hand.**

Throttle cables

1 Make sure the throttle twistgrip rotates easily from fully closed to fully open with the front wheel turned at various angles. Also check that the twistgrip returns automatically from fully open to fully closed when released.

2 If the throttle operates smoothly, check the cable adjustment as follows.

3 There should be a small amount of freeplay in the opening cable between the twistgrip and the carburettor, measured in the amount of twistgrip rotation before the throttle opens (see illustration). Compare the throttle cable freeplay to that listed in this Chapter's Specifications.

4 If the freeplay is incorrect, remove the fuel tank to access the adjusters on the carburettor end of the cables (see Chapter 4).

5 Pull back the boot on the lower (opening) cable adjuster (see illustration). Loosen the locknut, then turn the adjuster until the specified amount of twistgrip freeplay is achieved, then tighten the locknut. **Note:** *If the adjuster has reached the limit of its adjustment, renew the cable (see Chapter 4).*

6 Undo the screw securing the cable pulley cover and lift the cover off to check the operation of the pulley. When the throttle is closed, the pulley stop should rest on the top of the idle adjuster screw (see

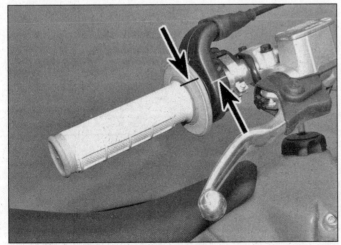

6.3 Check for a small amount of freeplay in the throttle cable at the twistgrip (arrowed)

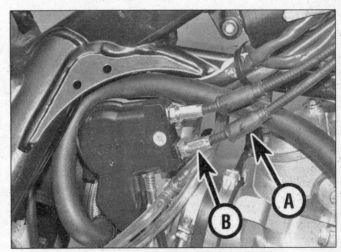

6.5 Opening cable boot (A) and adjuster (B)

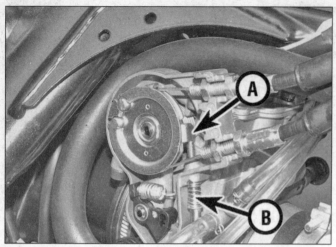

6.6 Location of the cable pulley stop (A) and idle adjuster screw (B)

6.7 Tighten the locknuts after cable adjustment

illustration). If necessary, adjust the upper (closing) cable.

7 Once the throttle cables have been correctly adjusted, ensure that the locknuts are tight **(see illustration)**. Clean any dust out of the pulley housing with compressed air and a small paint brush, taking care not to disturb

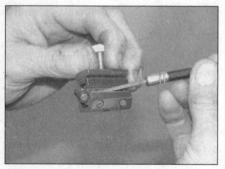

6.8a Fitting the cable lubricating adapter onto the inner throttle cable

the accelerator pump setting. Install the pulley cover and refit the boots on the cable adjusters.

8 If the throttle sticks, this is probably due to a cable fault. Remove the opening and closing cables (see Chapter 4) and lubricate them with a pressure adapter and aerosol lubricant suitable for nylon-lined cables **(see illustrations)**.

9 If an inner cable still does not run smoothly in the outer cable, renew the cable. Note that in very rare cases the fault could lie in the carburettor rather than the cables (see Chapter 4). Check the condition of the boots on the throttle cable adjusters and renew them if they are damaged or deteriorated.

10 With the cables removed, check that the twistgrip turns smoothly around the handlebar – dirt combined with a lack of lubrication can cause the action to be stiff. Clean and lubricate the twistgrip pulley and the inside of the twistgrip housing with dry film lubricant.

11 Install the lubricated or new cables,

making sure they are correctly routed (see Chapter 4).

12 Install the fuel tank. Start the engine and check that the idle speed does not rise as the handlebars are turned. If it does, a cable is routed incorrectly or is badly adjusted. This is a dangerous condition that can cause loss of control of the bike. Be sure to correct this problem before riding the bike.

Decompressor cable

13 If the decompressor cable does not operate smoothly this is probably due to a cable fault. Remove the cable and lubricate it as follows.

14 Remove the fuel tank (see Chapter 4). Pull back the boot on the lower end of the cable and loosen the adjuster locknut. Turn the adjuster to slacken the cable, then unhook the inner cable end from decompressor lever. Pull back the boot on the upper end of the cable and loosen the adjuster locknut **(see**

6.8b Ensure that the adapter grips the inner and outer cables firmly

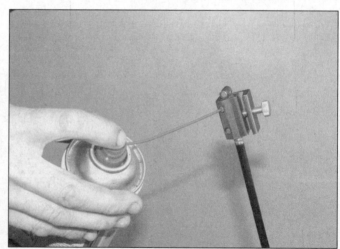

6.8c Connect the can of cable lubricant to the adapter

Routine maintenance and Servicing 1•17

6.14 Cable adjuster is underneath the boot (arrowed)

7.4 Location of the ignition coil (arrowed)

illustration). Unscrew the adjuster from the lever bracket and release the inner cable end from the lever.

15 Lubricate the cable with a pressure adapter and aerosol lubricant **(see illustrations 6.8a, 8b and 8c)**.

16 If the inner cable still does not run smoothly in the outer cable, renew the cable.

17 If the handlebar lever is stiff, undo the pivot screw and remove the lever from its bracket, then check for damage or distortion, or any other cause, and remedy as necessary. Clean and lubricate the pivot and contact areas with dry film lubricant.

18 Install the cable in the reverse of the removal procedure, leaving a small amount of freeplay. Tighten the adjuster locknut on the lower end of the cable and refit the boot, then install the fuel tank (see Chapter 4).

19 Check the cable adjustment as follows. Start the engine and allow it to idle. Slowly pull back the handlebar lever until the rocker arm can be felt knocking against the decompressor lever – there should be approximately 10 mm of freeplay in the handlebar lever before the knocking is felt **(see illustration 6.14)**. If necessary, turn the adjuster on the upper end of the cable until the freeplay is correct, then tighten the locknut and refit the boot.

20 Routine adjustments can now be made at the upper end of the cable.

7 Ignition system

Warning: The energy levels in electronic systems can be very high. On no account should the ignition be switched on whilst the plug or plug cap is being held in the hand – shocks from the HT circuit can be most unpleasant. Secondly, it is vital that the spark plug is soundly earthed when the system is checked for sparking. The ignition system components can be seriously damaged if the HT circuit becomes isolated.

1 All models covered in this manual are fitted with a fully transistorised capacitor discharge ignition (CDI) system which, due to its lack of mechanical parts, is totally maintenance-free. SX models have an ignition system only; on EXC models, the ignition, starting and lighting systems are combined in one wiring loom. Refer to Chapter 5 for full details of the ignition system.

2 On EXC models, before checking that the ignition system is producing a good spark at the plug, ensure that the battery is fully charged and that the main fuse is good. On 2000 and 2001 models, the capacitor should provide sufficient power for the ignition system in the event of a discharged battery (see Chapter 5).

3 Remove the fuel tank (see Chapter 4).

4 Check that the ignition coil, CDI unit and, where fitted, capacitor, are securely mounted and that the wiring connectors are tight **(see illustration)**.

5 Disconnect the HT lead from the spark plug **(see illustration)**. Connect the lead to a known good spark plug that is correctly gapped, and lay the plug on the engine with its threads contacting the engine. If necessary, hold the spark plug with an insulated tool.

Warning: Do not remove the spark plug from the engine to perform this check – atomised fuel being pumped out of the open spark plug hole could ignite, causing severe injury!

6 Having observed the above precautions, check that the ignition kill switch is in the RUN position, then turn the engine over on the kickstarter or starter motor. If the system is in good condition a regular, fat blue spark should be evident at the plug electrodes. If the spark appears thin or yellowish, or is non-existent, further investigation will be necessary, otherwise fit a new spark plug (see Section 24).

7 The ignition system must be able to produce a spark which is capable of jumping a particular size gap. KTM do not provide a specification, but a healthy system should produce a spark capable of jumping at least 5 to 6 mm. A simple testing tool can be purchased to test the minimum gap across which the spark will jump **(see illustration)**.

8 Connect the HT lead to the terminal on the test tool and clip the tool to a good earth on the engine. Turn the engine over – if everything is in good condition a regular, fat blue spark should be seen to jump the gap set on the tool.

7.5 Pull the cap off the spark plug

7.7 An adjustable spark gap tester

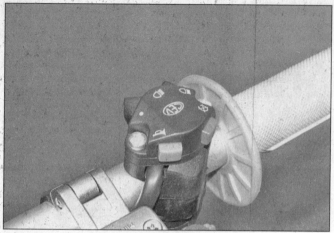
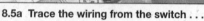

8.5a Trace the wiring from the switch . . .

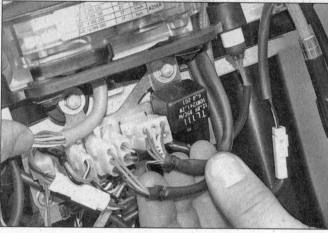

8.5b . . . to the wiring connector

9 If the ignition system fails to produce a satisfactory spark, unscrew the plug cap from the HT lead. Using an insulated tool, hold the end of the lead approximately 5 mm from a good earth point on the engine such as a clean cylinder head bolt, and test for a spark between the end of the lead and the bolt. If a regular, fat blue spark is seen to jump the gap then it is possible that either the plug cap is faulty or there was a poor connection between the cap and the HT lead.

10 Using a multimeter, check the cap resistance. Set the meter to the K-ohms scale and connect the meter probes to the terminals inside the cap. If the reading obtained differs significantly from the figure shown in the Specifications, the cap is proven faulty and must be renewed. If the cap is good, cut back the end of the HT lead by a small amount so that the core wire is visible, then screw the cap on firmly.

11 If the ignition system still fails to produce a satisfactory spark, refer to Chapter 5 for further tests.

8 Handlebar switches and headlight aim

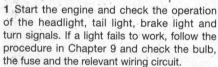

1 Start the engine and check the operation of the headlight, tail light, brake light and turn signals. If a light fails to work, follow the procedure in Chapter 9 and check the bulb, the fuse and the relevant wiring circuit.

2 Check the operation of the headlight main beam and turn signal warning lights next to the speedometer. If a warning light fails to illuminate, refer to Chapter 9 and check the relevant warning light bulb and wiring circuit.

Handlebar switches

3 Most troubles, when they do occur, are caused by dirty or corroded contacts, but wear and breakage is a possibility that should not be overlooked. If breakage does occur, the switch will have to be replaced with a new one.

4 The switches can be checked for continuity using a multimeter or a continuity test light (see Chapter 9). Always disconnect the battery negative (-ve) lead to prevent the possibility of a short circuit, before making the checks.

5 Remove the headlight panel (see Chapter 8). Trace the wiring from the switch to be tested to the connector and disconnect it (see illustrations). Check for continuity between the terminals on the switch side of the connector with the switch in various positions, i.e. switch OFF – no continuity, switch ON – continuity. Use the wire colours to identify the switch terminals (see *Wiring Diagrams*, Chapter 9).

6 If the check indicates a problem exists, undo the screws securing the two halves of the switch housing and lift them off the handlebar. Clean and inspect the switch wiring terminals for damage, then smear the contacts with silicone grease before reassembly (see illustration). If any of the switch components are damaged or broken, fit a new switch assembly (see Chapter 9).

7 Ensure that the headlight wiring is secure and that the panel is correctly installed on reassembly.

Headlight aim

Note: *An improperly adjusted headlight may cause problems for oncoming traffic or provide poor, unsafe illumination of the road ahead. Before adjusting the headlight aim, be sure to consult with local traffic laws and regulations.*

For UK owners refer to 'MOT test checks' in the Reference section at the back of this manual.

8 The headlight beam can be adjusted vertically. Make any adjustments to the headlight aim with the machine on level ground, with the fuel tank half full and with an assistant sitting on the seat.

9 The headlight adjuster is on the front of the headlight panel below the headlight (see illustration). Turn the adjuster clockwise to raise the beam, and anti-clockwise to lower it.

10 Start the engine and check the operation of the headlight dip and main beam before riding the bike on the road.

9 Fasteners

1 Since vibration of the machine tends to loosen fasteners, all nuts, bolts, screws, etc. should be periodically checked for proper tightness.

2 Pay particular attention to the following:
   Spark plug
   Engine oil drain plug
   Gearchange lever, brake and clutch lever, and brake pedal mounting bolts
   Sidestand bolts
   Engine mounting bolts
   Rear shock absorber and swingarm pivot bolts

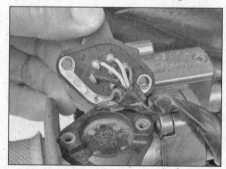

8.6 Inspect the switch wiring terminals for damage

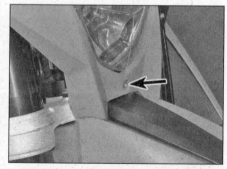

8.9 Location of the headlight adjuster (arrowed)

10.2 Keep the exterior of the carburettor clean

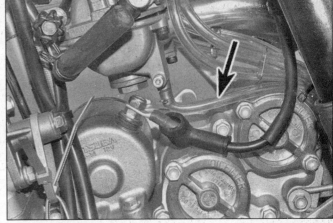

10.6a Trace the drain hose (arrowed) from the carburettor . . .

Handlebar clamp bolts
Front axle and axle clamp bolts
Front fork clamp bolts (top and bottom yoke)
Rear axle nut
Brake caliper mounting bolts
Brake hose banjo bolts and caliper bleed valves
Brake disc bolts
Exhaust system bolts

3 If a torque wrench is available, use it along with the torque specifications at the beginning of this and other Chapters.

10 Carburettor

Warning: Petrol (gasoline) is extremely flammable, so take extra precautions when you work on any part of the fuel system. Don't smoke or allow open flames or bare light bulbs near the work area, and don't work in a garage where a natural gas-type appliance is present. If you spill any fuel on your skin, rinse it off immediately with soap and water. When you perform any kind of work on the fuel system, wear safety glasses and have a fire extinguisher suitable for a Class B type fire (flammable liquids) on hand.

Cleaning

1 Remove the fuel tank (see Chapter 4).
2 The exterior of the carburettor should be kept clean and free of oil and dirt **(see illustration)**. If necessary, wash it carefully with hot soapy water and dry it with compressed air. Clean away any grit with a small paint brush. Oil deposits can be removed with a rag soaked in a suitable solvent. Take care not to disturb the idle speed setting during cleaning.
3 Undo the screw securing the throttle cable pulley cover and lift the cover off. Clean any dust out of the pulley housing and check the operation of the cables (see Step 6).
4 Provided the air filter element is kept clean (see Section 11) the carburettor will give many hours of satisfactory service. However, dirt particles will gradually accumulate inside the body, and vibration will wear to the throttle slide, needle and needle jet. Consequently, the carburettor should be removed and disassembled at the specified service interval to avoid poor running (see Chapter 4).

Draining

5 After every wet cleaning procedure the carburettor float chamber should be drained to remove any traces of water.
6 Ensure that the fuel tap is OFF. Trace the drain hose from the bottom of the float chamber and position a suitable container under its lower end **(see illustrations)**.
7 Undo the drain screw several turns and allow the contents of the float chamber to drain into the container, then tighten the screw securely **(see illustration)**.
8 Finally, open the fuel tap and check that the drain screw is fully closed.

11 Air filter element

1 On 2000 to 2003 models, first remove the number plate panel (see Chapter 8). Turn the two quick-release fasteners securing the left-hand side panel anti-clockwise, then pull them outwards. Draw the panel forwards and off.
2 On 2004 to 2007 models, pull the front edge of the left-hand side panel away carefully to

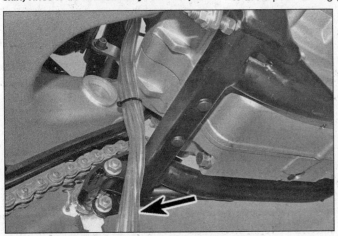

10.6b . . . to the underside of the bike

10.7 Undo the drain screw on the bottom of the float chamber

11.2a Pull the front edge of the panel away . . .

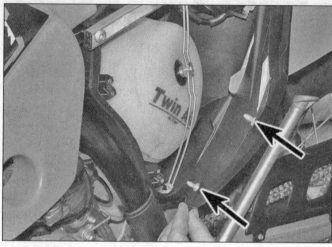

11.2b . . . to release the clips (arrowed) on the inside

release the pegs on the inside of the panel from the clips on the frame, then lift the panel off **(see illustrations)**.

3 Release the lower end of the wire clip securing the filter assembly, then raise the clip and lift the assembly out of its housing **(see illustrations)**. Where fitted, separate the outer cover from the element.

4 Note how the inside edge of the filter element is secured by pegs on the supporting frame, then ease the element off the frame **(see illustrations)**.

11.3a Release the lower end of the wire clip . . .

11.3b . . . and lift out the filter assembly

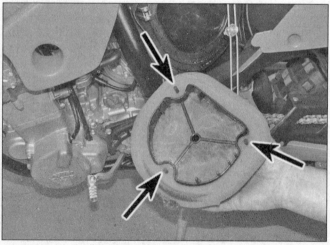

11.4a Release the filter element from the pegs (arrowed) . . .

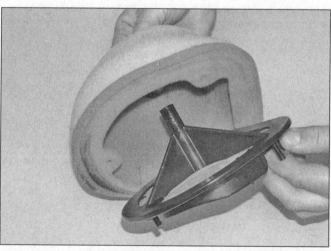

11.4b . . . and separate the element from the frame

11.10a Ensure that the filter locates all the way round the housing . . .

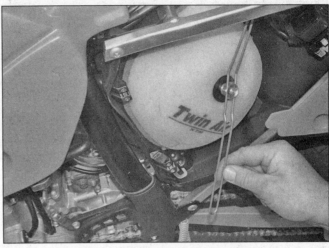

11.10b . . . and secure it with the wire clip

5 Check the element for signs of damage. If it is torn or is obviously beyond further use, replace it with a new one.

6 If the element is undamaged but dirty, wash it in a warm detergent solution. KTM recommend Motorex Bio Dirt Remover – never use a solvent cleaner or petrol/gasoline as these will damage the foam. Once the element has been washed, rinse it thoroughly in clean water and dry it. Never wring the filter dry as it may tear.

7 Soak the element in clean air filter oil – KTM recommend Motorex Liquid Bio Power. If necessary, lay the element on an absorbent surface to absorb any excess oil. Make sure you do not damage the foam by twisting it.

8 Ensure that the filter housing is clean and dry inside. Check that the seal between the housing and the carburettor is correctly located and tightened securely.

9 Install the filter element onto the support frame and ensure that it is correctly secured by the pegs. If applicable, fit the outer cover.

10 Install the filter assembly in the housing, making sure that it locates correctly into the rim of the housing (see illustration). Secure the assembly with the wire clip (see illustration).

11 Install the left-hand side panel, making sure it is correctly aligned with the tabs on the mudguard unit (see illustration). On 2000 to 2003 models, push the quick-release fasteners in, then turn them clockwise to lock. On 2004 to 2007 models, press the pegs firmly into the clips on the frame.

12 Stand and lever pivots

1 Since the stand and control levers are exposed to the elements, they should be inspected and cleaned regularly to ensure safe and trouble-free operation.

2 The footrest pivots, handlebar lever pivots, brake pedal, gearchange lever and kickstart lever pivots, and the stand pivot will all benefit from light lubrication to ensure smooth operation and to deter corrosion.

3 When working on the handlebar levers, draw the covers off to ensure that no dirt is trapped inside (see illustration).

4 Ideally, in order that the lubricant is applied where it will do the most good, the component should be disassembled. However, if an aerosol lubricant is being used, it can be applied to the pivot joint gaps and then worked into the areas where friction occurs. Note: One of the best lubricants for the control lever pivots is a dry-film lubricant (available from motorcycle and accessory shops). If motor oil or light grease is being used, apply it sparingly as it will attract dirt (which could cause the controls to bind or wear at an accelerated rate).

5 Lubricate the stand pivot and check the operation of the stand. The stand return springs must be capable of retracting the stand fully and holding it retracted when

11.11 Align the left-hand panel with the tabs (arrowed)

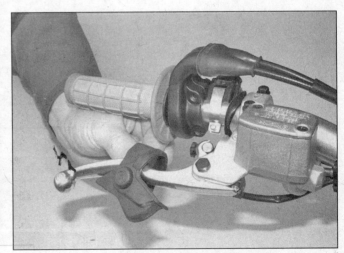

12.3 Pull the covers off to inspect the handlebar levers

12.5 Check that the springs (arrowed) hold the stand up securely

13.3 Unscrew the oil filler cap

the motorcycle is in use **(see illustration)**. If a spring has sagged or broken, it must be replaced with a new one (see Chapter 6).

13 Engine oil and filters

⚠️ *Warning: Be careful when draining the oil, as the exhaust pipes, the engine, and the oil itself can cause severe burns.*

1 Regular oil and filter changes are the single most important maintenance procedure you can perform on a motorcycle. The oil not only lubricates the internal parts of the engine, transmission and clutch, but it also acts as a coolant, a cleaner, a sealant, and a protector. Because of these demands, the oil takes a terrific amount of abuse and should be drained and the engine refilled with new oil

of the correct type and grade at the specified service interval. The oil strainers should be cleaned and both filters should be changed at the same time.
2 Before changing the oil, warm up the engine so the oil will drain easily.
3 Support the bike securely on level ground, and position a drain tray below the engine. Unscrew the oil filler cap (dipstick on early models) from the front of the clutch cover to vent the crankcase and to act as a reminder that there is no oil in the engine **(see illustration)**.
4 Next, unscrew the oil drain plug from the sump on the bottom of the engine and allow the oil to flow into the drain tray **(see illustration)**. Note the magnet on the plug and clean off any metal swarf **(see illustration)**. Check the condition of the sealing washer on the drain plug and discard it if it is damaged or worn. It is good practice to fit a new washer whenever the drain plug is removed.
5 When the oil has completely drained, fit

HAYNES HiNT *Place a strainer between the engine and the drain tray so that any debris in the oil is filtered out and can be examined. If there are flakes or chips of metal in the oil or on the drain plug magnet, then something is drastically wrong internally and the engine will have to be disassembled for inspection and repair.*

the plug into the sump, using a new sealing washer if necessary, and tighten it to the torque setting specified at the beginning of this Chapter. Avoid overtightening, as damage to the sump will result.
6 A short oil strainer for the transmission oil feed is located forward of the drain plug and is secured by a hex socket plug. Insert a socket into the plug and tap it lightly with a hammer to relieve stress on the plug threads, then

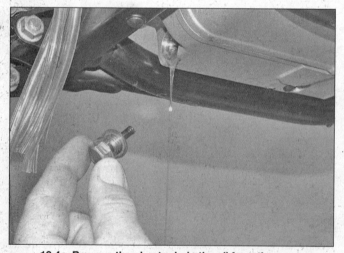

13.4a Remove the plug to drain the oil from the sump

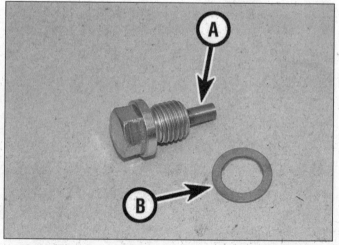

13.4b Clean the magnet (A) and fit a new sealing washer (B)

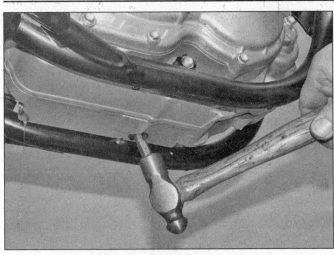

13.6a Tap the hex socket . . .

13.6b . . . then remove the plug and short strainer

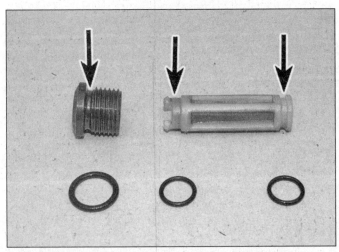

13.7 Note the locations (arrowed) for the O-rings

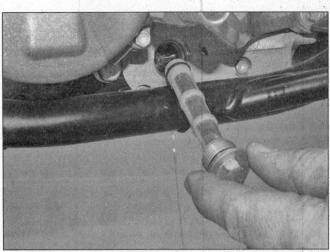

13.9 Unscrew the plug and withdraw the long strainer

unscrew the plug and withdraw the strainer **(see illustrations)**.

7 Withdraw the strainer from the plug, noting the location of the O-rings on the strainer and the plug **(see illustration)**. Clean the strainer using a suitable solvent and dry it with compressed air, if available. Check the condition of the O-rings and renew them if they are damaged or flattened.

8 Lubricate the O-rings with clean engine oil and press the strainer into the plug. Lubricate the threads of the plug with oil, then install the plug and tighten it to the specified torque setting.

9 A long oil strainer for the camshaft oil feed is located below the gearchange lever – if required, secure the lever with a cable-tie around the cam chain tensioner to aid access.

Unscrew the plug and withdraw the strainer **(see illustration)**.

10 Withdraw the strainer from the plug, noting the location of the O-rings on the strainer and the plug **(see illustration)**. Clean the strainer using a suitable solvent and dry it with compressed air, if available. Check the condition of the O-rings and renew them if they are damaged or flattened **(see illustrations)**.

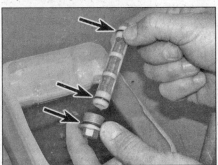

13.10a Note the locations (arrowed) for the O-rings

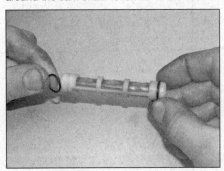

13.10b Renew the O-rings . . .

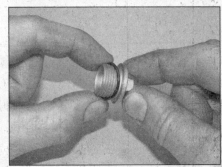

13.10c . . . if they are damaged or flattened

13.12a Insert the rod into the crankcase . . .

13.12b . . . slide the strainer into position . . .

11 To install the long strainer you will require a piece of rod, approximately 300 mm long, that will pass through the middle of the strainer.
12 First lubricate the O-rings with clean engine oil. Insert the rod into the crankcase and locate it in the seat of the strainer on the opposite side of the engine **(see illustration)**.

Slide the strainer along the rod and press it carefully into its seat, then withdraw the rod **(see illustrations)**.
13 Ensure that the strainer is correctly located in its seat, then install the plug and tighten it to the specified torque setting **(see illustration)**.
14 The oil filters are located on the left-hand side above the transmission. If required,

displace the lead from the starter motor terminal to aid access.
15 Place a rag below the filter housings to absorb any residual oil, then undo the bolts securing the filter covers and lift them off **(see illustrations)**. Note the O-rings on the covers and renew them if they are damaged or flattened.

13.12c . . . then hold the strainer and withdraw the rod

13.13 Install the plug and tighten it as specified

13.15a Undo the bolts (arrowed) . . .

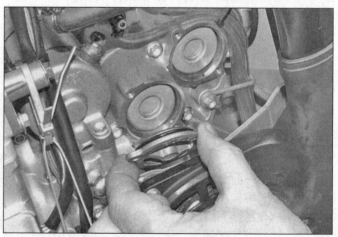

13.15b . . . and remove the oil filter covers

13.16 Pull the filters out from their housings

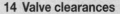

13.18 Prime the lubricating system as described

16 Withdraw the filters from their housings using a pair of needle-nose pliers **(see illustration)**. Note that the long filter fits in the front housing and the short filter fits in the rear housing.

17 Wipe the inside of the housings and the covers with clean rag to remove any old oil.

18 Lay the bike over on its right-hand side, then pour a small amount of clean engine oil into each housing to prime the lubricating system **(see illustration)**. **Note:** *KTM recommends half-filling the filter housings, but in our experience this resulted in a considerable amount of spillage when the filters were installed.*

19 Coat the outside of the new filters with engine oil, then insert them slowly into their respective housings **(see illustration)**.

20 Install the filter covers and tighten the bolts to the specified torque setting **(see illustration)**.

21 Support the bike upright and refill the engine to the correct level using the specified type and grade of oil (see *Pre-ride checks*). Install the filler cap **(see illustration 13.3)**. **Note:** *If the valve clearances are going to be checked, wait until this has been done before refilling with oil - see Note at the beginning of Section 14.*

22 Start the engine and let it run for two or

three minutes. Shut it off, wait a few minutes, then check the oil level. If necessary, add more oil to correct the level. Check around the drain plug, the strainer plugs and the filter covers for leaks.

 HAYNES HiNT *Saving a little money on the difference between good and cheap oils won't pay off if the engine is damaged as a result.*

23 The oil drained from the engine cannot be re-used and should be disposed of properly. Check with your local refuse disposal company, disposal facility or environmental agency to see whether they will accept the used oil for recycling and the old filters for disposal. Don't pour used oil into drains or onto the ground.

 **OIL CARE**

0800 66 33 66
www.oilbankline.org.uk

Note: It is antisocial and illegal to dump oil down the drain. To find the location of your local oil recycling bank, call this number free.
In the USA, note that any oil supplier must accept used oil for recycling.

14 Valve clearances

Note: *When installed without its thick sealing washer, the crankshaft position screw holds the crankshaft at TDC (compression). For this reason, checking the valve clearances is best done during the oil change procedure, before the engine is filled with fresh oil (see Section 13).*

1 Drain the engine oil (see Section 13).

2 The engine must be completely cold for this procedure, so let the machine sit overnight before beginning.

3 Position a support underneath the crankcase so that the bike is upright with the rear wheel off the ground **(see illustration 1.2)**.

4 Remove the fuel tank (see Chapter 4).

5 Disconnect the lead from the negative terminal of the battery. Remove the spark plug (see Section 24) so that the crankshaft is easier to turn.

6 If required, the aid access, displace or remove the right-hand radiator (see Chapter 3).

13.19 Install the filters into their respective housings

13.20 Ensure that each cover is fitted with an O-ring (arrowed)

14.7 Note the sealing washers on the rocker cover bolts (arrowed)

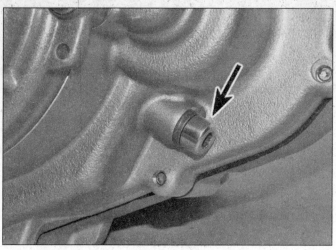

14.9a Location of the crankshaft position screw

7 Undo the bolts and remove the front and rear rocker covers (see illustration). Discard the sealing washers on the bolts and the cover gaskets as new ones must be fitted.

8 Turn the engine with the kickstart lever until the piston is at top dead centre (TDC) on the compression stroke – all valves closed. To check the position of the piston, insert a small screwdriver through the spark plug hole so that it rests on the top of the piston. Select a high gear and have an assistant turn the rear wheel slowly by hand backwards and forwards until the piston is at the mid-point between rising and falling.

9 The exact point of TDC (compression) can be determined using the crankshaft position screw which is located on the front, right-hand side of the crankcase (see illustration). Undo the screw and remove the thick sealing washer. Next, install the screw by hand – if the crankshaft is in the exact TDC (compression) position, the screw will go all the way in and locate in a notch in the right-hand flywheel (see illustrations). If the screw does not go all the way in, repeat the procedure in Step 8 to rock the crankshaft backwards and forwards until the screw locates in the notch.

10 With the piston at TDC (compression) there should be discernable freeplay in the rocker arms in the form of a clearance between the adjusters and the valve stems (see illustration). If one pair of valves is open, rotate the crankshaft a further 360° to realign the TDC position on the compression stroke.

11 Check the clearance on each valve by inserting a feeler gauge of the correct thickness (see Specifications) between the rocker arm adjuster screw and the valve stem – the gauge should be a firm sliding fit (see illustration).

12 If the clearance is incorrect on the valve

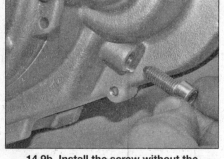

14.9b Install the screw without the washer . . .

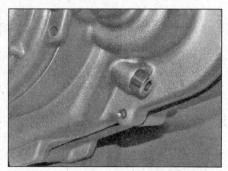

14.9c . . . at TDC (compression) it will go all the way in

14.10 Check for clearance between the valves and the rocker adjusters (arrowed)

14.11 Checking the valve clearance with a feeler gauge

14.12a Using a cranked screwdriver to adjust the valve clearance

14.12b Hold the adjuster and tighten the locknut securely

14.15 Fit new rocker cover gaskets

15.2a Camshaft cover banjo union (A). Note the spacer (B)

being checked, loosen the adjuster locknut and turn the adjuster using a suitable screwdriver until the correct clearance is obtained (see illustrations). Hold the adjuster in position and tighten the locknut securely, then re-check the clearance to ensure that it hasn't changed and readjust it if necessary.

13 When all four valves have been checked, undo the crankshaft position screw, install a new, thick sealing washer, then tighten the screw to the torque setting specified at the beginning of this Chapter.

14 Turn the engine with the kickstart lever and check the operation of the rocker arms.

15 Install new gaskets on the camshaft cover, holding them in position with a dab of grease of required (see illustration). Install the rocker covers, fit new sealing washers to the cover bolts, then tighten the bolts to the specified torque setting.

16 Install the remaining components in the reverse order of removal.

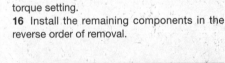

15 Camshaft oil feed

1 Remove the fuel tank (see Chapter 4). The oil feed pipe runs from the top of the crankcase behind the cylinder to the top of the camshaft cover.

2 Inspect the pipe for damage and check for leaks at the banjo unions at both ends (see illustrations).

3 If any leaks are found, first check that the banjo bolts are tightened to the torque setting specified at the beginning of this Chapter. If the bolts are tight, renew the sealing washers fitted to both sides of each union (see illustration).

15.2b Oil feed banjo union on the top of the crankcase (arrowed)

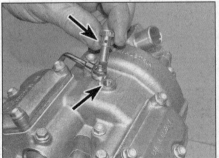

15.3 Sealing washers should be fitted to both sides of the banjo union (arrowed)

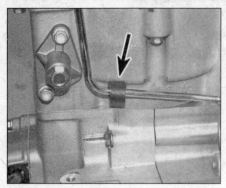

15.5 Make sure the spacer (arrowed) is in place on the oil feed pipe

4 If the pipe is damaged it must be renewed. Note the spacer on the cable-tie securing the wiring and clutch hose to the pipe **(see illustration 15.2a)**. If the tie is renewed it is important that the spacer is

not lost – in use, the pipe gets very hot and without the spacer the wiring may become damaged.

5 Check that the spacer is in position between the pipe and the back of the cylinder and fit a new one if it is deteriorated or missing **(see illustration)**.

16 Brake and clutch hoses

Brake

1 Look for leaks at the hose connections and check for deterioration or damage in the hoses themselves **(see illustrations)**. To check the connection to the rear brake master cylinder, first undo the screw securing the protective cover and lift the cover off **(see illustrations)**.

2 Twist and flex each hose while looking for cracks, bulges and seeping fluid. Check extra carefully around the areas where the hose connects with the master cylinder and caliper banjo unions, as these are common areas for hose failure. If any faults are found, renew the brake hose (see Chapter 7).

3 If the lever or pedal feels spongy, bleed the brakes (see Chapter 7). The brake fluid should be changed every year and the hoses renewed if they deteriorate, or every four years irrespective of their condition (see Chapter 7). Check the master cylinder and caliper for leaks and renew the seals if necessary (see Chapter 7).

Clutch

4 Remove the fuel tank (see Chapter 4), then inspect the clutch hose, its connections, the master cylinder on the handlebars and the release cylinder on the left-hand side of the crankcase for signs of fluid

16.1a Inspect each brake hose connection (arrowed) . . .

16.1b . . . and check the hose (arrowed) for damage

16.1c Remove the cover . . .

16.1d . . . to check the rear brake master cylinder connection (arrowed)

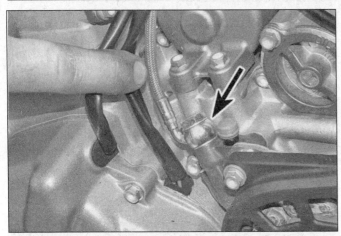

16.4 Clutch hose connection to the release cylinder

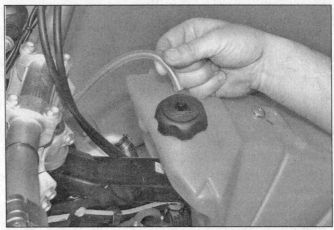

17.1a Check the breather hose on the fuel tank filler cap ...

17.1b ... the radiator filler neck ...

17.1c ... and the carburettor

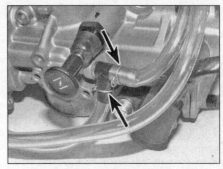

17.3 Carburettor breather hoses are secured by clips (arrowed)

leakage, deterioration and wear **(see illustration)**.

5 If any leaks or damage are found they must be rectified immediately. Refer to Chapter 2 for details of the clutch release cylinder.

6 Check the operation of the clutch. If there is evidence of air in the system (spongy feel to the lever, difficulty in engaging gear), bleed the system (see Chapter 2). If the lever feels stiff or sticky, check the operation of the lever and/or overhaul the master cylinder and the release cylinder (see Chapter 2).

17 Breather hoses

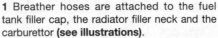

1 Breather hoses are attached to the fuel tank filler cap, the radiator filler neck and the carburettor **(see illustrations)**.
2 Inspect the hoses for damage and deterioration, and check the ends for dirt which may cause blockages.
3 Ensure that the hoses are pressed firmly onto their unions and that any clips

(where fitted) are secure **(see illustration)**.
4 Ensure that the hoses are routed clear of the engine and exhaust system, and clear of the drive chain.

18 Exhaust system

1 The unions between the exhaust header pipes and silencer are secured by springs **(see illustrations)**. Considerable force should

18.1a Exhaust header pipes are secured by stiff springs

18.1b Springs (arrowed) secure pipes and silencer assembly

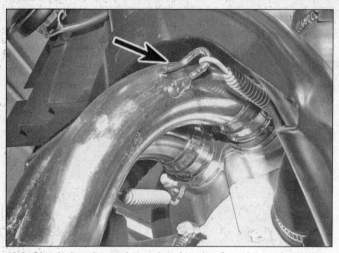

18.2 Check that the anchor points (arrowed) are in good condition

18.4 Water entering the silencer will damage the packing inside

be required to remove and install the springs – check that they are under tension and that the hooked ends are not sprained.

2 Check that the anchor points for the springs are secure **(see illustration)**.

3 Check that the exhaust-to-frame mounting bolts are tightened to the specified torque setting, and check that the mounting bushes are not deformed or deteriorated (see Chapter 4).

4 When washing the bike, block the open end of the silencer to prevent water getting inside and saturating the glass fibre packing **(see illustration)**.

5 The silencer packing should be renewed at the appropriate service interval (see Chapter 4).

19 Idle speed

⚠ **Warning: Take great care not to burn your hand on the hot engine unit when adjusting the engine idle speed. Do not allow exhaust gases to build up in the work area; either perform the adjustment outside or use an exhaust gas extraction system.**

1 The idle speed should be checked and adjusted whenever it is obviously too high or

too low, and after the carburettor has been overhauled.

2 Before adjusting the idle speed, make sure the spark plug is clean and correctly gapped, and that the air filter is clean.

3 The mixture screw is located on the underside of the carburettor **(see illustration)**. If required, KTM provide a service tool (Part No. 590.29.034.000) to make access to the mixture screw easier, although aftermarket alternatives are available **(see illustration)**. The idle speed adjuster is located on the left-hand side of the carburettor **(see illustration)**.

4 Turn the mixture screw all the way in (clockwise), then turn it out the number of turns specified in the standard settings (see Chapter 4).

5 Start the engine and warm it up to normal operating temperature, which is usually reached after 10 to 15 minutes of stop-and-go riding. Make sure the transmission is in neutral, and support the bike upright on an auxiliary stand.

6 With the engine running, turn the idle speed adjuster to achieve the normal idle speed (1400 to 1500 rpm). Turn the adjuster clockwise to increase idle speed, and anti-clockwise to decrease it.

7 Slowly turn the mixture screw in until the idle speed starts to decrease, noting the amount it's moved from its standard position.

Now turn the screw out until the idle speed again starts to decrease. Finally, turn the screw back to the point where the idle speed is the highest between these two positions.

8 If, after this procedure, the idle speed is too high, turn the idle speed adjuster anti-clockwise to correct it, then repeat the procedure.

> **HAYNES HINT** *For competition use, to speed engine warm-up, turn the mixture screw in 1/4 turn from the setting achieved above.*

9 If a satisfactory idle speed cannot be achieved, an incorrectly sized idle jet may be fitted. Compare the results with the following characteristics.

10 If the mixture screw can be turned all the way in without any change in idle speed, select a smaller idle jet.

11 If the engine dies with the mixture screw 2 full turns out, select a larger idle jet.

12 If the idle jet is changed, repeat the procedure to adjust the idle speed.

13 Finally, snap the throttle open and shut a few times and ensure that the idle speed returns to normal.

14 If a smooth, steady idle cannot be

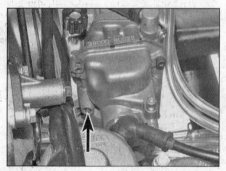

19.3a Location of the carburettor mixture screw

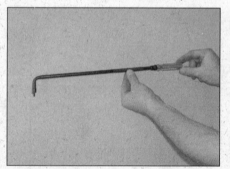

19.3b Aftermarket mixture screw adjuster

19.3c Location of the idle speed adjuster

20.1 Inspect the brake discs for damage

20.2 Measuring the thickness of a brake disc

achieved, refer to Chapter 4 and check the following:

● Inspect the intake manifold for cracks that will cause an air leak, resulting in a weak mixture.
● Check that the carburettor is correctly seated in the manifold and clamped securely.
● Check that the carburettor top cover is correctly fitted.
● Dirt may have entered the carburettor or it may be worn and require overhauling.

⚠️ **Warning: Turn the handlebars all the way through their travel with the engine idling. Idle speed should not change. If it does, the throttle cables may be routed incorrectly or badly adjusted. Correct this condition before riding the bike.**

20 Brake discs

1 Inspect the surface of both brake discs for score marks and other damage **(see illustration)**. Light scratches are normal after use and won't affect brake operation, but deep grooves and heavy score marks will reduce braking efficiency and accelerate pad wear. If

a disc is badly grooved it must be machined or renewed (see Chapter 7).
2 Note that dirt and small stones from off-road riding which become trapped between the pads and disc will accelerate pad and disc wear. Using a micrometer, measure the thickness of the disc in the brake pad contact area **(see illustration)**. Take measurements at several places around the disc. Compare the results with the specifications at the beginning of this Chapter. If a disc has worn down to the service limit a new one must be fitted, together with new pads.
3 Ensure that the disc mounting bolts are tightened to the torque setting specified at the beginning of this Chapter.
4 Follow the procedure in Chapter 7 to check brake disc runout – an out-of-true disc will normally cause a pulsing movement in the brake lever or pedal when the brake is applied. If the disc appears to be out-of-true, first check that the wheel bearings are good (see Section 5).

21 Steering head bearings

1 All the machines covered in this manual are fitted with tapered roller bearings at the top

and bottom of the steering stem. The bearings can become dented, rough or loose during use and, in extreme cases, worn or loose bearings can cause steering wobble – a condition that is potentially dangerous.

Check

2 Support the motorcycle using an auxiliary stand so that the front wheel is off the ground **(see illustration 1.2)**.
3 Slowly turn the handlebars from side to side. Any dents or roughness in the bearing races will be felt and if the bearings are too tight the bars will not move smoothly and freely. If the bearings are damaged or the action is rough, they should be renewed (see Chapter 6). If the bearings are too tight they should be adjusted as described below.
4 Next, point the wheel straight ahead and grasp the bottom of the forks and try to pull and push them forwards and backwards **(see illustration)**. Any freeplay in the steering head bearings will be felt as front-to-rear movement of the forks. If play is felt in the bearings, adjust them as follows.

> **HAYNES HINT** *Freeplay in the fork due to worn fork bushes can be misinterpreted as steering head bearing play – do not confuse the two.*

Adjustment

5 Ensure that the bike is supported securely in an upright position. If required, to aid access to the steering stem nut, displace the handlebars (see Chapter 6).
6 Loosen the two fork clamp bolts on both sides of the top yoke and loosen the steering stem clamp bolt **(see illustration)**.
7 Tighten the steering stem bolt a little at a time until all freeplay is removed **(see illustration 21.6)**. Tap both sides of the top yoke with a plastic mallet to relieve any

21.4 Checking for play in the steering head bearings

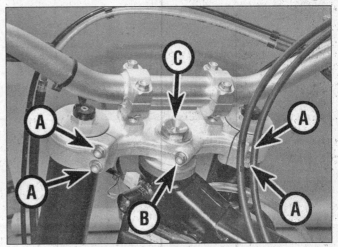

21.6 Fork clamp bolts (A), steering stem clamp bolt (B) and steering stem bolt (C)

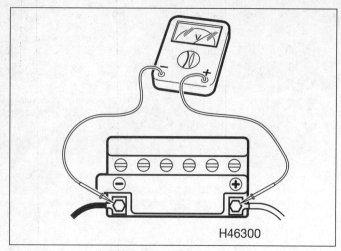

22.3 Checking battery voltage

H46300

H46302

22.5 Checking for current leakage

tension between the yoke and the fork legs, then check the bearing adjustment again.
Caution: Take great care not to overtighten the steering stem bolt because this will cause premature failure of the bearings.
8 Turn the steering from lock to lock several times to settle the bearings and ensure that there is no roughness or notchiness in the movement. If there is, the bearings are damaged and must be renewed (see Chapter 6).
9 If the steering turns smoothly the bearings are correctly adjusted. Tighten all clamp bolts to the torque settings specified at the beginning of Chapter 6.
10 Install the remaining components in the reverse order of removal.

22 Electrical system

1 All EXC models covered in this manual are fitted with a three-phase alternator with separate regulator/rectifier. The alternator provides power for the ac lighting system and charges the battery, which in turn provides power for the starter motor, horn and turn signals. Refer to Chapter 9 for full details. On SX models, the alternator provides power for the ignition system (see Chapter 5).

Battery

Caution: Be extremely careful when handling or working around the battery. The electrolyte inside is very caustic and an explosive gas (hydrogen) is given off when the battery is charging.
2 Remove the seat (see Chapter 8).
3 The condition of the battery can be assessed by measuring the voltage at the battery terminals with the engine stopped. Connect the positive (+ve) probe of a multimeter, set to the volts (DC) scale, to the battery positive (+ve) terminal and the negative (-ve) probe to the battery negative (-ve) terminal **(see**

illustration). When fully charged there should be more than 12.5 volts present. If the voltage falls below 12.0 volts the battery must be removed and recharged (see Chapter 9).
4 If the battery voltage falls repeatedly during use, refer to the procedure in Chapter 9 and check the alternator regulated voltage output.
5 An electrical system fault can cause current leakage from the battery – test as follows. Disconnect the battery negative (-ve) terminal, then connect an ammeter between the earth lead and the negative (-ve) terminal **(see illustration)**. A reading above 1 mA (milliamp) indicates leakage. Refer to Chapter 9 and check the regulator/rectifier, the starter switch and the starter relay. Also check the connections between the various components. Where fitted, check the capacitor (see Chapter 5).
Caution: Always connect an ammeter in series, never in parallel with the battery, otherwise it will be damaged. Do not operate the starter motor when the ammeter is connected – a sudden surge in current will blow the meter's fuse.
6 The battery is of the maintenance free (sealed) type, requiring no regular maintenance other than the following checks of the terminals and damage to the case.
7 Ensure that the battery leads are securely connected to the terminals **(see illustration)**. If

22.7 Check that the battery connections are clean and secure

corrosion is evident, undo the terminal screws and disconnect the leads from the battery, disconnecting the negative (-ve) terminal first. Clean the terminals and lead ends with a wire brush, knife or steel wool. Reconnect the leads, connecting the positive (+ve) terminal first, and apply a thin coat of petroleum jelly or battery terminal grease to the connections to slow further corrosion.
8 The battery case should be kept clean to prevent current leakage, which can discharge the battery over a period of time (especially when it sits unused). Remove the battery (see Chapter 9), then wash the outside of the case with a solution of baking soda and water. Rinse the battery thoroughly, then dry it.
9 Look for cracks in the case and renew the battery if any are found. If acid has been spilled on the frame or battery box, neutralise it with a baking soda and water solution, dry it thoroughly, then touch up any damaged paint.
10 If the motorcycle sits unused for long periods of time, disconnect the leads from the battery terminals, negative (-ve) terminal first. Charge the battery once every month to six weeks (see Chapter 9).

Lighting system

11 The alternator provides power for the headlight, tail light and brake light. Start the engine and check their operation. If none of the lights operate, first check the output of the appropriate alternator coil (see Chapter 9).
12 If the headlight, tail light or brake light fails to work individually, follow the procedure in Chapter 9 and check the bulb, the switch and the relevant wiring circuit.
13 If the turn signals fail to operate, check the main fuse located in the starter relay (see Chapter 9). Note that the electric starter, horn and electronic speedometer are also protected by the fuse. If one signal light fails to work, check the bulb and the bulb terminal first, then the wiring connector; also check the operation of the turn signal relay (see Chapter 9).

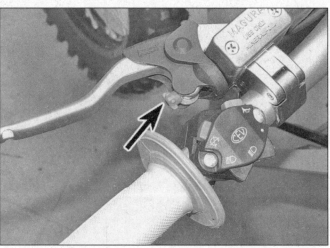

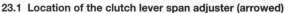

23.1 Location of the clutch lever span adjuster (arrowed)

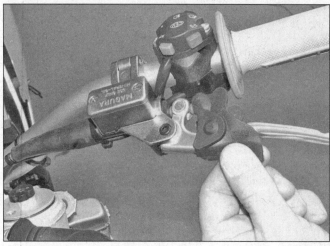

23.2 Pull back the cover to inspect the lever and its bracket

14 Check the operation of the headlight main beam and turn signal warning lights on the instrument cluster. If a warning light fails to illuminate, refer to Chapter 9 and check the relevant warning light bulb and wiring circuit.

23 Clutch lever, springs and plates

Clutch lever

1 The lever has a span adjuster which alters the distance of the lever from the handlebar **(see illustration)**. Turn the adjuster by hand until the setting which best suits the rider is obtained.

2 If the lever feels stiff, pull off the cover and check the lever and the lever bracket for damage **(see illustration)**. If necessary, remove the lever and clean then lubricate the pivot bolt (see Chapter 2, Section 17). Note that it is not necessary to remove the clutch master cylinder from the bike to check the operation of the lever.

3 If the lever action feels spongy, or it becomes difficult to select gears, bleed the operating system (see Chapter 2).

Clutch springs and plates

4 The internal clutch components should be disassembled and inspected for wear at the specified service interval. Note that specifications differ according to year of manufacture – ensure that you compare the parts on your bike with the correct specifications.

5 Refer to Chapter 2 for the disassembly, inspection and reassembly procedure.

24 Spark plug

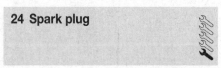

1 Make sure you have a spark plug socket of the correct size before attempting to remove the plug – 16 mm hex.

2 Remove the fuel tank (see Chapter 4). Disconnect the battery negative (-) lead (see Section 22) .

3 If necessary, clean the area around the spark plug to prevent any dirt falling into the engine when the plug is removed.

4 Pull the spark plug cap off the spark plug.

5 If required, to aid access to the plug, undo the right-hand fuel tank support **(see illustration)**.

6 Unscrew the plug from the cylinder head **(see illustration)**.

7 A new spark plug should be fitted at the specified service interval – it is unwise to clean and re-gap an old plug which may then fail in competition use.

8 Before installing the new plug, make sure it is the correct type (see Specifications at the beginning of this Chapter). Check the gap between the electrodes **(see illustrations overleaf)**. Compare the gap to that specified and adjust as necessary. If the gap must be adjusted, bend the side electrode only and be very careful not to chip or crack the insulator

24.5 Unscrew the right-hand tank support . . .

24.6 . . . to gain access with a deep socket plug spanner

24.8a Using a wire type gauge to measure the spark plug electrode gap

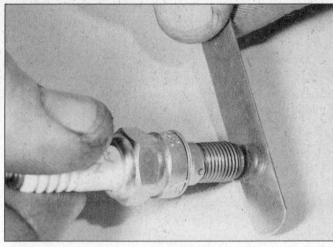

24.8b Using a feeler gauge to measure the spark plug electrode gap

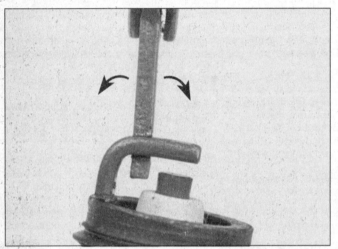

24.8c Adjust the electrode gap by bending the side electrode only

24.9 Thread the plug in by hand to start with

nose **(see illustration)**. Make sure the washer is in place before installing the plug.

9 Since the cylinder head is made of aluminium, which is soft and easily damaged, thread the plug into the head by hand **(see illustration)**. Once the plug is finger-tight, the job can be finished with the plug spanner. Take care not to over-tighten the plug.

> **HAYNES HiNT**
> *A stripped plug thread in the cylinder head can be repaired with a thread insert – refer to the Reference section at the end of this manual.*

10 Reconnect the spark plug cap.
11 If removed, install the right-hand tank support and tighten the bolt to the torque setting specified at the beginning of this Chapter.
12 Connect the battery negative (-) lead (see Section 22) .
13 Install the fuel tank (see Chapter 4).

Chapter 2
Engine, clutch and transmission

Contents

Degrees of difficulty

| Easy, suitable for novice with little experience 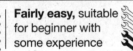 | Fairly easy, suitable for beginner with some experience 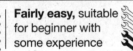 | Fairly difficult, suitable for competent DIY mechanic 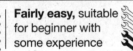 | Difficult, suitable for experienced DIY mechanic 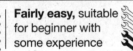 | Very difficult, suitable for expert DIY or professional |

Specifications

General

250 EXC

Bore x stroke . . . . 75 x 56.5 mm
Displacement . . . . 249 cc
Compression ratio . . . . 12 to 1

400 EXC, SX and MXC

Bore x stroke . . . . 89 x 64 mm
Displacement . . . . 398 cc
Compression ratio . . . . 11 to 1

450 EXC and MXC

Bore x stroke . . . . 89 x 72 mm
Displacement . . . . 448 cc
Compression ratio . . . . 11 to 1

450 SX, SXS, 450 SMR, 450 XC

Bore x stroke . . . . 95 x 63.4 mm
Displacement . . . . 449 cc
Compression ratio . . . . 12 to 1

520 EXC, SX and MXC, 525 EXC, SX and MXC/XC, 525 SMR

Bore x stroke . . . . 95 x 72 mm
Displacement . . . . 510 cc
Compression ratio . . . . 11 to 1

540 SXS

Bore x stroke . . . . 100 x 68 mm
Displacement . . . . 534 cc
Compression ratio . . . . 11 to 1

560 SMR

Bore x stroke . . . . 100 x 72 mm
Displacement . . . . 566 cc
Compression ratio . . . . 11 to 1

Rocker arms

Rocker arm end-float
  Specified clearance .... 0.05 mm
  Acceptable variance...................................... 0.02 to 0.10 mm
Valve clearances.. see Chapter 1

Cylinder head and valves

Cylinder head warpage limit................................ 0.10 mm
Valve head runout limit.................................... 0.05 mm
Valve guide inside diameter (intake and exhaust)
  Service limit .... 6.05 mm
Valve seat width
  Intake (service limit) .... 1.5 mm
  Exhaust (service limit)................................. 2.0 mm
Spring seat thickness
  Standard... 0.5 mm
  Service limit .... 0.4 mm
Valve spring free length service limit (intake and exhaust)
  400/520 EXC and MXC, and 450/525 EXC and MXC/XC
    Outer spring .... 39.20 mm
    Inner spring... 36.45 mm
  250 EXC (conical) .... 37.70 mm
  450/525 SX and 450/525/560 SMR (conical).................. 38.30 mm
  450/525 SX, SXS and SMR
    Outer spring .... 32.40 mm
    Inner spring... 30.20 mm
  540 SXS (2004 and 2006)
    Outer spring .... 32.40 mm
    Inner spring... 30.20 mm
  540 SXS (2005)
    Outer spring .... 32.90 mm
    Inner spring... 30.70 mm

Cylinder

Bore diameter (standard)
  250 EXC
    Size I .... 75.000 to 75.012 mm
    Size II .... 75.013 to 75.025 mm
  400 EXC, SX and MXC, 450 EXC and MXC
    Size I .... 89.000 to 89.012 mm
    Size II .... 89.013 to 89.025 mm
  450, 520 and 525 SX, SXS and SMR
    Size I.. 95.000 to 95.012 mm
    Size II .... 95.013 to 95.025 mm
  540 SXS and 560 SMR
    Size I.. 100.000 to 100.012 mm

Piston

Piston diameter
  250 EXC
    Size I diameter .... 74.950 to 74.980 mm
    Piston-to-cylinder clearance (standard) .... 0.020 to 0.062 mm
    Piston-to-cylinder clearance (service limit)............... 0.12 mm
    Size II diameter..................................... 74.960 to 74.990 mm
    Piston-to-cylinder clearance (standard) .... 0.022 to 0.065 mm
    Piston-to-cylinder clearance (service limit)............... 0.12 mm
  400 EXC and MXC
    Size I diameter .... 88.920 to 88.950 mm
    Piston-to-cylinder clearance (standard) .... 0.050 to 0.092 mm
    Piston-to-cylinder clearance (service limit)............... 0.12 mm
    Size II diameter..................................... 88.930 to 88.960 mm
    Piston-to-cylinder clearance (standard) .... 0.052 to 0.095 mm
    Piston-to-cylinder clearance (service limit)............... 0.12 mm
  450 EXC and MXC
    Size I diameter .... 88.916 to 88.946 mm
    Piston-to-cylinder clearance (standard) .... 0.055 to 0.096 mm
    Piston-to-cylinder clearance (service limit)............... 0.12 mm
    Size II diameter..................................... 88.926 to 88.958 mm
    Piston-to-cylinder clearance (standard) .... 0.056 to 0.099 mm
    Piston-to-cylinder clearance (service limit)............... 0.12 mm

Piston (continued)

Piston diameter (continued)

450 SX, XC, SMR and SXS

Size I diameter	94.932 to 94.960 mm
Piston-to-cylinder clearance (standard)	0.040 to 0.080 mm
Piston-to-cylinder clearance (service limit).	0.12 mm
Size II diameter.	94.940 to 94.968 mm
Piston-to-cylinder clearance (standard)	0.044 to 0.085 mm
Piston-to-cylinder clearance (service limit).	0.12 mm

520 EXC and MXC

Size I diameter	94.942 to 94.950 mm
Piston-to-cylinder clearance (standard)	0.060 to 0.070 mm
Piston-to-cylinder clearance (service limit).	0.12 mm
Size II diameter.	94.951 to 94.956 mm
Piston-to-cylinder clearance (standard)	0.064 to 0.075 mm
Piston-to-cylinder clearance (service limit).	0.12 mm

525 SX, SXS and SMR

Size I diameter	94.922 to 94.950 mm
Piston-to-cylinder clearance (standard)	0.050 to 0.090 mm
Piston-to-cylinder clearance (service limit).	0.12 mm
Size II diameter.	94.951 to 94.978 mm
Piston-to-cylinder clearance (standard)	0.034 to 0.075 mm
Piston-to-cylinder clearance (service limit).	0.12 mm

540 SXS and 560 SMR

Size I	99.940 to 99.948 mm
Piston-to-cylinder clearance (standard)	0.060 to 0.090 mm
Size II	99.950 to 99.958 mm
Piston-to-cylinder clearance (standard)	0.060 to 0.090 mm
Piston-to-cylinder clearance (service limit).	0.10 mm

Piston ring end gap

Measured approx. 10 mm below top of cylinder

Top ring service limit.	0.80 mm
Oil ring service limit	1.0 mm

Clutch

Friction plate thickness

2000 to 2003 (all 7 plates)

Standard.	1.8 mm
Service limit	1.7 mm

2004 to 2007 (all 7 plates)

Standard.	2.0 mm
Service limit	1.9 mm

Plain plate thickness

2000 to 2001 (all 8 plates)	not available

2002, 2003, 2006 and 2007

2 inner and 2 outer plates.	1.0 mm
4 middle plates	1.4 mm
2004 and 2005 (all 8 plates)	1.0 mm
Plain plate warpage limit	0 mm

Spring free length

Standard.	43.0 mm
Service limit	42.0 mm

Gearchange mechanism

Selector fork end thickness

Standard.	4.8 to 4.9 mm
Service limit	4.6 mm
Pawl assembly sliding clearance	0.4 to 0.8 mm

Oil pressure relief valve

Oil pressure relief valve spring service limit	23.5 mm

Oil pump

Inner-to-outer rotor clearance – service limit	0.20 mm
Outer rotor-to-housing clearance – service limit	0.20 mm
Drive shaft axial play (end-float).	0.15 mm

Crankshaft, connecting rods and bearings

Crankshaft runout (max)	0.12 mm
Crankshaft assembly width	65 ± 0.05 mm
Crankshaft axial clearance (end-float)	0.25 to 0.35 mm
Connecting rod big-end side clearance (max)	1.10 mm
Connecting rod big-end radial clearance (max)	0.05 mm

Transmission

Input and output shaft axial clearance	0.10 to 0.40 mm

Torque settings

Alternator rotor nut	60 Nm
Alternator cover screws	10 Nm
Automatic decompressor stop bolt	8 Nm (see text)
Balancer shaft drive gear screws	10 Nm***
Camshaft cover bolts	10 Nm
Cam chain tensioner bolts	10 Nm
Cam chain tensioner centre bolt	10 Nm
Camshaft sprocket bolts	28 Nm***
Cam chain tensioner blade bolt	
2000 to 2005	8 Nm***
2006-on	6 Nm***
Cam chain guide bolt	
2000 to 2005	8 Nm***
2006-on	6 Nm***
Clutch centre nut (2003-on)	120 Nm* and ***
Clutch pressure plate screws	8 Nm***
Crankcase bolts and crankcase cover bolts	10 Nm
Cylinder head bolts (M10) – oiled	
Initial torque	40 Nm
Final torque	50 Nm
Cylinder head bolts (M6)	10 Nm
Decompressor bolt	8 Nm
Decompressor mechanism bob weight stop nut	8 Nm*
Engine cover screws	10 Nm
Engine mounting bolts	
2000 to 2004	45 Nm
2005-on	60 Nm
Engine oil pressure relief valve	20 Nm
Exhaust manifold bolts	10 Nm***
Front sprocket cover bolts	10 Nm
Front sprocket bolt	60 Nm***
Gearchange rotor centre bolt	10 Nm***
Gearchange stopper arm pivot bolt	6 Nm***
Gearchange lever bolt	10 Nm***
Ignition pick-up coil bolts	10 Nm***
Kickstart lever bolt	25 Nm***
Kickstart lever stop plate bolts	10 Nm***
Kickstart return spring bolt	10 Nm***
Lower cam chain guard bolts	6 Nm
Oil pump cover bolts	6 Nm**
Primary gear nut	150 Nm***
Selector drum bearing retaining screw	6 Nm***
Starter clutch bolts	16 Nm****
Starter motor mounting bolts	
2000 to 2005	8 Nm***
2006-on	10 Nm***
Swingarm pivot bolt nut	100 Nm
Transmission input shaft bearing retaining screw	5 Nm***
Water pump cover bolts	
2000 to 2005	8 Nm
2006-on	10 Nm

*   *Use a new lock washer*
**   *Use thread locking compound Loctite 222*
*** *Use thread locking compound Loctite 243*
**** *Use thread locking compound Loctite 648*

1 General information

The engine unit is a single cylinder four-stroke, with liquid cooling. There are four valves in the cylinder head, operated by a single overhead camshaft via a pair of rocker arms. The camshaft is chain driven off the left-hand side of the crankshaft. A gear-driven balancer shaft is located in the front of the crankcase.

The crankshaft assembly is pressed together, incorporating the connecting rod, with the big-end running on the crankpin on a roller bearing. The piston runs on a plain bearing pressed in the small-end of the connecting rod. The crankshaft turns on caged roller main bearings. The crankcase divides vertically.

Two separate oil pumps draw oil from the sump to lubricate the engine and transmission respectively.

The alternator is on the left-hand end of the crankshaft. On EXC and MXC/XC models, the starter motor connects to the crankshaft via a reduction gear and sprag clutch.

Power from the crankshaft is routed to the transmission via a multi-plate clutch which is located on the right-hand side of the engine unit. Final drive to the rear wheel is by chain and sprockets.

Read the *Safety first!* **section of this manual carefully before starting work.**

2 Component access

Operations possible with the engine in the frame

The components and assemblies listed below can be removed without having to remove the engine from the frame. If, however, a number of areas require attention at the same time, engine removal is recommended.

Cam chain tensioner
Camshaft cover and rockers
Camshaft
Cylinder head and valves
Cylinder, piston and piston rings
Alternator
Cam chain, tensioner blade and guide
Clutch
Primary drive gear and starter clutch
Kickstart mechanism
External gearchange mechanism
Oil pumps

Operations requiring engine removal

It is necessary to remove the engine from the frame to gain access to the following components.

Crankcase halves and main bearings
Crankshaft assembly and big-end bearing
Balancer shaft and bearings
Selector drum and forks
Transmission shafts

3 Cylinder compression test

 Warning: Be careful when working on the hot engine – the exhaust pipe, the engine and engine components can cause severe burns.

Special tools: *A compression gauge with an appropriate threaded adapter (see Step 5) is required for this procedure.*

1 Among other things, poor starting and engine performance may be caused by leaking valves, a leaking head gasket or worn piston, rings and/or cylinder wall. A cylinder compression check will help pinpoint these conditions.
2 Before carrying out the test, check that the valve clearances are correct (see Chapter 1). Also, where fitted, check that there is sufficient freeplay in the decompressor cable (see Chapter 1, Section 6).
3 Run the engine until it reaches normal operating temperature, then turn the ignition OFF. Support the machine securely on an auxiliary stand.
4 Follow the procedure in Chapter 1, Section 24, and remove the spark plug. Fit the plug back into the cap and position the plug with its threads contacting the engine.
5 Thread the gauge adapter into the spark plug hole then install the compression gauge **(see illustration)**.
6 Open the throttle fully and crank the engine over on the kickstarter or starter motor until the gauge reading stabilises – after four or five revolutions the pressure should build up to a maximum figure and then remain stable. Make a note of the pressure reading.
7 Release the pressure on the gauge, then repeat the procedure. If the reading is different this time, repeat the procedure until you obtain several readings that are the same.
8 KTM provide no specification for cylinder compression, but a good engine should have at least 100 psi in the cylinder.
9 If the compression builds up quickly and

evenly, you can assume that the engine top-end is in good mechanical condition. Worn or sticking piston rings, or a worn cylinder, will produce very little initial movement of the gauge, but compression will tend to build-up as the engine turns over. Valve seat leakage, or head gasket leakage, is indicated by low initial compression which does not build-up.
10 To confirm your findings, use a squirt-type oil can to add a small amount of engine oil into the cylinder through the spark plug hole. The oil will tend to seal the piston rings if they are leaking. Check the compression again and if it increases significantly after the addition of the oil, the rings or cylinder are definitely worn. If the compression remains low, the pressure is leaking past the valves or head gasket.
11 When the test is complete, follow the procedure in Chapter 1, Section 24, and install the spark plug.
Note: *High compression pressure indicates excessive carbon build-up in the combustion chamber and on the top of the piston. If this is the case, remove the cylinder head and clean the carbon deposits off. Note that excessive carbon build-up is less likely with the use of modern fuels.*

4 Engine removal and installation

Caution: *Although the engine is not heavy, removal and installation is a lot easier with the aid of an assistant. Personal injury or damage could occur if the engine falls or is dropped.*

Removal

1 Support the motorcycle securely in an upright position using an auxiliary stand **(see illustration)**. Work can be made easier by raising the machine to a convenient working height on an hydraulic ramp or a suitable platform – make sure it is secure and will not topple over. When disconnecting any wiring, cables and hoses, it is advisable to mark or tag them as a reminder of where they connect.
2 If the engine is dirty, particularly around its mountings, wash it thoroughly before starting any major dismantling work. This will make work much easier and rule out the possibility of dirt falling into some vital component.

3.5 Checking cylinder compression as described

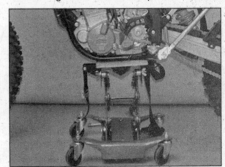

4.1 Use of an auxiliary stand to support the engine

4.8a Release the wiring – note the spacer (arrowed) on the cable tie

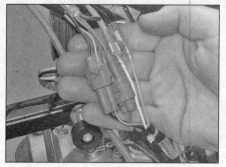

4.8b Disconnect the connectors . . .

4.8c . . . by releasing the small clip first

3 Drain the engine oil (see Chapter 1).
4 Remove the seat (see Chapter 8). Disconnect the negative (–ve) lead from the battery (see Chapter 9).

4.10 Disconnect the lead from the starter motor terminal

5 Remove the fuel tank and the left and right-hand tank support brackets (see Chapter 4).
6 Remove the radiators and disconnect the coolant hoses from the water pump housing and cylinder (see Chapter 3).
7 Remove the exhaust system (see Chapter 4). **Note:** *If the rear wheel has to be removed, loosen the final drive front sprocket bolt before removing the drive chain (see Chapter 7).*
8 Release the wiring from any clips or ties, noting its routing, then disconnect the ignition and alternator wiring connectors **(see illustrations)**. Remove the spacer from the old cable-tie for safekeeping – it must be used on reassembly. Secure the wiring clear of the engine.
9 Pull the cap off the spark plug.
10 Pull back the boot, then undo the nut and disconnect the lead from the starter motor terminal **(see illustration)**.
11 Where fitted, loosen the adjuster on the

decompressor cable, then disconnect the cable end from the decompressor lever. Secure the cable clear of the engine.
12 Release the clips securing the crankcase breather hose and remove the hose **(see illustration)**.
13 On 2004-on models, release the cable-tie securing the wiring for the throttle position sensor, then disconnect the throttle position sensor wiring connector **(see illustrations)**.
14 Position a suitable container under the lower end of the carburettor float chamber drain hose, then loosen the drain screw several turns and drain any residual fuel out of the carburettor **(see illustration)**. Tighten the screw securely.
15 If required, the carburettor can be displaced with the throttle cables in place, otherwise remove the throttle pulley cover and disconnect the cables (see Chapter 4).
16 Draw the carburettor breather hoses up from behind the crankcases **(see illustration)**.

4.12a Release the clips . . .

4.12b . . . securing the crankcase breather hose

4.13a Release the throttle position sensor wiring . . .

4.13b . . . then disconnect the connector

4.14 Draining the carburettor float chamber

4.16 Carburettor breather hoses are secured behind the crankcase

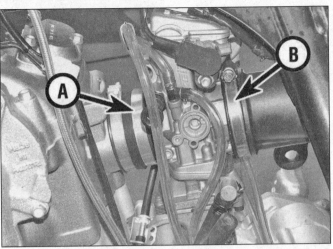

4.17a Clips secure the carburettor to the intake manifold (A) and air filter housing (B)

4.17b Detach the carburettor from the intake manifold . . .

17 Loosen the clips securing the carburettor to the intake manifold and to the air filter housing (see illustration). Ease the carburettor back to detach it from the intake manifold, then draw it forward and off the bike (see illustrations).
18 Undo the screw(s) securing the right-hand frame cover and, if fitted, the clip, then draw the cover off (see illustration).
19 Disconnect the rear brake pedal return spring (see illustration).
20 On 2000 to 2003 models, undo the bolt securing the rear brake fluid reservoir bracket to the crankcase and displace the reservoir. Secure the reservoir in an upright position to prevent fluid loss.
21 Undo the bolts and, where fitted, the cable-tie securing the final drive front sprocket cover; note that the longer bolt fits at the front and secures the chain guide and the clutch release cylinder (see illustrations). Lift the cover off, noting the location of the spacers fitted in the rear of the cover (see illustration).

4.17c . . . then from the air filter housing

4.18 Remove the right-hand frame cover

4.19 Disconnect the rear brake pedal return spring

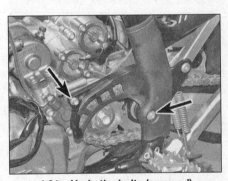

4.21a Undo the bolts (arrowed)

4.21b Note the location of the longer bolt

4.21c Lift the cover off . . .

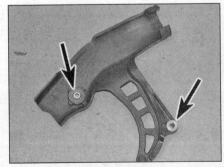

4.21d . . . noting the location of the spacers (arrowed)

4.22a Undo the bolt (arrowed) . . .

4.22b . . . and lift off the chain guide assembly

4.22c Note the arrangement of roller, washers (arrowed) and guide

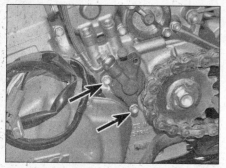

4.24a Undo the bolts (arrowed) . . .

4.24b . . . and displace the clutch release cylinder

Note that it is not necessary to disconnect the clutch hose from the release cylinder.

25 If not already done, remove the rear wheel (see Chapter 7). Unclip the rear brake hose from the swingarm and secure the brake caliper to the rear sub-frame to prevent damage **(see illustration)**. Remove the rear shock absorber (see Chapter 6).

26 Undo the nut on the left-hand end of the swingarm pivot bolt, noting the location of the threaded sleeve for the sprocket cover bolt **(see illustration)**.

27 Support the swingarm and withdraw the pivot bolt, then draw the swingarm off from either side of the crankcase **(see illustrations)**. Note the location of the threaded sleeve for the right-hand frame cover **(see illustration)**.

28 Pivot the lower chain guide back so that it is clear of the crankcase **(see illustration)**.

29 Check that all wiring, cables and hoses

22 Undo the rear bolt securing the chain guide and roller and lift the assembly off **(see illustrations)**.

23 Remove the final drive chain (see Chapter 7). **Note:** *If the final drive front sprocket is*

going to be removed, loosen the sprocket bolt before removing the chain.

24 Undo the two remaining bolts securing the clutch release cylinder and position the cylinder clear of the engine **(see illustrations)**.

4.25 Secure the rear brake caliper to the sub frame

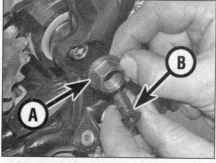

4.26 Undo the nut (A) noting the location of the sleeve (B)

4.27a Withdraw the pivot bolt . . .

4.27b . . . then draw the swingarm off

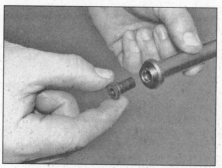

4.27c Note the location of the threaded sleeve in the pivot bolt

4.28 Pivot the lower chain guide back as shown

4.30a **Undo the engine mounting bolts (arrowed) . . .**

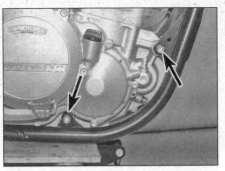

4.30b **. . . noting the location of the captive nuts (arrowed)**

4.31a **Withdraw the front . . .**

are disconnected and positioned clear of the engine.

30 Undo the two engine mounting bolts – note that the nuts on the right-hand side are captive in the engine mounting brackets **(see illustrations)**.

31 Have an assistant support the engine, then withdraw the mounting bolts and carefully manoeuvre the engine out of the frame **(see illustrations)**.

Installation

32 Clean the threads of the engine mounting bolts and the swingarm pivot bolt. Apply a smear of grease to the bolts to help prevent further corrosion. Ensure that the lower chain guide is still pivoted back clear of the crankcase **(see illustration 4.28)**.

33 With the aid of an assistant, carefully lift the engine into position in the frame. Ensure no wires or cables have become trapped between the engine and the frame, then insert the two mounting bolts and tighten them finger-tight.

34 Ensure that the seal caps are in place on the swingarm, then position the swingarm between the frame and the crankcase and insert the pivot bolt from the right-hand side **(see illustration 4.27b)**. Ensure that the flat edge on the head of the bolt is correctly located in the recess in the frame **(see illustration)**.

35 Tighten the mounting bolts to the torque setting specified at the beginning of this Chapter, then tighten the swingarm pivot bolt to the specified torque.

36 Push the lower chain guide forward into

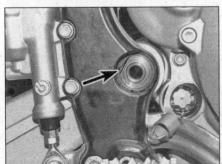

4.34 **Ensure that the flat edge is correctly located**

4.31b **. . . and lower mounting bolts . . .**

its correct position **(see illustration)**.

37 The remainder of the installation procedure is the reverse of removal, noting the following:

● Make sure all wires, cables and hoses are correctly routed and connected, and secured by the relevant clips or ties.

● Don't forget to fit the spacer on the cable-tie around the camshaft oil feed pipe (see Step 8).

● Tighten all bolts to the specified torque settings.

● On 2004 to 2007 models fitted with a two-piece exhaust system, fit the exhaust before installing the rear shock and wheel.

● Follow the procedure in Chapter 4 to install the carburettor.

● Follow the procedure in Chapter 3 to install the coolant hoses and radiators.

● If the throttle cables have been disconnected, adjust the freeplay (see Chapter 1).

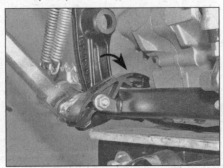

4.36 **Push the lower chain guide forward**

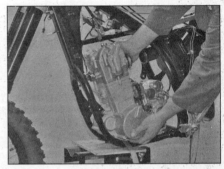

4.31c **. . . then manoeuvre the engine out carefully**

● If the decompressor cable has been disconnected, adjust the freeplay (see Chapter 1).

● Adjust the drive chain (see Chapter 1).

● Refill the engine with oil (see Chapter 1).

● Refill the engine with coolant (see Chapter 3).

● Before riding the bike, start the engine and check that there are no coolant or oil leaks.

● Check the operation of the clutch and the rear brake.

5 Engine disassembly and reassembly – general information

Disassembly

1 Before disassembling the engine, the external surfaces of the unit should be thoroughly cleaned and degreased. This will prevent contamination of the engine internals, and will also make working a lot easier and cleaner. A high flash-point solvent, such as paraffin (kerosene) can be used, or better still, a proprietary engine degreaser such as Gunk. Use a paraffin brush or old paintbrush to work the solvent into the recesses of the engine casings. Take care to exclude solvent or water from the electrical components and intake and exhaust ports.

 Warning: The use of petrol (gasoline) as a cleaning agent should be avoided because of the risk of fire.

2 When the engine is clean and dry, clear a suitable area for working – a workbench is desirable for all operations once a component has been removed from the machine. Gather a selection of small containers and plastic bags so that parts can be grouped together in an easily identifiable manner. Some paper and a pen should be on hand so that notes can be made and labels attached where necessary. A supply of clean rag is also required. If he engine has been removed from the bike (see Section 4), have an assistant help you lift it onto the workbench.

3 Before commencing work, read through the appropriate section so that some idea of the necessary procedure can be gained. When removing components it should be noted that great force is seldom required. In many cases, a component's reluctance to be removed is indicative of an incorrect approach or removal method – if in any doubt, re-check with the text. In cases where fasteners have corroded, apply penetrating oil or WD40 before disassembly.

4 When disassembling the engine, keep 'mated' parts together (e.g. camshaft and rockers, valve assemblies, piston and rings, clutch plates etc. that have been in contact with each other during engine operation). These 'mated' parts must be reused or renewed as assemblies.

5 A complete engine/transmission disassembly should be done in the following general order with reference to the appropriate Sections.

> Remove the cam chain tensioner
> Remove the camshaft cover
> Remove the camshaft
> Remove the cylinder head
> Remove the cylinder
> Remove the piston
> Remove the starter motor (see Chapter 9)
> Remove the alternator
> Remove the cam chain, tensioner blade
> and guide
> Remove the clutch
> Remove the primary drive gear and starter
> clutch
> Remove the oil pumps
> Remove the kickstart mechanism
> Remove the external gearchange
> mechanism

6.1 Unscrew the centre bolt and sealing washer and withdraw the spring

> Separate the crankcase halves
> Remove the selector drum and forks
> Remove the transmission shafts/gears
> Remove the balancer shaft
> Remove the crankshaft and connecting rod
> assembly

Reassembly

6 Reassembly is accomplished by reversing the general disassembly sequence.

6 Cam chain tensioner

Note: *This procedure can be carried out with the engine in the frame. If the engine has been removed, ignore the steps that do not apply.*

Removal

1 Unscrew the tensioner centre bolt and sealing washer and withdraw the spring **(see illustration)**.
2 Unscrew the tensioner fixing bolts and withdraw the tensioner from the engine **(see illustration)**. Discard the gasket as a new one must be fitted.

Inspection

3 Examine the tensioner components for signs of wear, scoring or damage.

6.2 Withdraw the tensioner from the engine

4 Pull the plunger out from the tensioner body and examine the teeth on the ratchet **(see illustration)**. Now try to press the plunger back into the body – it should be locked in position.
5 Release the catch on the ratchet and ensure that the plunger moves freely in and out of the tensioner body.
6 Press the plunger into the body and temporarily install the tensioner on the back of the cylinder, then fit the spring and centre bolt **(see illustration 6.1)**. Now unscrew the centre bolt and withdraw the spring. Insert a small screwdriver into the tensioner and try to push the plunger out further against the pressure of the tensioner blade **(see illustration)**. If the plunger moves, then the spring has lost its tension.
7 A check on the condition of the cam chain can be done at this stage. Unscrew the fixing bolts and withdraw the tensioner body carefully, noting the position of the plunger. Press the screwdriver into the tensioner to see how much adjustment remains on the plunger – if there are only two or three clicks of movement left, the chain and tensioner blade should be inspected for wear (see Section 16).
8 If any of the tensioner components are worn or damaged, a new tensioner will have to be fitted – individual components are not available.

Installation

9 Ensure the mating surfaces of the tensioner

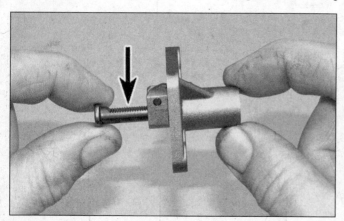

6.4 Examine the teeth (arrowed) on the ratchet

6.6 Checking the spring tension

6.9 Fit a new tensioner body gasket on assembly

7.3 Unscrew the fuel tank support brackets on both sides

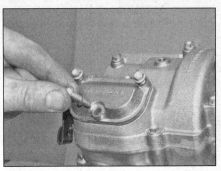

7.7 Remove the front and rear rocker covers

and cylinder are clean and fit a new gasket onto the tensioner **(see illustration)**.
10 Press the plunger into the body and install the tensioner on the back of the cylinder, then tighten the fixing bolts to the torque setting specified at the beginning of this Chapter.
11 Fit the spring and centre bolt with a new sealing washer and tighten the bolt to the specified torque **(see illustration 6.1)**.

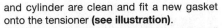

7 Camshaft cover

Note: *The camshaft cover can be removed with the engine in the frame. If the engine has been removed, ignore the steps which do not apply.*

Removal

1 Drain the engine oil (see Chapter 1).
2 Position a support underneath the crankcase so that the bike is upright with the rear wheel off the ground **(see illustration 4.1)**.
3 Remove the fuel tank (see Chapter 4). Undo the left and right-hand tank support brackets **(see illustration)**.
4 Disconnect the lead from the negative (-) terminal of the battery (see Chapter 1, Section 22).
5 Remove the spark plug (see Chapter 1) so the crankshaft is easier to turn.
6 Drain the cooling system and disconnect the

coolant hose from the top of the water pump housing (see Chapter 3). If required, to aid access, remove the radiators (see Chapter 3).
7 Undo the bolts and remove the front and rear rocker covers **(see illustration)**. Discard the sealing washers on the bolts and the cover gaskets as new ones must be fitted.
8 Turn the engine with the kickstart lever until the piston is at top dead centre (TDC) on the compression stroke – all valves closed. To check the position of the piston, insert a small screwdriver through the spark plug hole so that it rests on the top of the piston. Select a high gear and have an assistant turn the rear wheel slowly by hand backwards and forwards until the piston is at the mid-point between rising and falling.
9 The exact point of TDC (compression)

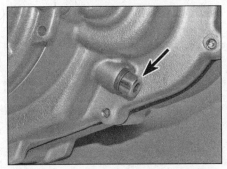

7.9a Location of the crankshaft position screw

can be determined using the crankshaft position screw which is located on the front of the crankcase on the right-hand side **(see illustration)**. Undo the screw and remove the thick sealing washer. Next, install the screw by hand – if the crankshaft is in the exact TDC (compression) position, the screw will go all the way in and locate in a notch in the right-hand flywheel **(see illustrations)**. If the screw does not go all the way in, repeat the procedure in Step 8 to rock the crankshaft backwards and forwards until the screw locates in the notch.
10 With the piston at TDC (compression) there should be discernable freeplay in the rocker arms in the form of a clearance between the adjusters and the valve stems **(see illustration)**. If one pair of valves is open,

7.9b Install the screw without the washer . . .

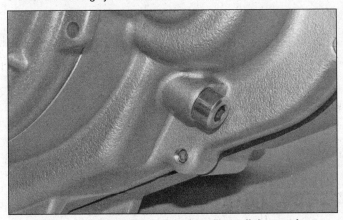

7.9c . . . at TDC (compression) it will go all the way in

7.10 Check for clearance between the valves and the rocker adjusters (arrowed)

7.13a Undo the banjo union on the camshaft cover . . .

7.13b . . . and on the top of the crankcase (arrowed)

7.13c Note the spacer (arrowed) on the oil feed pipe

rotate the crankshaft a further 360° to realign the TDC position on the compression stroke.
11 Follow the procedure in Section 6 to remove the cam chain tensioner.
12 Where fitted, loosen the adjuster on the decompressor cable, then disconnect the cable end from the decompressor lever.
13 Release the cable-tie securing the wiring and the clutch hose to the camshaft oil feed

pipe **(see illustration 4.8a)**. Remove the spacer from the old cable-tie for safekeeping – it must be reused on reassembly. Undo the banjo bolts at both ends of the camshaft oil feed pipe, noting the location of the sealing washers **(see illustration)**. Note that the shorter bolt screws into the camshaft cover. Lift off the pipe, noting the location of the spacer **(see illustrations)**.
14 Undo the bolts and remove the water

pump cover **(see illustrations)**. Discard the cover gasket as a new one must be fitted.
15 Undo the bolts securing the camshaft cover **(see illustration)**. Note the location of the bolts as they are of different lengths **(see illustration)**. Note the location of the sealing washers – keep the washers with the bolts as a reminder, but note that new washers must be fitted on reassembly.

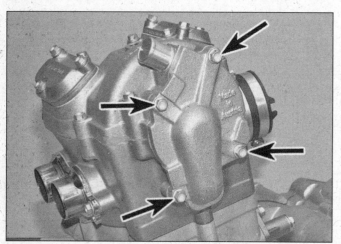

7.14a Undo the bolts (arrowed) . . .

7.14b . . . and remove the water pump cover

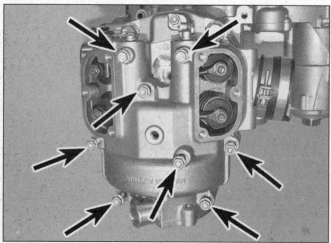

7.15a Undo the camshaft cover bolts

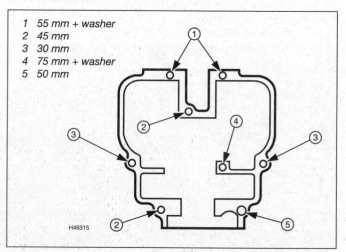

7.15b Location of camshaft cover bolts and sealing washers

1 55 mm + washer
2 45 mm
3 30 mm
4 75 mm + washer
5 50 mm

7.16 Lift off the camshaft cover

7.21 Apply an even bead of sealant to the cover

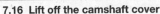

HAYNES HiNT *Make a cardboard template of the camshaft cover and punch a hole for each bolt location. As each bolt is removed, store it in its relative position in the template. This will ensure all bolts are installed correctly on reassembly.*

16 Lift the cover off **(see illustration)**. If the cover sticks, tap around the joint with a soft-faced mallet to free the sealant bond. Do not attempt to lever the cover off with a screwdriver – you'll damage the sealing surfaces. Note the location of the two cover dowels – they may be in the cover or the mating surface of the cylinder head. Remove the dowels for safekeeping if they are loose.

Installation

17 Before installing the camshaft cover, check the O-ring seals on the water pump seal carrier. If the seals are damaged or flattened, or if there is evidence of water or oil leakage from either side of the carrier, renew the O-rings (see Chapter 3).
18 Remove all traces of old sealant from the mating surfaces. If a scraper must be used, be very careful not to nick or gouge the soft aluminium or oil leaks will result.
19 Clean the threads of all the cover bolts.
20 Ensure that the holes in the rocker shafts, end caps and cover are aligned **(see illustrations 8.11 and 8.3a)**.
21 Make sure that the dowels are in place, then apply a thin, even bead of suitable sealant to the mating surface of the cover **(see illustration)**.
Caution: Don't apply an excessive amount of sealant as it will ooze out when the cover is installed and may obstruct the water pump drain passages.
22 If there was insufficient clearance to remove the centre cover bolt with the engine in the frame, install the bolt now.
23 Carefully lower the cover down onto the cylinder head, making sure that it aligns with the camshaft bearings and the dowels. Once

the cover is correctly seated, install the bolts finger-tight ensuring that they are in their correct locations **(see illustration 7.15b)**. Don't forget to fit new sealing washers where applicable.
24 Before tightening the cover bolts, refer to the Specifications at the beginning of this Chapter and check the rocker arm end-float as follows.
25 Working on one rocker arm at a time, insert a suitable feeler gauge between the arm and the end cap, then press the cap inwards to remove any freeplay between the other end of the arm and the cover **(see illustration)**. Now tighten the bolt that passes through the shaft and end cap to the torque setting specified at the beginning of this Chapter.
26 Follow the same procedure on the other arm, then tighten all the cover bolts to the specified torque setting.
27 Re-check that the rocker arm end-float is within acceptable limits (see Specifications).
28 Install the remaining components in the reverse order of removal, noting the following:
● Tighten all bolts to the specified torque settings.
● Fit a new gasket on the water pump cover (see Chapter 3).
● Fit new sealing washers to both sides of the camshaft oil feed pipe banjo unions (see Step 13).
● Don't forget to fit the spacer on the cable-tie around the camshaft oil feed pipe (see Step 13).

● Follow the procedure in Section 6 to install the cam chain tensioner.
● Check the valve clearances (see Chapter 1).
● Fit new gaskets on the rocker covers.
● Don't forget to fit a new, thick sealing washer to the crankshaft position screw before turning the engine.
● If the decompressor cable has been disconnected, adjust the freeplay (see Chapter 1).
● Refill the engine with oil to the correct level (see Chapter 1).
● Refill the cooling system with fresh coolant (see Chapter 3).
● Before riding the bike, start the engine and check that there are no coolant or oil leaks.

8 Rocker arms and shafts

Removal

1 Follow to the procedure in Section 7 to remove the camshaft cover.
2 Note how the return spring on the decompressor arm locates against the end cap of the exhaust rocker shaft **(see illustration)**. To remove the decompressor arm, first remove

7.25 Checking the rocker arm end float

8.2a Note location of return spring (arrowed)

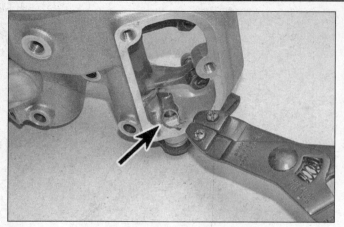

8.2b Remove the circlip (arrowed) . . .

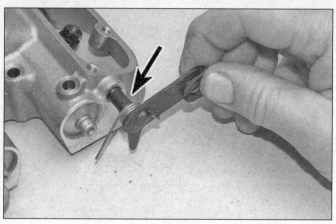

8.2c . . . then draw out the arm, noting the O-ring (arrowed)

the circlip on the inside of the cover, then draw the arm out **(see illustrations)**. Note the location of the O-ring on the pivot shaft.

3 Working on one rocker arm at a time, pull out the end cap, noting the location of the O-ring **(see illustration)**. Hook a suitable tool

through the end of the rocker shaft and draw out the shaft **(see illustration)**.

4 Note which way round the rocker arm is fitted, then lift it out of the cover **(see illustration)**.

5 Mark each rocker shaft, arm and end cap

according to its position (i.e. intake or exhaust valve), and keep matched assemblies together **(see illustration)**.

Inspection

6 Clean the components with a suitable

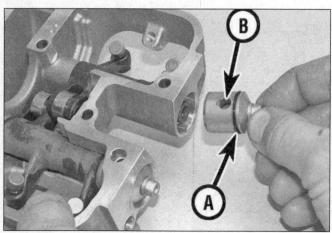

8.3a Note the O-ring (A) and the alignment of the hole (B) in the end cap

8.3b Pull out the rocker shaft as described

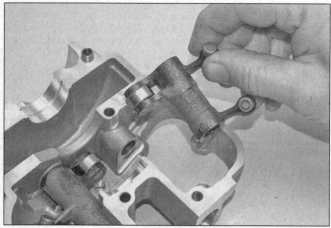

8.4 Lift out the rocker arm

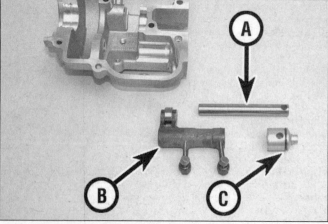

8.5 Keep matched assemblies together – (A) exhaust rocker shaft, (B) arm and (C) end cap

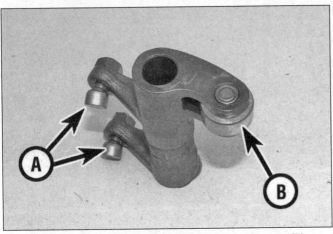

8.6 Check the articulated tips (A) and the roller foot (B)

8.7 Check for freeplay between the rocker arm and shaft

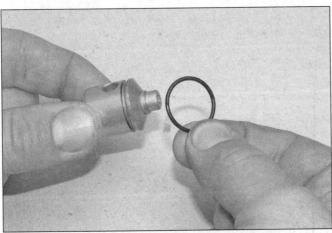

8.10 Lubricate the O-rings before installation

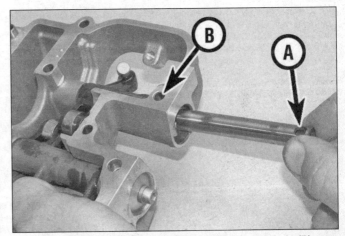

8.11 Align the hole (A) in the shaft with the bolt hole (B)

solvent, then inspect the rocker arm contact points for wear, pitting, spalling, score marks and cracks (see illustration). Check that the articulated tips of the adjusting screws are free to move, but not loose. Check that the roller feet that bear on the camshaft rotate smoothly without any radial freeplay.

7 Inspect the surface of the rocker shafts for wear and score marks, then assemble each arm on its shaft and check for freeplay between the two – there should be no discernable freeplay (see illustration).

8 If any components are worn or damaged, they must be renewed.

9 Ensure that the oil holes in both rocker shafts are clear.

Installation

10 Fit new O-rings to both shaft end caps (see illustration). Fit a new O-ring to the decompressor arm pivot shaft.

11 Working on one rocker arm at a time, lubricate the shaft with clean engine oil, then position the arm in the cover, making sure that it is the right way round, and press the shaft into position (see illustration). Ensure that the hole in the outer end of the shaft aligns with the appropriate cover bolt hole.

12 Lubricate the end caps with a smear of oil and press them into place – ensure that the holes in the end caps align with the holes in the shafts (see illustration 8.3a).

13 To check the alignment between the holes in the camshaft cover, rocker shafts and end caps, carefully ease a cover bolt through all three.

14 Lubricate the decompressor arm pivot shaft and fit the return spring onto the arm, then install the arm and secure it with a new circlip (see illustration).

15 Assembled in the camshaft cover, the rocker arms should look like this (see illustration).

16 Lubricate the articulated tips and roller feet on the rocker arms, then follow the procedure in Section 7 to install the camshaft cover.

8.14 Secure the decompressor arm shaft with a new circlip (arrowed)

8.15 Complete camshaft cover assembly should look like this

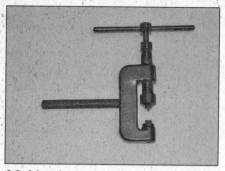

9.2 A breaker and riveting tool suitable for working on the cam chain

9.3 Operating the cam chain breaker

9.4a Lift off the free sideplate

9 Camshaft

Note: *The camshaft can be removed with the engine in the frame.*
Special tools: *A chain breaker and riveting tool is required for this procedure (see Step 2).*

Removal

1 Follow the procedure in Section 7 to remove the camshaft cover.
2 Before the camshaft can be removed, the cam chain must be broken. KTM provide a service tool (Part No. 590.29.020.000) for this purpose; alternatively, a similar proprietary tool can be used (see illustration). Note that a new chain link must be fitted on reassembly – under no circumstances re-use the old link.
3 Stuff clean rag into the cam chain tunnel to prevent anything falling into the engine, then follow the manufacturer's instructions to assemble the breaker tool on a convenient pin of the cam chain – any of the chain links can be broken (see illustration).
4 Tighten the tool and press the selected pin out of one sideplate, then assemble the tool on the adjacent pin of the same chain link and press that out also. Remove the tool and lift the free sideplate off (see illustration). Press the remaining sideplate out to separate the two ends of the chain (see illustration). Pull the ends of the chain back under tension and secure them with cable-ties or wire to prevent them falling into the engine (see illustration).
5 Note that at TDC (compression) the timing dots on the camshaft sprocket align with the mating surface of the cylinder head and the stop for the automatic decompressor mechanism is facing up (see illustration). Note also that both cam lobes are facing down (see illustration).

9.4b Remove the sideplate and separate the ends of the chain

9.4c Secure the ends of the chain to prevent them falling into the engine

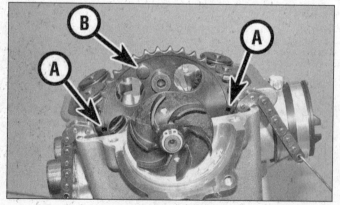

9.5a Note the alignment of the timing dots (A) and the decompressor stop (B)

9.5b Note the position of the camshaft lobes (arrowed)

9.6 Lift out the complete camshaft assembly

9.7 Inspect the cam lobes carefully for wear and damage

9.8a Set-up for drawing-off the right-hand bearing

6 Lift the camshaft out **(see illustration)**.

Inspection

Note: *If the water pump seal carrier is removed during camshaft inspection, the two internal seals must be renewed (see Chapter 3).*

7 Check the camshaft lobes for heat discoloration (blue appearance), score marks, chipped areas, flat spots and spalling **(see illustration)**. If either lobe appears worn or damaged, a new camshaft must be fitted.

8 Refer to *Tools and Workshop Tips* in the *Reference* section and check the bearings. Only remove the bearings if new ones are to be fitted. Use a two-legged puller to draw the bearings off **(see illustration)**. Follow the procedure in Chapter 3, Section 5, and remove the water pump impeller and seal carrier to gain access to the left-hand bearing **(see illustration)**. Press the new bearings on carefully (see *Tools and Workshop Tips*).

9 Check the operation of the automatic decompressor – the return spring should hold the bob weight in the rest position, and the mechanism should turn smoothly to the running position against the stop **(see illustrations)**. Check the contact surface of the decompressor shaft for wear.

10 To renew the decompressor mechanism, first draw off the left-hand camshaft bearing (see Step 8). Note the location of the ends of the return spring, then pull the shaft out

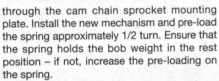

9.8b Remove the water pump components to access the left-hand bearing

9.9a Automatic decompressor return spring (arrowed)

through the cam chain sprocket mounting plate. Install the new mechanism and pre-load the spring approximately 1/2 turn. Ensure that the spring holds the bob weight in the rest position – if not, increase the pre-loading on the spring.

11 Note that on 2000 and 2001 models, the bob weight stop is retained by a self-locking nut, and on 2002 models it is retained by a plain nut secured with Loctite 222. If the stop is loose, either fit a new self-locking nut or, on 2002 models, unscrew the nut, clean the threads and apply a fresh drop of Loctite. Tighten the nut to the torque setting specified at the beginning of this Chapter.

12 Examine the camshaft sprocket – check for wear on the sides and tips of the teeth and for chipped or hooked teeth **(see illustration)**. If the sprocket needs renewing, then a new chain must also be fitted, and it is very likely the sprocket on the crankshaft will be worn also. Refer to Section 16 for details of sprocket wear and chain renewal.

13 To renew the sprocket, follow the procedure in Chapter 3 and remove the water pump impeller and seal carrier, then draw off the bearing and remove the decompressor mechanism (see Steps 8 and 10). Undo the two bolts securing the sprocket to the camshaft and lift the sprocket off.

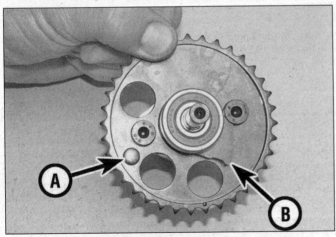

9.9b Decompressor stop (A) and bob weight (B)

9.12 Inspect the sprocket teeth for wear and damage

9.17 Note the location of the washer (A) and the hole in the seal carrier (B)

9.19 Join the ends of the cam chain with the new link

14 Install the new sprocket with the automatic decompressor stop facing towards the water pump and directly opposite the tops of the camshaft lobes. Tighten the bolts to the torque setting specified at the beginning of this Chapter.

Installation

15 Before installing the camshaft, renew the O-ring seals on the water pump seal carrier (see Chapter 3).

16 Ensure that the piston is at TDC (compression) and that the crankshaft position screw is located in the notch in the right-hand flywheel (see Section 7, Step 9).

17 Position the camshaft in the cylinder head with both cam lobes facing down **(see illustration 9.5b)**. Ensure that on 2002 to 2007 models the washer is located in its groove, and that on 2003 to 2007 models the hole in the water pump seal carrier is facing up **(see illustration)**.

18 Check that the timing dots on the camshaft sprocket align with the mating surface of the cylinder head and the stop for the automatic decompressor mechanism is facing up **(see illustration 9.5a)**.

19 Bring the two ends of the cam chain together on the top of the sprocket and secure them with the new link **(see illustration)**. If the ends do not meet, the chain has probably bunched-up around the crankshaft sprocket – if necessary, temporarily unscrew the crankshaft position screw and rock the crankshaft backwards and forwards to release the chain.

20 If not already done, stuff clean rag into the cam chain tunnel to prevent anything falling into the engine, then install the new sideplate over the pins of the new link and press it all the way on using the hollow adapter on the riveting tool **(see illustration)**. The sideplate must be pressed firmly over both pins – the installed link and sideplate should look like this **(see illustration)**.

21 Follow the manufacturer's instructions to assemble the riveting tool on one of the pins of the new link, then tighten the tool to rivet the end of the pin over the sideplate **(see illustration)**. Repeat the procedure to rivet the remaining pin over the sideplate – when correctly installed, the new riveted link should look like this **(see illustration)**.

22 Follow the procedure in Section 7 to install the camshaft cover.

9.20a Press the new sideplate on with the chain tool

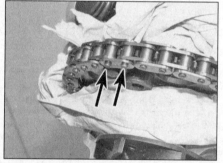

9.20b With the sideplate correctly installed the ends of the pins (arrowed) should be exposed

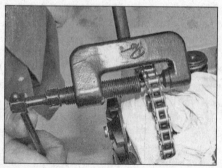

9.21a Riveting the pins on the new chain link

9.21b The ends of the pins should be spread evenly by the tool

10 Cylinder head

Note: *The cylinder head can be removed with the engine in the frame.*

Removal

1 Follow the procedure in Section 7 to remove the camshaft cover, then follow the procedure in Section 9 to remove the camshaft.

2 If not already done, remove the radiators and the coolant hoses (see Chapter 3).

3 Remove the carburettor and the exhaust system (see Chapter 4).

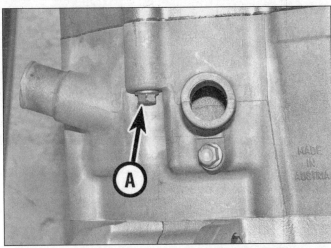

10.4a Undo the bolts securing the head at the front (A) . . .

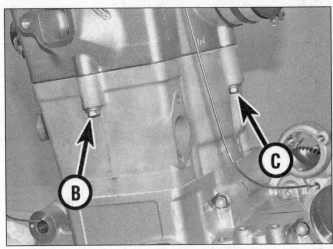

10.4b . . . left-hand side (B) and rear (C)

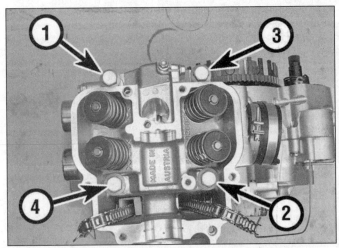

10.5a Undo the cylinder head bolts in a criss-cross pattern . . .

10.5b . . . then lift them out noting the washers

4 Undo the three 6 mm bolts securing the cylinder head to the front, left-hand side and rear of the cylinder **(see illustrations)**. Note the location of the sealing washer on the bolt below the water pump housing and discard it as a new one must be fitted.

5 Undo the cylinder head bolts evenly and in a criss-cross pattern, then lift out the bolts and washers **(see illustrations)**.

6 Ease the head up off the cylinder **(see illustration)**. Note that the cylinder is secured to the crankcase via the head bolts and the base gasket seal will be broken if the cylinder is disturbed during this process. If the head is stuck, tap around the joint face between the head and the cylinder with a soft-faced mallet to free it. Do not attempt to free the head by levering with a screwdriver between the head and cylinder –

you'll damage the sealing surfaces. Once the head has separated from the cylinder, secure the cam chain so that the head can be lifted off.

7 Remove the cylinder head gasket and secure the cam chain **(see illustration)**.

8 Check that the two dowels are a tight fit in the top of the cylinder **(see illustration 10.14)**.

9 Check the old cylinder head gasket and the sealing surfaces on the head and cylinder for signs of leakage, which could indicate a warped head. Discard the gasket once it has been inspected as a new one must be used.

10 Clean all traces of old gasket material from the head and cylinder. If a scraper is used, take care not to scratch or gouge the soft aluminium. Be careful not to let any of the gasket material fall into the crankcase or cylinder water jacket.

Installation

11 If the seal between the cylinder and crankcase has been broken, fit a new cylinder base gasket (see Section 12).

10.6 Don't allow the cam chain to drop as the head is lifted off

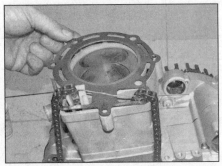

10.7 Remove the gasket. Note wire through cam chain

10.14 Fit the new gasket over the dowels (arrowed)

10.17 Tighten the head bolts with a torque wrench as described

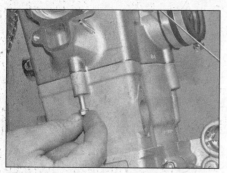

10.18 Fit a new sealing washer on the bolt below the water pump

12 Ensure that the piston is at TDC (compression) and that the crankshaft position screw is located in the notch in the right-hand flywheel (see Section 7, Step 9).

13 If removed, install the two dowels into the top of the cylinder.

14 Fit the new head gasket in place on the cylinder, making sure all the holes are correctly aligned **(see illustration)**. If one side of the gasket is marked ALTO, that side should face up. Never re-use the old gasket.

15 Carefully fit the cylinder head over the ends of the cam chain and onto the cylinder **(see illustration 10.6)**.

16 Lubricate the seats of the M10 cylinder head bolts in the head and the bolt threads with clean engine oil, then install the bolts with

their washers **(see illustration 10.5b)**. Tighten the bolts finger-tight.

17 Tighten the bolts evenly, a little at a time and in a criss-cross sequence, until light resistance is felt. Now tighten each bolt in the same sequence, first to the initial torque setting specified at the beginning of this Chapter, then to the final torque setting **(see illustration)**.

18 Install the three M6 bolts – don't forget the new sealing washer on the bolt below the water pump housing **(see illustration)**. Tighten the bolts to the specified torque setting.

19 Install the remaining components in the reverse order of removal.

11 Cylinder head and valves

1 Because of the complex nature of this job and the special tools and equipment required, most owners leave servicing of the valves, valve seats and valve guides to a professional. However, you can make an initial assessment of whether the valves are seating, and therefore sealing, correctly by pouring a small amount of solvent into each of the valve ports. If the solvent leaks past any valve into the combustion chamber the valve is not sealing.

2 Using a valve spring compressor, you can also remove the valves and associated components from the cylinder head, then

clean them and check for wear to assess the extent of the work needed. Unless seat cutting or guide renewal is required, you can then reassemble the cylinder head.

3 A dealer service department or specialist engineer can replace the guides and re-cut the valve seats.

4 After the valve service has been performed, be sure to clean it very thoroughly before installation on the engine to remove any metal particles or abrasive grit that may still be present from the valve service operations. Use compressed air, if available, to blow out all the holes and passages.

Disassembly

Special tool: *A valve spring compressor suitable for motorcycle work is absolutely necessary for this procedure (see Step 7).*

5 Before proceeding, arrange to label and store the valves along with their related components in such a way that they can be returned to their original locations without getting mixed up. A good way to do this is to obtain a container which is divided into four compartments, and to label each compartment with the identity of the valve which will be stored in it (i.e. intake left or right-hand valve, and exhaust left or right-hand valve). Alternatively, labelled plastic bags will do just as well.

6 If not already done, clean any traces of old gasket material from the cylinder head. If a scraper is used, take care not to scratch or gouge the soft aluminium.

 HAYNES HINT *Refer to Tools and Workshop Tips for details of gasket removal methods.*

7 Using a suitable valve spring compressor, compress the spring on the first valve, making sure the tool is correctly located onto each end of the valve assembly **(see illustration)**. Do not compress the spring any more than is absolutely necessary, then remove the collets, using either needle-nose pliers, tweezers, a magnet, or a screwdriver with a dab of grease on it **(see illustration)**.

11.7a Ensure the spring compressor is correctly located on the valve

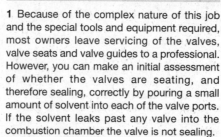

11.7b Lift out the collets carefully

11.8a Lift off the spring retainer . . .

11.8b . . . then lift off the spring(s)

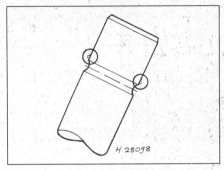

11.9 If necessary, deburr the area above the collet groove

8 Carefully release the valve spring compressor and remove the spring retainer, noting which way up it fits, and the spring(s) **(see illustrations)**. Note that some models are fitted with one spring per valve only (see *Specifications* at the beginning of this Chapter).

9 Push the valve down into the head and withdraw it from the underside. If the valve binds in the guide (won't pull through), push it back into the head and deburr the area above the collet groove with a very fine file or whetstone **(see illustration)**.

10 Repeat the procedure for the remaining valves. Remember to keep the components for each valve assembly together and in order so they can be reinstalled in the same location **(see illustration)**.

11 Once the valves have been removed and labelled, pull the valve stem seals off the top of the valve guides using either a special removing tool or pliers **(see illustration)**. Discard the old seals as new ones must be fitted.

12 Lift off the spring seats, noting which way up they fit **(see illustration)**.

13 Carefully scrape all carbon deposits out of the combustion chamber area. A hand held wire brush or a piece of fine emery cloth can be used once the majority of deposits have been scraped away. Do not use a wire brush mounted in a drill motor as the head material is soft and may be eroded away. Next, wash the cylinder head with solvent and dry it thoroughly. Compressed air will speed the drying process and ensure that all holes, recessed areas and oil passages are clean.

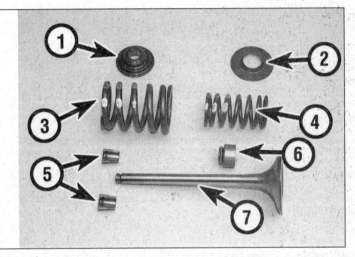

11.10 Valve components

1 Spring retainer
2 Spring seat
3 Outer spring
4 Inner spring (if fitted)
5 Collets
6 Valve stem seal
7 Valve

14 Scrape off any deposits that may have formed on the valves, then use a motorized wire brush to remove deposits from the valve heads and stems. Make sure the valves do not get mixed up.

15 Clean the valve springs, collets, retainers and spring seats with solvent and dry them thoroughly. Clean the parts from one valve at a time so as not to mix them up.

Inspection

16 Inspect the head very carefully for cracks and other damage. If cracks are found, a new head will be required.

17 Using a precision straight-edge and a feeler gauge, check the head gasket mating surface for warpage. Refer to *Tools and*

Workshop Tips in the Reference section for details of how to use the straight-edge. If the head is warped beyond the limit specified at the beginning of this Chapter, consult your KTM dealer or take it to a specialist repair shop for rectification.

18 Examine the valve seats in the combustion chamber. If they are pitted, cracked or burned, the head will require work beyond the scope of the home mechanic. Check that the width of the valve seat-to-valve contact area is the same around the entire circumference of the seat, and compare the result with the specifications at the beginning of this Chapter **(see illustration)**. If the width varies, or is smaller than the service limit, professional valve overhaul is required. Note that the valve

11.11 Pull off the valve stem seals . . .

11.12 . . . then lift out the spring seats

11.18 Measuring the valve seat width

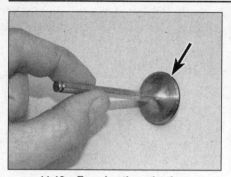

11.19a Examine the valve face (arrowed) . . .

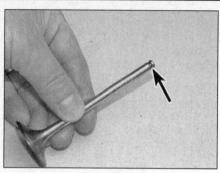

11.19b . . . and the valve stem and collet groove (arrowed)

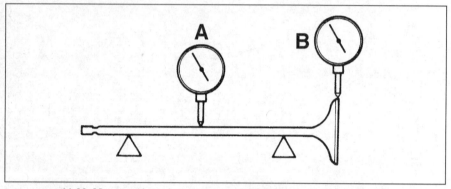

11.20 Measure the valve stem runout (A) and valve head runout (B)

seat width service limits are different for intake and exhaust valves.

19 Carefully inspect each valve face for cracks, pits and burned spots, and check the valve stem and the collet groove area for scoring and cracks **(see illustrations)**. Check the end of the stem for pitting and excessive wear. Any of these conditions indicates the need for a new valve.

20 Rotate the valve and check for any obvious indication that it is bent. If available, use V-blocks and a dial gauge to measure the valve head runout and compare the result with the specification **(see illustration)**. If the runout exceeds the service limit, a new valve must be fitted.

21 If available, measure the inside diameter of the valve guides with a small hole gauge and micrometer **(see illustration)**. Measure the guides at each end and at the centre to determine if they are worn unevenly. Compare the results with the specification. If the guides are worn unevenly, or beyond the service limit, they must be renewed. **Note:** *Carbon build-up inside the lower ends of the exhaust valve guides indicates worn valve guides. Have the head inspected by a KTM dealer.*

22 Check the end of each valve spring for wear and pitting. Measure the spring free length and compare it to that listed in the specifications **(see illustration)**. If any spring is shorter than specified it has sagged and must be renewed – always renew the valve springs as a set.

23 Measure the thickness of the spring seats

and renew any seat that is worn to the service limit **(see illustration)**.

24 Check the spring retainers and collets for

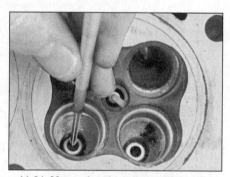

11.21 Measuring the valve guide inside diameter with a small hole gauge

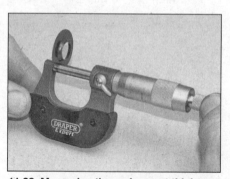

11.23 Measuring the spring seat thickness

obvious wear and cracks. Any questionable parts should not be reused, as extensive damage will occur in the event of failure during engine operation.

25 If the inspection indicates that no overhaul work is required, the valve components can be reinstalled in the head.

Reassembly

26 Unless a valve service has been performed, before installing the valves in the head they should be ground-in (lapped) to ensure a positive seal between the valves and seats. This procedure requires coarse and fine valve grinding compound and a valve grinding tool. If a grinding tool is not available, a piece of rubber or plastic hose can be slipped over the valve stem (after the valve has been installed in the guide) and used to turn the valve.

⚠️ *Warning: Do not grind-in the titanium valves fitted to SX models because the process will destroy the coating – use a steel valve to grind-in the seats on these machines.*

27 Apply a small amount of coarse grinding compound to the valve face, then oil the valve stem and insert it into the guide **(see illustration)**. **Note:** *Make sure each valve is installed in its correct guide and be careful not to get any grinding compound on the valve stem.*

28 Attach the grinding tool (or hose) to the valve and rotate the tool between the palms of your hands. Use a back-and-forth motion

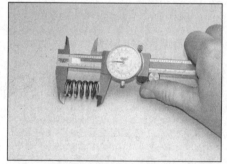

11.22 Measuring valve spring free length

11.27 Apply the grinding compound in small dabs to the valve face only

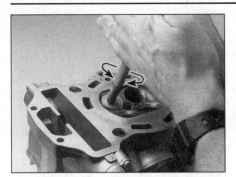

11.28a Rotate the grinding tool back-and-forth between the palms of your hands

11.28b The grinding process should leave the valve face (arrowed) . . .

11.28c . . . and seat (arrowed) as an unbroken ring of uniform width

(as though rubbing your hands together) rather than a circular motion (i.e. so that the valve rotates alternately clockwise and anti-clockwise rather than in one direction only) **(see illustration)**. Lift the valve off the seat and turn it at regular intervals to distribute the grinding compound properly. Continue the grinding procedure until the valve face and seat contact area is of uniform width and unbroken around the entire circumference of the valve face and seat **(see illustrations)**.

29 Carefully remove the valve from the guide and wipe off all traces of grinding compound. Use solvent to clean the valve and wipe the seat area thoroughly with a solvent soaked cloth.

30 Repeat the procedure with fine valve grinding compound, then repeat the entire procedure for the remaining valves.

31 Working on each valve in turn, lubricate the stem with clean engine oil and install the valve into its guide **(see illustration)**.

32 Slide a suitable plastic sleeve over the upper end of the valve stem – electrical heat shrink sleeving is ideal **(see illustration)**. The purpose of the plastic sleeve is to prevent the edges of the collet groove damaging the inside of the stem seal when it is fitted. If a suitable sleeve is not available, take great care when installing the seal.

33 Install the spring seat with its shouldered

side facing up, then lubricate the stem seal and slide it down over the sleeve **(see illustrations)**.

34 If used, remove the sleeve, then press the seal over the end of the valve guide with an appropriate size deep socket until it is felt to clip into place **(see illustration)**. Don't twist or cock the seal, or it will not seal properly against the valve stem. Also, don't remove it again or it will be damaged.

35 Install the valve springs as follows.

36 If a single, conical spring is fitted, install it with the wide end against the spring seat.

37 If two springs are fitted, install the inner spring, then install the outer spring – on 2000 and 2001 models, install the outer spring with

11.31 Lubricate each valve stem prior to installation

11.32 Slide a plastic sleeve over the valve stem

11.33a Install the spring seat . . .

11.33b . . . then lubricate the stem seal . . .

11.33c . . . and slide it down over the sleeve

11.34 Press the seal over the end of the guide with a deep socket

11.37a Install the valve springs . . .

11.37b . . . as described in the text

11.39 A dab of grease will hold the collets in place

11.41 Tap each valve stem gently to seat the collets in their grooves

the tighter wound end against the spring seat (see illustrations).

38 Install the spring retainer, with its shouldered side facing down so that it fits into the top of the spring (see illustration 11.8a).

39 Apply a small amount of grease to the collets to hold them in place during installation, then compress the spring with the valve spring compressor and install the collets (see illustration). Do not compress the spring any more than is absolutely necessary to slip the collets into position. Make certain that the collets are securely located in the collet groove, then release the spring compressor.

40 Repeat the procedure for the remaining valves.

41 Support the cylinder head on blocks so the valves can't contact the workbench top, then gently tap each of the valve stems to seat the collets in their grooves (see illustration).

 HAYNES HiNT *Check for proper sealing of the valves by pouring a small amount of solvent into each of the valve ports. If the solvent leaks past any valve into the combustion chamber the valve grinding operation on that valve should be repeated.*

12 Cylinder

Note: *The cylinder can be removed with the engine in the frame.*
Special tool: *Use of a piston ring clamp is*

advised when installing the cylinder, although it's not essential (see Step 17).

Removal

1 Remove the cylinder head (see Section 10).
2 Ease the cylinder up off the crankcase. If it is stuck, tap around the joint face between the cylinder and the crankcase with a soft-faced mallet to free it. Do not attempt to free the cylinder by levering with a screwdriver between the cylinder and crankcase – you'll damage the sealing surfaces.
3 Once the cylinder has separated from the crankcase, secure the cam chain so that the cylinder can be lifted off. Support the piston to prevent the connecting rod hitting the crankcase. Once the cylinder has been removed, stuff clean rag around the connecting rod to protect it and to prevent anything falling into the crankcase (see illustration).
4 To prevent the camchain slipping into the crankcase, wrap an elastic band around the chain and guide blade (see illustration).
5 Remove the two dowels from the crankcase if they are loose (see illustration 12.15a).
6 Clean any traces of old gasket material from the cylinder and crankcase mating surfaces. If a scraper is used, take care not to scratch or gouge the soft aluminium. Be careful not to let any of the gasket material fall into the crankcase.

Inspection

7 The cylinder bore has a wear resistant coating which should last the life of the engine unless damage, caused by a broken piston ring or seizure, has occurred.
8 Inspect the cylinder walls carefully for scratches and score marks (see illustration). Its Nikasil coating should last the life of the machine and significant wear is unlikely. If damage is noted, yet the bore diameter is still within the service limit, seek the advice of a KTM dealer or engine specialist as to the suitability of the cylinder for continued use. The cylinder cannot be rebored, but the coating can be renewed.
9 Cylinders and pistons are fitted as paired sets; there are two sets, Size I or Size II, for every engine capacity (see *Specifications* at the beginning of this Chapter).
10 The size code is stamped into the

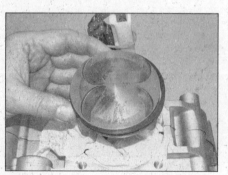

12.3 Stuff clean rag in the crankcase opening

12.4 Secure the cam chain with an elastic band

12.8 Inspect the cylinder wall (arrowed) for scratches and score marks

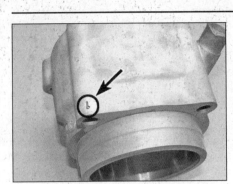

12.10 Location of the cylinder size code

12.11a Using a telescoping gauge . . .

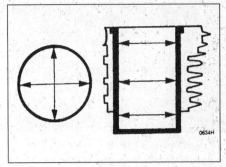

12.11b . . . measure the cylinder bore in the directions shown

bottom of the cylinder **(see illustration)**. New components must match the size code.

11 Using a telescoping gauge and a micrometer (see *Tools and Workshop Tips* in the *Reference* section), check the dimensions of the cylinder to assess the amount of wear **(see illustration)**. Take measurements about half-way down the bore, both parallel with the piston pin and at 90° to it **(see illustration)**.

12 Any difference between the two measurements indicates that the bore is wearing oval, which will reduce the efficiency of the piston rings to achieve a seal in the bore, resulting in loss of compression and increased oil consumption.

13 Next, compare the results with the appropriate specification; if either measurement indicates that the bore is worn beyond the specification, it must either be re-coated or a new cylinder fitted. Make sure you supply the dealer with the size code when purchasing new parts.

Installation

Note: *Installing the cylinder is a lot easier with the aid of an assistant to hold the cam chain while the piston rings are being fed into the bottom of the cylinder.*

14 Ensure that the piston is at TDC (compression) and that the crankshaft position screw is located in the notch in the right-hand flywheel (see Section 7, Step 9).

15 If removed, install the two dowels in the crankcase **(see illustration)**. Fit a new cylinder base gasket **(see illustration)**.

16 Ensure that the piston ring end gaps are correctly staggered (see Section 14).

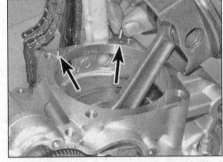

12.15a Install the dowels (arrowed)

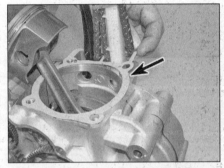

12.15b Fit the base gasket carefully to avoid damage

17 If a piston ring clamp is being used, proceed as follows, otherwise go to Step 21. Lubricate the piston, rings and the inside of the clamp with clean engine oil. Install the clamp over the rings and tighten it enough to compress the rings into their grooves, but not so tight that it locks onto the piston – as the piston is pressed into the cylinder bore, the clamp must be able to slide off. Once the clamp is in place, don't rotate it as the position of the ring end gaps will alter.

18 Lubricate the cylinder bore with clean engine oil. Remove the elastic band and secure the cam chain so that the cylinder can be lowered down over the chain and piston and onto the crankcase **(see illustration)**.

19 Position the top of the piston in the bottom of the cylinder bore, then slowly ease the cylinder down over the piston. If the top ring snags on the lip of the bore, tighten the clamp slightly to compress the rings further into their grooves.

20 Once both rings are safely inside the cylinder, remove the clamp **(see illustration)**. Remove the rag from around the connecting rod and press the cylinder down onto the crankcase, then secure the cam chain **(see illustration)**. Follow the procedure in Section 10 to install the cylinder head.

21 To install the cylinder without a ring clamp, first lubricate the piston, rings and cylinder bore with clean engine oil.

22 Remove the elastic band and secure the cam chain so that the cylinder can be lowered down over the chain and piston and onto the crankcase **(see illustration 12.18)**.

23 Position the top of the piston in the bottom of the cylinder bore, then carefully compress and feed the top ring into the bore as the cylinder is pressed down – use your finger-tips and a small screwdriver to do this. Don't press the cylinder down too hard as this will only cause the ring to snag and take care

12.18 Support the cam chain while installing the cylinder

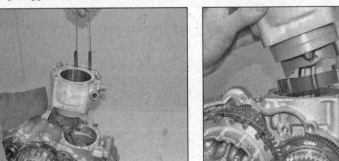

12.20a Remove the piston ring clamp carefully

12.20b Secure the cam chain once the cylinder is installed

13.3a Prise out the circlip . . .

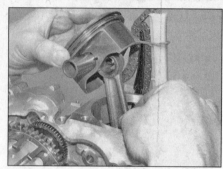

13.3b . . . and push out the piston pin to free the piston

13.7a Remove the piston rings with your thumbs . .

not to score the surface of the piston skirt with the screwdriver.

24 Continue lowering the cylinder over the piston and feed the oil ring in using the same method.

25 Once both rings are safely inside the cylinder, remove the rag from around the connecting rod and press the cylinder down onto the crankcase, then secure the cam chain (see illustration 12.20b).

26 Follow the procedure in Section 10 to install the cylinder head.

13 Piston

Note: *The piston can be removed with the engine in the frame.*

Removal

1 Remove the cylinder (see Section 12). Once the cylinder has been removed, don't forget to stuff clean rag around the connecting rod to protect it and to prevent anything falling into the crankcase.

2 The piston should be marked with a direction of installation arrow, but this may not be visible until the piston has been cleaned. Before removing the piston, use a scriber or marker pen to mark the front of the piston crown or the inside of the skirt.

Note: *The piston and cylinder will be supplied as a paired set – check for the size code on the bottom of the cylinder (see Section 12, Step 10).*

3 Carefully prise out the circlip on one side of the piston pin using needle-nosed pliers or a small, flat-bladed screwdriver inserted into the notch **(see illustration)**. Push the piston pin out from the other side using a suitably sized socket to free the piston from the connecting rod **(see illustration)**.

> **HAYNES HINT** *If the piston pin is a tight fit in the piston bosses, heat the piston with a hot air gun to release the pin. Support the piston (wrap rag around the piston to avoid burning your hands) and press the pin out with a suitable length of rod. Never drive the piston pin out with a hammer and drift.*

4 Remove the other circlip and discard them both as new ones must be used.

5 Once the piston has been removed, fit the pin back into the piston to ensure it can be installed the right way round on reassembly.

Inspection

6 Before the inspection process can be carried out, remove the piston rings and clean the piston.

7 Using your thumbs or a thin blade (an old

feeler gauge is ideal), carefully remove the rings from the piston **(see illustrations)**. Do not nick or gouge the piston in the process. Note which way up each ring fits and in which groove as they must be installed in their original positions if being re-used. The upper surface of the top ring is marked 'TOP' and the upper surface of the oil ring is marked 'O'. Note that the oil ring has an expander fitted behind it **(see illustration 14.6)**.

8 Scrape all traces of carbon from the piston crown. A hand-held wire brush or a piece of fine emery cloth can be used once most of the deposits have been scraped away. Do not, under any circumstances, use a wire brush mounted in a drill motor to remove deposits from the piston – the piston material is soft and will be eroded away by the wire brush.

9 Use a piston ring groove cleaning tool to remove any carbon deposits from the ring grooves. If a tool is not available, a piece broken off an old ring will do the job. Be very careful to remove only the carbon deposits. Do not remove any metal and do not nick or gouge the sides of the ring grooves.

10 Once the deposits have been removed, wash the piston with solvent and dry it thoroughly. Make sure the oil return holes in the back of the oil ring groove are clear. If the identification mark made on removal is cleaned off, make sure that the direction of installation arrow is visible, or re-mark the piston **(see illustration)**.

13.7b . . . or with a thin blade

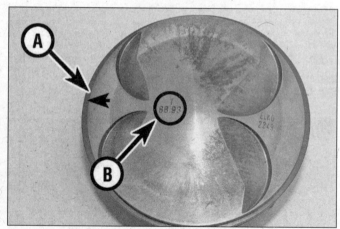

13.10 Direction of installation arrow (A) and size code (B)

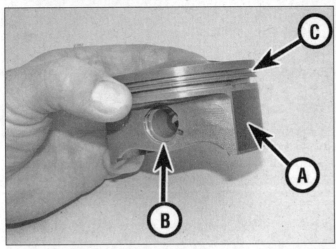

13.11 Inspect the piston skirt (A), pin bosses (B) and ring lands (C)

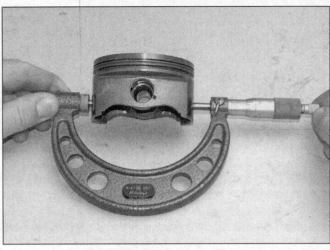

13.14 Measuring the piston diameter

11 Inspect the piston for cracks and damage around the skirt, at the pin bosses and at the ring lands **(see illustration)**. Normal wear appears as light, vertical marks on the thrust surfaces of the skirt and slight looseness of the top ring in its groove. If the skirt is scored or scuffed, the piston and cylinder are probably worn beyond the service limit. Alternatively, the engine may have been suffering from overheating caused by lack of lubrication or abnormal combustion. Check the operation of the oil pumps (see Section 22).

12 A hole in the top of the piston (only likely in extreme circumstances) or burned areas around the edge of the piston crown, indicate that pre-ignition or knocking under load have occurred. If you find evidence of any problems, the causes must be corrected or the damage will occur again (see *Fault Finding* in the *Reference* section).

13 Make sure the piston is matched correctly to its cylinder. The size code is stamped into the top of the piston **(see illustration 13.10)**. This should correspond with the code stamped into the bottom of the cylinder **(see illustration 12.10)**.

14 Calculate the piston-to-cylinder clearance by measuring the cylinder bore (see Section 12) and the piston diameter. Measure the piston across the skirt at 90° to the piston pin axis **(see illustration)**. Subtract the piston diameter from the bore diameter to obtain the clearance and compare the result with the service limit specified at the beginning of this Chapter.

15 If the clearance is greater than the service limit, first check to see if fitting a new piston will reduce the clearance to within the specification. If so, fit a new piston; if not, a new cylinder and piston will be required. Make sure you supply the dealer with the size code when purchasing new parts. **Note:** *In most cases, only the piston will have worn.*

16 Apply clean engine oil to the piston pin, insert it part way into the piston and check for any freeplay between the two. There should be no discernable freeplay.

13.17a Measuring the diameter of the piston pin . . .

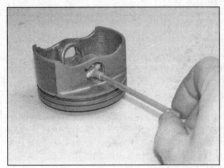

13.17b . . . and the pin bore in the piston

17 Measure the pin external diameter in several places to determine if the pin has worn unevenly and, if available, use a small hole gauge to measure the internal diameter of the pin bore in the piston **(see illustrations)**. Any discrepancies in the measurements are indicative of uneven wear – renew the piston or the pin as required. Repeat the checks between the pin and the connecting rod small-end (see Section 25).

Installation

18 Ensure that the piston is at TDC (compression) and that the crankshaft position screw is located in the notch in the right-hand flywheel (see Section 7, Step 9).

19 Install the piston rings (see Section 14).

13.22a Install the piston pin . . .

20 Install a **new** circlip into one side of the piston – never re-use old circlips. Position the open end of the circlip facing either straight up or straight down. Use a small, flat-bladed screwdriver inserted into the notch to ease the circlip into its groove **(see illustration 13.3a)**.

21 Lubricate the piston pin, the piston pin bore and the connecting rod small-end bore with clean engine oil.

22 Align the piston with the connecting rod, making sure the direction of installation arrow points forwards, then insert the piston pin from the side without the circlip **(see illustration)**. Secure the pin with the other **new** circlip **(see illustration)**. When installing

13.22b . . . and secure it with a new circlip

13.22c Open end of the circlip must be away from the notch (arrowed)

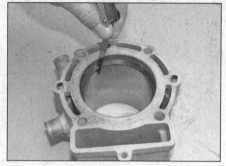

14.3 Measuring piston ring installed end gap

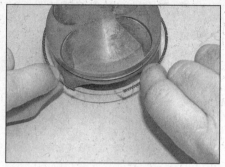

14.6 Fitting the oil ring expander as described

the circlips, compress them only just enough to fit them in the piston, and make sure they are properly seated in their grooves with the open end away from the removal notch **(see illustration)**.

23 Follow the procedure in Section 12 to install the cylinder.

14 Piston rings

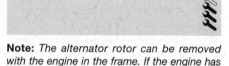

1 It is good practice to renew the piston rings when the engine is being overhauled. Before installing the new piston rings, the ring end gaps must be checked with the rings installed in the cylinder.

2 Lay out the new ring set – the upper surface of the top ring is marked 'TOP' and the upper surface of the oil ring is marked 'O'. The oil ring has an expander fitted behind it.

3 To measure the installed ring end gap, insert each ring into the top of the cylinder and square it up with the cylinder walls by pushing it in with the top of the piston. The ring should be about 10 mm below the top edge of the cylinder. To measure the end gap, slip a feeler gauge between the ends of the ring and compare the measurement to the specifications at the beginning of the Chapter **(see illustration)**. Note that the end gap for the top ring is different from the oil ring.

4 If the gap is larger or smaller than specified,

double check to make sure that you have the correct rings before proceeding.

5 If the gap is too large, check to ensure that the cylinder bore is not worn beyond the service limit (see Section 12).

6 The oil ring (lowest on the piston) is installed first. It is composed of two separate components – the expander and the ring. Pull the ends of the expander apart enough to fit it over the top of the piston and slip it into its groove, then press the ends back together **(see illustration)**. Ensure that the straight wire is not pulled out of either end of the coiled wire. Now install the oil ring over the expander. Make sure that the 'O' mark is facing up and that the end gap in the ring is on the opposite side of the piston to the end gap in the expander. Do not expand the ring any more than is necessary to slide it into place. To avoid breaking the ring, slide a thin blade around the piston while easing the ring on **(see illustration 13.7b)**. After the oil ring components have been installed, check that the ring can be turned smoothly in the ring groove.

7 Install the top ring, ensuring that the 'TOP' mark is facing up. Use a thin blade, as with the oil ring, to ease the ring on without breaking it. Check that the ring moves freely without snagging.

8 Before fitting the piston into the cylinder, stagger the ring end gaps as follows: the oil ring end gap should be facing to the back of the engine and the top ring end gap should be offset from it by approximately 90°.

15 Alternator rotor

Note: *The alternator rotor can be removed with the engine in the frame. If the engine has been removed, ignore the steps which do not apply.*

Special tool: *A crankshaft/clutch holding tool or strap, and an alternator rotor puller, are required for this procedure (see Step 7).*

Removal

1 Drain the engine oil (see Chapter 1).

2 Remove the seat (see Chapter 8). Disconnect the negative (–ve) lead from the battery (see Chapter 9).

3 Remove the fuel tank (see Chapter 4).

4 Trace the alternator wiring from the left-hand engine cover **(see illustration)**. If the cover is just going to be displaced, free the wiring from any clips or ties **(see illustration 4.8a)**. Remove the spacer from the old cable-tie for safekeeping – it must be reused on reassembly. If the cover is going to be removed from the bike, free the wiring and disconnect the wiring connectors **(see illustration 4.8b)**.

5 Position a drain tray underneath the alternator cover to catch any residual oil when the cover is removed.

6 Undo the alternator cover screws, noting their locations, and remove the cover **(see illustrations)**. Discard the gasket as a new one

15.4 Trace the alternator wiring (arrowed) from the left-hand engine cover

15.6a Undo the cover screws (arrowed) . . .

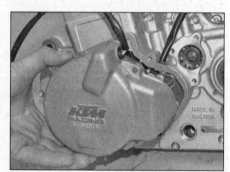

15.6b . . . and lift off the cover

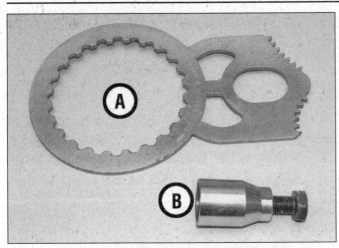

15.7 KTM service tools for holding the crankshaft (A) and pulling-off the alternator rotor (B)

15.8 Remove the nut and washer

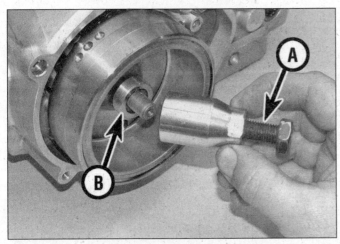

15.10a Unscrew the bolt (A) and install the puller on the boss of the rotor (B)

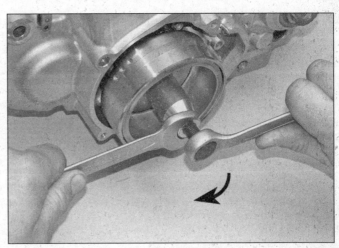

15.10b Turn the bolt clockwise . . .

must be fitted on reassembly. Remove the two dowels from either the cover or the crankcase for safekeeping if they are loose. If required, follow the procedure in Chapter 9, Section 20, to remove and install the alternator stator.

⚠ **Warning: If the crankshaft position screw has been installed to locate TDC, remove it now. If the crankshaft rotates under pressure**

while the rotor nut is being loosened, the screw will bend.

7 To remove the rotor nut it is necessary to stop the crankshaft from turning. KTM provide a service tool (Part No. 590.29.003.100) for this purpose **(see illustrations)**. The tool is used to hold the crankshaft by locking the primary gear and clutch housing together (see Section 19). If the piston has been removed, the crankshaft can

be held by passing a suitable bolt through the small-end eye of the connecting rod (see Section 19). Alternatively, a rotor strap can be used **(see illustration 15.15)** – refer to the procedure in Chapter 5 and remove the ignition pick-up coil first. If the engine is in the frame, and neither tool is available, place the transmission in gear and have an assistant apply the rear brake.

8 Unscrew the nut and remove the washer **(see illustration)**.

9 To remove the rotor from the crankshaft taper it is necessary to use a rotor puller. KTM provide a service tool (Part No. 580.12.009.000) for this purpose **(see illustration 15.7)**.

10 Unscrew the puller bolt, then thread the puller body all the way onto the centre boss of the rotor **(see illustration)**. Hold the puller body with a large spanner to stop the crankshaft turning, then turn the puller bolt clockwise until the rotor is displaced **(see illustration)**.

11 Lift the rotor off **(see illustration)**. Note the location of the Woodruff key in the crankshaft and remove it for safekeeping if it is loose **(see illustration)**.

15.11a . . . to displace the alternator rotor

15.11b Note the location of the Woodruff key

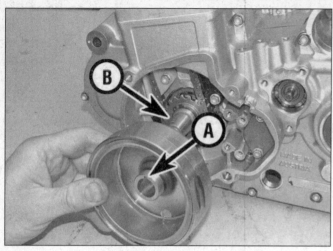

15.14 Align the slot (A) with the key (B)

15.15 Holding the alternator rotor with a rotor strap

Installation

12 Clean the end of the crankshaft and the corresponding mating surface on the inside of the rotor with a suitable solvent. Make sure that no metal objects have attached themselves to the magnet on the inside of the rotor.

13 Remove all traces of old gasket from the crankcase and the alternator cover surfaces.

14 If removed, fit the Woodruff key into its slot (see illustration 15.11b). Align the slot in the centre of the rotor with the key, then slide the rotor onto the shaft (see illustration).

15 Install the rotor nut with its washer and

15.18a Apply sealant to the grommet in the crankcase . . .

tighten it to the torque setting specified at the beginning of this Chapter, using the method employed on removal to prevent the crankshaft from turning (see illustration).

16 If removed, install the ignition pick-up coil (see Chapter 5).

17 If required, follow the procedure in Section 7 and install the crankshaft position screw with the crankshaft at TDC (compression).

18 Apply a small bead of sealant across the wiring grommets in the crankcase and the alternator cover (see illustrations).

19 If removed, fit the dowels into the crankcase and fit a new cover gasket, making sure it locates correctly onto the dowels (see illustration).

20 Install the cover, then install the cover screws in their correct locations (see illustration 15.6a). Tighten the screws evenly in a criss-cross pattern to the specified torque setting.

21 Install the remaining components in the reverse order of removal, noting the following:
● Ensure all wiring connectors are secure.
● Don't forget to fit the spacer on the cable-tie around the camshaft oil feed pipe (see Step 4).
● Refill the engine with oil (see Chapter 1).

16 Cam chain, sprockets, tensioner blade and guide

Special tool: *A two-legged puller is required for this procedure (see Step 8). A chain breaker and riveting tool is required to remove the camshaft (see Section 9).*

1 An indication of cam chain wear can be obtained by removing the cam chain tensioner and checking the position of the plunger (see Section 6).

2 To check the camshaft sprocket, follow the procedure in Section 9 and remove the camshaft.

3 To gain access to the remaining components, first remove the cylinder (see Section 12) and the alternator rotor (see Section 15).

Removal

4 Undo the screws securing the lower guide and lift it off (see illustration). Note the location of the spacers on the bolts.

5 If installed, undo the crankshaft position screw. Ensure that the connecting rod is supported so that it will not hit the crankcase,

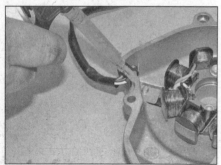

15.18b . . . and in the alternator cover

15.19 Install a new gasket on the dowels (arrowed)

16.4 Remove the lower cam chain guide

16.5 Draw the cam chain off the crankshaft sprocket

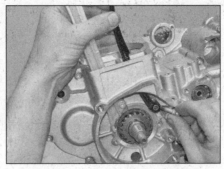

16.6a Remove the tensioner blade . . .

16.6b . . . and the cam chain guide

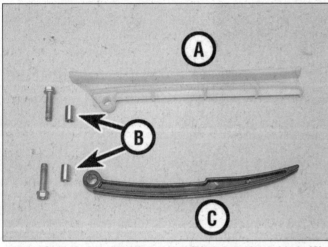

16.6c Cam chain guide (A), spacers (B) and tensioner blade (C)

16.7 Crankshaft sprocket is retained by a circlip (arrowed)

then carefully draw the cam chain off the crankshaft sprocket (see illustration).
6 Undo the bolts securing the tensioner blade and the guide, and lift them out (see illustrations). Note the location of the spacers on the bolts (see illustration). Note: On 2003 to 2007 models, two mounting holes are provided for the tensioner blade bolt. Note which hole is used and ensure that the same hole is used on reassembly.
7 The crankshaft sprocket can be inspected in position – follow the procedure in Step 10 (see illustration).
8 To remove the sprocket, first use circlip pliers to remove the retaining circlip, then draw

the sprocket off using a two-legged puller (see illustration). If required, KTM provide a service tool for this purpose (Part No. 590.29.033.000). Note the location of the sprocket's Woodruff key in the crankshaft and remove it for safekeeping if it is loose (see illustration).

Inspection

9 Clean all the components in a suitable solvent, then inspect the contact surfaces of the tensioner blade and guide for wear.
10 Examine the crankshaft and camshaft sprockets – check for wear on the sides and tips of the teeth and for chipped or hooked teeth (see illustration). If either of the sprockets

needs renewing, then both sprockets and the cam chain should be renewed
11 Over an extended period, the cam chain will stretch – indicated by play between the links. Lay the chain on a flat surface and compress the links as much as possible, then pull the ends of the chain apart. If any movement between the links, or stretch overall, is evident fit a new chain.

Installation

12 If removed, fit the Woodruff key into its slot (see illustration 16.8b).
13 Heat the crankshaft sprocket, then install it onto the crankshaft, making sure that the

16.8a Use a two-legged puller to remove the sprocket

16.8b Note the location of the Woodruff key (arrowed)

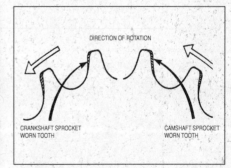

16.10 Check the sprockets in the areas indicated to see if they are worn excessively

16.13a Heat the sprocket . . .

16.13b . . . then drive it onto the crankshaft until the circlip groove is visible

16.17 Arrangement of the cam chain, tensioner blade and guides

slot in the centre of the sprocket aligns with the key (see illustrations). Drive the sprocket on with a suitable length of tube or punch until the circlip groove is visible, then install a new circlip with its sharp edge facing outwards (see illustration 16.7).

14 Clean the threads of the mounting bolts for the tensioner blade and both guides, then apply a fresh drop of the specified thread locking compound to the threads as the bolts are installed.

15 Install the spacer in the lower end of the long guide, then position the guide in the crankcase and secure it with the bolt (see illustration 16.6b). Follow the same procedure to install the tensioner blade (see illustration 16.6a). Tighten the bolts to the torque setting specified at the beginning of this Chapter.

16 Ensure that the connecting rod is

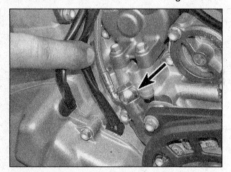

17.4 Location of the release cylinder banjo union

supported so that it will not hit the crankcase, then carefully feed the cam chain around the crankshaft sprocket (see illustration 16.5). Make sure that the chain is located correctly around the sprocket and not kinked, then secure the ends of the chain.

17 Install the spacers in the lower guide, then position the guide in the crankcase and secure it with the bolts (see illustration 16.4). Tighten the bolts to the specified torque setting. The installed cam chain, crankshaft sprocket, tensioner blade and guide should look like this (see illustration).

18 Install the remaining components in the reverse order of removal.

17 Clutch operating system

Special tool: A suitable large syringe or bleeding kit is required to bleed the clutch system (see Step 42).
Note: The clutch operating system can be removed with the engine in the frame.

1 All the models covered in this manual are fitted with an hydraulic clutch. The operating system comprises the master cylinder on the handlebar, the hose and the release cylinder on the left-hand side of the crankcase (see illustration 17.24).

2 The system requires no maintenance other than regular inspection for damage, and

changing the fluid at the specified service interval (see Chapter 1).

3 If there is evidence of air in the system (spongy feel to the lever, difficulty in engaging gear), bleed the system (see Steps 41 to 52).

4 If clutch fluid is leaking from any part of the system, first check that the hose unions are tight. If necessary, renew the sealing washers on both sides of the banjo union on the release cylinder (see illustration). If either the master cylinder or the release cylinder is leaking, new seals will have to be fitted.

Master cylinder

Removal

Note: If the clutch release cylinder is being overhauled at the same time, hydraulic pressure can be used to ease out the piston (see Step 29) before the fluid is extracted and the hose is disconnected from the master cylinder.

5 Before starting, make sure you have some new clutch fluid – KTM specify Shell Naturelle HF-E15 or Magura Blood biohydraulic oil, depending upon year of manufacture. You will also need some clean rags and a suitable container for the old fluid.

6 Undo the screws securing the reservoir cover and lift off the cover and diaphragm (see illustrations). Siphon the old fluid out of the reservoir. Note that on machines fitted with a decompressor, the lever bracket is integral with the reservoir cover – it is not necessary to disconnect the decompressor cable in order to remove the cover (see illustration).

17.6a Remove the reservoir cover . . .

17.6b . . . and lift off the diaphragm

17.6c It is not necessary to disconnect the decompressor cable (arrowed)

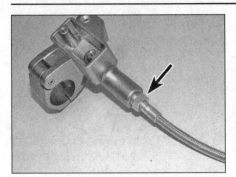

17.7 Disconnect the hose union (arrowed) from the master cylinder

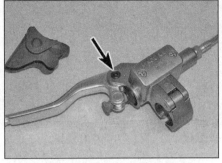

17.9 Remove the cover to access the pivot bolt (arrowed)

17.10a Undo the pivot bolt . . .

7 Pull back the boot and undo the clutch hose union and separate the hose from the master cylinder **(see illustration)**. Be prepared to catch any residual fluid in the union. Wrap a clean plastic bag over the end of the hose to prevent dirt entering the system, and secure the hose in an upright position to minimise fluid loss.

8 Note the alignment of the master cylinder with the handlebar, then undo the handlebar clamp screw and lift the master cylinder off.

Overhaul

9 Pull off the lever cover to access the pivot bolt **(see illustration)**.

10 Undo the nut on the underside of the pivot bolt, then withdraw the bolt and separate the lever assembly from the master cylinder **(see illustrations)**. Note how the push rod on the lever passes through the boot to locate on the master cylinder piston. Note the location of the tensioner spring.

11 Clean the contact surfaces of the lever, bracket and pivot bolt. If they are in good condition, lubricate the components with dry film lubricant prior to assembly.

12 Carefully remove the boot from the master cylinder to reveal the piston retaining circlip **(see illustration)**.

13 Depress the piston and use circlip pliers to remove the circlip, then slide out the washer, piston assembly and the spring, noting how they fit **(see illustrations)**. If the piston is difficult to remove, apply low pressure compressed air to the fluid outlet. Lay the parts out in the proper order to prevent confusion during reassembly.

14 If required, clean the inside of the master cylinder with fresh clutch fluid. If compressed air is available, blow it through the fluid galleries to ensure they are clear (make sure the air is filtered and unlubricated).

Caution: Do not, under any circumstances, use a petroleum-based solvent to clean the master cylinder.

15 Check the master cylinder bore for corrosion, scratches, nicks and score marks. If damage or wear is evident, the master cylinder must be renewed.

16 The circlip, washer, piston assembly and spring are all included in the master cylinder rebuild kit. Use all of the new parts, regardless of the apparent condition of the old ones. It is good practice to renew the boot at this time.

17 Install the spring on the inner end of the piston. Lubricate the piston assembly with clean clutch fluid and install it in the master cylinder, making sure it is the correct way round **(see illustration 17.13b)**.

18 Depress the piston and install the washer and new circlip, making sure the circlip locates properly in its groove **(see illustration 17.13a)**.

19 Install the boot, making sure the lip is seated correctly in the groove **(see illustration 17.12)**.

20 Align the clutch lever with the bracket – note the recess for the tensioner spring and insert the push rod into the boot **(see illustration 17.10b)**. Secure the lever with the pivot bolt and tighten the nut securely. Install the lever cover.

21 Inspect the reservoir cover and diaphragm

and renew any parts if they are damaged or deteriorated. On machines fitted with a decompressor, check the reservoir cover/ lever bracket for signs of damage **(see illustration 17.6c)**.

Installation

22 Installation is the reverse of removal, noting the following:

● Align the master cylinder as noted on removal and tighten the handlebar clamp screw securely.

● Tighten the hose union nut securely – don't push the boot over the union until the system has been refilled with fluid and checked for leaks.

● Fill the system with new clutch fluid and bleed out any air (see Steps 41 to 52).

● Check the operation of the clutch before riding the bike.

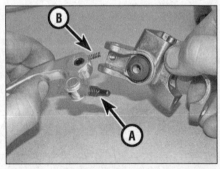

17.10b . . . and lift off the lever assembly. Note the push rod (A) and spring (B)

17.12 Location of the piston retaining circlip (arrowed)

17.13a Remove the circlip . . .

17.13b . . . then slide out the washer, piston assembly and the spring

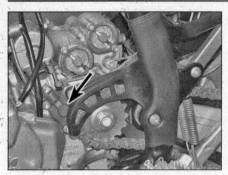

17.24 Location of the clutch release cylinder (arrowed)

17.28a Undo the bolts (arrowed) . . .

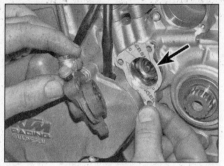

17.28b . . . and remove the release cylinder and gasket (arrowed)

Release cylinder

Removal

23 Before starting, make sure you have some new clutch fluid – KTM specify Shell Naturelle HF-E15 or Magura Blood biohydraulic oil, depending upon year of manufacture. You will also need some clean rags and a suitable container for the old fluid.

24 The release cylinder is located on the left-hand side of the crankcase **(see illustration)**.

25 Follow the procedure in Section 4, Steps 21 and 22, to remove the final drive front sprocket cover and the chain guide and roller.

26 Follow the procedure in Chapter 7 and remove the drive chain and, if required, the front sprocket.

27 Clean the area around the release cylinder to prevent any dirt getting into the transmission input shaft bearing or release cylinder mechanism.

28 Slacken the clutch hose banjo bolt, then tighten it lightly as an aid to removal. Undo the two remaining release cylinder mounting bolts and lift the cylinder off **(see illustrations)**. Note the location of the gasket between the release cylinder and the crankcase and the O-ring on the release cylinder – discard both as new ones must be fitted.

29 If compressed air is not available to extract the piston from the release cylinder, remove the circlip now (see Step 32) and ease the piston out by applying light pressure with the clutch lever. Cover the piston with clean rag to avoid fluid spillage.

30 Undo the clutch hose banjo bolt and separate the hose from the release cylinder, noting its alignment. Be prepared to catch any residual fluid in the union. Discard the sealing washers as new ones must be fitted. Wrap a clean plastic bag over the end of the hose to prevent dirt entering the system, and secure the hose in an upright position to minimise fluid loss.

Caution: Do not operate the clutch lever while the hose is disconnected.

Overhaul

31 Check that the clutch pushrod is free to move inside the transmission input shaft – if necessary, withdraw the pushrod and check that it is clean and free from corrosion **(see illustration 17.28c)**. Lubricate the pushrod with a smear of clutch assembly grease before installation.

32 Use circlip pliers to remove the circlip, then cover the piston with rag and apply low pressure compressed air to the fluid inlet and ease out the piston, seal and ball bearing **(see illustration)**.

33 If required, clean the inside of the release cylinder with fresh clutch fluid. If compressed air is available, blow it through the fluid galleries to ensure they are clear (make sure the air is filtered and unlubricated).

Caution: Do not, under any circumstances, use a petroleum-based solvent to clean the release cylinder.

34 Check the cylinder bore for corrosion, scratches, nicks and score marks. If damage or wear is evident, the release cylinder must be renewed.

35 The piston, seal and ball bearing are all included in the release cylinder rebuild kit. Use all of the new parts, regardless of the apparent condition of the old ones. It is good practice to renew the retaining circlip at this time.

36 Lubricate the piston and seal with clean clutch fluid and install it and the ball bearing in the release cylinder, then secure the piston with the circlip **(see illustration 17.32)**. Ensure that the circlip locates properly in its groove.

Installation

37 If removed, install the clutch pushrod. Fit a new O-ring and gasket onto the release cylinder, then install the release cylinder and secure it with the two front mounting bolts **(see illustrations 17.28b and 28a)**.

38 Connect the clutch hose to the release

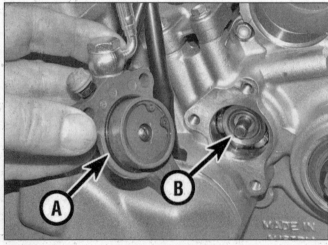

17.28c Note the location of the O-ring (A) and clutch pushrod (B)

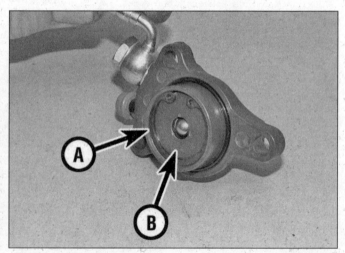

17.32 Remove the circlip (A) then ease out the piston assembly (B)

17.48a Attach the hose to the bleed valve (arrowed)

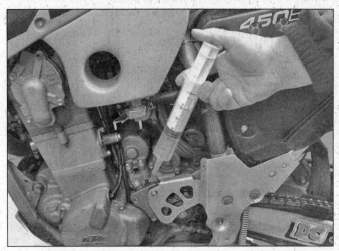

17.48b Pump fluid into the clutch system as described

cylinder, using new sealing washers on both sides of the banjo union. Align the union as noted on removal **(see illustration 17.4)**.

39 If removed, install the final drive front sprocket (see Chapter 7).

40 Install the remaining components in the reverse order of removal, noting the following:
- Fill the system with new clutch fluid and bleed out any air (see Steps 41 to 52).
- Check the banjo union for leaks.
- Check the operation of the clutch before riding the bike.

Bleeding the clutch release mechanism

41 Bleeding the clutch is simply the process of removing air from the master cylinder, hose and the release cylinder. Bleeding is necessary whenever an hydraulic connection is loosened, or when a component or hose is renewed. Leaks in the system may also allow air to enter, but leaking clutch fluid will reveal their presence and warn you of the need for repair.

42 To bleed the clutch, you will need a clutch bleeding syringe. If required, KTM provide a service tool for this purpose (Part No. 503.29.050.000). Alternatively, a bleeding kit designed to back-feed the system, or any commercial syringe with a capacity of approximately 40 cc and some clear plastic hose, will do. You will also need some new clutch fluid – KTM specify Shell Naturelle HF-E15 or Magura Blood biohydraulic oil, depending upon year of manufacture – some clean rags and a suitable container for the old fluid.

43 Support the motorcycle securely in an upright position using an auxiliary stand. Position the handlebars so that the top of the master cylinder reservoir is as level as possible, then undo the two cover screws and lift off the cover and the diaphragm **(see illustrations 17.6a and b)**.

44 If the reservoir is not already empty, siphon the old fluid out.

45 If you are using the KTM service tool, fill the syringe with clutch fluid, then unscrew

the bleed valve from the release cylinder and install the syringe in its place.

46 Pump fluid from the syringe into the clutch system – as the system fills, the fluid will emerge through the hole in the bottom of the master cylinder reservoir. If there is air in the system there will be air bubbles in the fluid. Keep pumping the fluid until no air bubbles are visible – it may be necessary to siphon excess fluid from the reservoir during this procedure.

47 When no more air bubbles are visible, unscrew the service tool and install the bleed valve. Tighten the valve securely and, if removed, fit the dust cap.

48 If you are using a commercially available kit, fill the syringe or pump reservoir with clutch fluid. Pull the dust cap off the bleed valve on the release cylinder and attach the plastic hose to the valve **(see illustration)**. Now open the valve (approximately 2 turns anti-clockwise) and pump the fluid through the hose into the clutch system as described in Step 45 **(see illustration)**.
Note: *To avoid damaging the bleed valve during the procedure, loosen it and then tighten it temporarily with a ring spanner before attaching the hose. With the hose attached, the valve can then be opened and closed with an open-ended spanner.*

49 When no more air bubbles are visible,

18.2 Kickstart lever is retained by bolt (arrowed)

tighten the bleed valve, disconnect the hose and fit the dust cap.

50 Once the clutch system has been filled and all the air has been bled out, correct the fluid level in the reservoir and install the cover and the diaphragm (see *Pre-ride checks*).

51 Wipe up any spilled brake fluid.

52 Check the operation of the clutch before riding the bike.

> **HAYNES HiNT** *If it's not possible to produce the correct feel to the lever the clutch fluid may be aerated. Let the fluid in the system stabilise for a few hours and then repeat the procedure. Also check to make sure that there are no 'high-spots' in the hose in which an air bubble can become trapped – moving the hose around will normally dislodge any trapped air.*

18 Clutch

Note: *This procedure can be carried out with the engine in the frame. If the engine has been removed, ignore the steps which do not apply.*
Special tool: *On 2003 models onward, a clutch holding tool is required for this procedure (see Step 17).*

Removal

1 Drain the engine oil (see Chapter 1).

2 Undo the retaining bolt and draw the kickstart lever off its shaft **(see illustration)**.

3 Remove the brake pedal (see Chapter 7).

4 Position a drain tray underneath the right-hand engine cover to catch any residual oil when the cover is removed. **Note:** *On 2007 models, a separate clutch cover is provided on the engine cover; it is not necessary to remove the entire right-hand engine cover to access the clutch on these models.*

18.5a Location of the right-hand engine cover screws

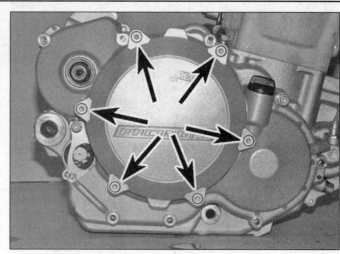

18.5b Location of the separate clutch cover screws – 2007 models

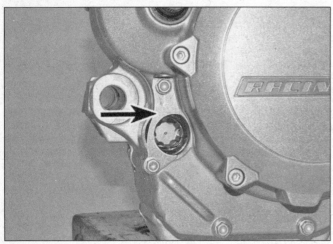

18.5c Location of the brake pedal return spring bracket

18.7 Note the location of the dowels (A) and steel pin (B)

5 Undo the cover screws **(see illustrations)**. Note the locations of the engine cover screws

> **HAYNES HiNT** *Make a cardboard template of the cover and punch a hole for each screw location. As each screw is removed, store it in its relative position in the template. This will ensure all screws are installed correctly on reassembly.*

as they are of different lengths. Also note the location of the bracket for the brake pedal return spring **(see illustration)**.

6 Lift the cover off. If it sticks, tap around the joint with a soft-faced mallet to free the bond. Do not attempt to lever the cover off with a screwdriver – you'll damage the sealing surfaces. Discard the gasket as a new one must be fitted on reassembly.

7 Note the location of the two cover dowels – they may be in the cover or the mating surface

of the crankcase **(see illustration)**. Remove the dowels for safekeeping if they are loose. On 2004-on models, also note the location of the steel pin and remove it for safekeeping.

8 Undo the clutch spring bolts a little at a time in a criss-cross pattern, then remove the bolts, the spring cups and the springs **(see illustration)**.

9 Remove the clutch pressure plate, then withdraw the clutch plates from the clutch housing as a set **(see illustrations)**. Unless

18.8 Remove the clutch bolts, spring cups and springs

18.9a Remove the pressure plate . . .

18.9b . . . withdraw the clutch plates as a set

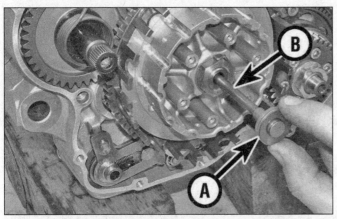

18.10 Remove the clutch lifter (A) and pushrod (B)

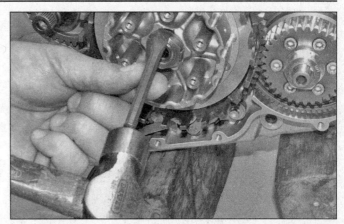

18.16 Bend back the tabs of the centre nut lock washer

18.17a Using the KTM service tool to hold the clutch

18.17b Using a proprietary tool to hold the clutch

18.18 Remove the clutch centre

the plates are being renewed, keep them in their original order.

10 Remove the clutch lifter and, if required, withdraw the pushrod from the centre of the input shaft (see illustration).

11 At this stage, if required, the KTM service tool (Part No. 590.29.003.100) should be used to loosen the alternator rotor nut (see Section 15) and/or the primary gear nut (see Section 19).

2000 to 2002 models

12 On 2000 to 2002 models, remove the circlip securing the clutch centre and draw the centre off. Discard the circlip as a new one must be used on reassembly.

13 On year 2000 models only, remove the outer thrust washer, then draw off the clutch housing, the bearing bush and the inner thrust washer.

14 On 2001 and 2002 models, remove the stepped washer, noting which way round it fits, then draw off the clutch housing, the two needle roller bearings, and the inner thrust washer.

15 On year 2002 models, note how the clutch plate sleeves locate in the clutch centre, then remove them for safekeeping.

2003-on models

16 Bend back the tabs of the clutch centre nut lock washer (see illustration).

17 To remove the nut it is necessary to stop the transmission input shaft from turning,

using either the KTM service tool (Part No. 590.29.003.100) or a suitable clutch holding tool (see illustrations). Note that before using a proprietary holding tool the clutch plate sleeves should be removed. Ensure that the tool engages in the slots for the sleeves without damaging them (see illustration 18.42a).

18 Unscrew the nut and remove the tab washer, noting how it fits. Draw off the clutch centre (see illustration). If not already done, remove the clutch plate sleeves for safekeeping.

19 Remove the stepped washer, noting which way round it fits, then remove the two keepers (see illustrations).

18.19a Remove the stepped washer . . .

18.19b . . . and the two keepers (arrowed)

18.20a Draw off the clutch housing . . .

18.20b . . . the needle roller bearings (arrowed) . . .

20 Draw off the clutch housing, the two needle roller bearings, and the inner thrust washer (see illustrations).

Inspection

21 Measure the free length of each clutch spring (see illustration). If any spring is shorter than the specified service limit, the clutch springs must be renewed as a set.
22 Measure the thickness of each friction plate using a Vernier caliper (see illustration). If any plate has worn to or beyond the service limit given in the specifications at the beginning of this Chapter, the friction plates must be renewed as a set. Also, if any of the

plates smell burnt or are glazed, they must be renewed as a set.
23 Inspect the tabs on the outer edge of each plate (see illustration). If they are burred, renew the plates as a set. Check the corresponding slots in the clutch housing for damage also (see Step 26).
24 Measure the thickness of each plain plate using a Vernier caliper, then compare the results with the specification at the beginning of this Chapter. **Note:** *On 2002, 2003 and 2006-on models, two different thicknesses of plain plate are fitted. The two inner and two outer plates are thinner than the four middle plates – see Specifications for details.* Inspect

the plain plates for signs of wear or scuffing on the surface. The plain plates should show no signs of excess heating (bluing). Check for warpage using a surface plate and feeler gauges (see illustration). If any plate is warped, or shows signs of wear or bluing, all plain plates must be renewed as a set.
25 Inspect the tabs on the inner edge of each plain plate (see illustration). If they are burred, renew the plates as a set. Check the corresponding slots on the clutch centre (2000 and 2001 models) or the surface of the clutch plate sleeves (2002-on models) for damage (see Step 28).
26 Inspect the slots in the clutch housing where

18.20c . . . and the inner thrust washer

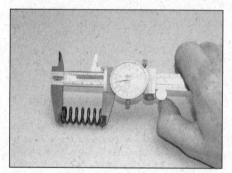

18.21 Measuring clutch spring free length

18.22 Measuring clutch friction plate thickness

18.23 Inspect the tabs on the outer edge of each friction plate

18.24 Check the plain plates for warpage

18.25 Inspect the tabs on the inner edge of each plain plate

18.26a Inspect the slots in the clutch housing

18.26b Inspect the gear teeth for wear and damage

18.27 Inspect the clutch housing bearing surface and bearing(s)

the tabs on the friction plates engage **(see illustrations)**. Check the teeth around the outer edge of the housing and the corresponding teeth on the primary gear on the crankshaft. Check the teeth on the pinion that engages with the kickstart intermediate gear and the oil pump drive gear. If any wear or damage is found, renew the appropriate components as sets.

27 Inspect the bearing surface of the clutch housing and the surface of the plain bush (year 2000 models) or needle roller bearings **(see illustration)**. If the bush is scored or damaged, fit a new bush and housing. If the needle rollers are pitted, but the bearing surface of the clutch housing shows no signs of wear, renew the needle bearings only.

28 Inspect the slots on the clutch centre (2000 and 2001 models) or the surface of the clutch plate sleeves (2002-on models) for damage **(see illustration)**. Ensure that the sleeves are a firm sliding fit in their slots.

29 Inspect the splines that engage with the transmission input shaft. The clutch centre should be a firm fit on the shaft **(see illustration)**.

30 Ensure the threads for the spring bolts in the clutch centre are in good condition.

31 Check the friction surface of the pressure plate for wear and scuff marks. On 2000 to 2002 models, refer to *Tools and Workshop Tips* in the *Reference* section and check the condition of the pressure plate thrust bearing.

32 On 2003-on models, the clutch lifter incorporates a radial needle bearing. If required, ease off the circlip, then remove the washer and bearing to clean and check the

lifter for wear **(see illustrations)**. If required, fit a new clutch lifter assembly – individual components are not available.

33 Check that the clutch pushrod is straight by rolling it on a flat surface.

Installation

34 Remove all traces of old gasket from the crankcase and right-hand engine cover surfaces. Note the location of the crankshaft and kickstart shaft seals in the cover and inspect them for wear and damage. If required, lever the seals out carefully using a flat-bladed screwdriver, then press in new seals using a suitably-sized socket (see *Tools and Workshop Tips* in the *Reference* section). When installed, the outer edge of both seals should be level with the lip of the seal housing in the cover.

2000 to 2002 models

35 On year 2000 models only, slide the inner thrust washer and bearing bush onto the transmission input shaft. Lubricate the bush with clean engine oil, then install the clutch housing. Ensure that the primary drive gears, clutch housing pinion, kickstart intermediate gear and the oil pump drive gear all engage correctly. Install the outer thrust washer.

36 On 2001 and 2002 models, slide the inner thrust washer and two needle roller bearings onto the transmission input shaft. Lubricate the bearings with clean engine oil, then install the clutch housing. Ensure that the primary drive gears, clutch housing pinion, kickstart intermediate gear and the oil pump drive gear all engage correctly. Install the stepped washer.

37 If required, heat the clutch centre with a hot air gun, then align the splines in the centre with the splines on the transmission shaft and press the centre on so that the groove in the shaft for the retaining circlip is visible. Using circlip pliers, secure the clutch centre with a new circlip. Now go to Step 44.

2003-on models

38 Slide the inner thrust washer and two needle roller bearings onto the transmission input shaft. Lubricate the bearings with clean engine oil, then install the clutch housing **(see illustration 18.20a)**. Ensure that the primary drive gears, clutch housing pinion, kickstart intermediate gear and the oil pump drive gear all engage correctly. Install the two keepers and secure them with the stepped washer **(see illustrations 18.19b and a)**.

39 Slide on the clutch centre **(see illustration 18.18)**.

18.28 Check the sleeves for wear and ensure they are a good fit

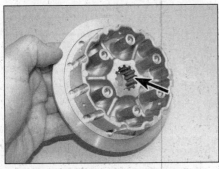

18.29 Check the clutch centre splines (arrowed) for wear

18.32a Remove the circlip . . .

18.32b . . . to inspect the clutch lifter bearing

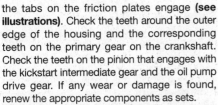

18.40a Note the tab washer location (arrowed) . . .

18.40b . . . then install the tab washer

18.41a Apply thread lock to the input shaft . . .

18.41b . . . then install the clutch centre nut

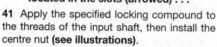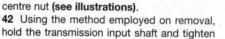

18.42a Ensure the holding tool is correctly located in the slots (arrowed) . . .

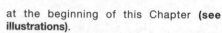

at the beginning of this Chapter (see illustrations).

43 Bend the remaining two tabs on the tab washer over the sides of the centre nut (see illustration).

44 Ensure that the clutch pushrod is installed in the input shaft, then fit the clutch lifter (see illustration 18.10)

45 On 2002-on models, install the clutch plate sleeves (see illustration).

46 Coat each clutch plate with clean engine oil, then build up the plates in the clutch housing, starting with a plain plate, then a friction plate and alternating friction and plain plates until all are installed (see illustrations). Note: On 2002, 2003 and 2006-on models, the two inner and two outer plain plates are thinner than the four middle plates – see Specifications for details.

47 Fit the pressure plate, ensuring it is correctly located over the clutch assembly (see illustration).

40 Clean the threads of the transmission input shaft and the clutch centre nut with suitable solvent. Note the location for the tab washer on the boss of the clutch centre and install the tab washer (see illustrations).

41 Apply the specified locking compound to the threads of the input shaft, then install the centre nut (see illustrations).

42 Using the method employed on removal, hold the transmission input shaft and tighten the centre nut to the torque setting specified

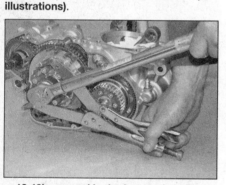

18.42b . . . and locked securely before tightening the centre nut

18.43 Bend the tabs up to secure the centre nut

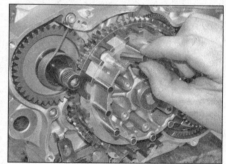

18.45 Install the clutch plate sleeves

18.46a Install the clutch plates, starting with a plain plate . . .

18.46b . . . followed by a friction plate

18.47 Ensure the pressure plate is correctly located

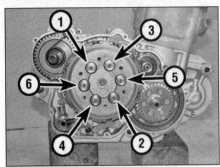

18.48 Tighten the bolts in a criss-cross pattern

18.50a Ensure the new gasket is correctly located

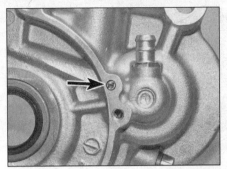

18.50b Take care not to block the oil jet (arrowed) in the sealing surface

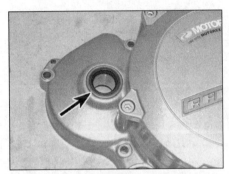

18.51a Lubricate the kickstart shaft seal (arrowed) . . .

18.51b . . . and the crankshaft seal (arrowed) with a smear of grease

18.51c Align the cover and install it carefully . . .

48 Clean the threads of the clutch pressure plate bolts and apply a drop of specified locking compound, then install the springs, spring cups and bolts **(see illustration 18.8)**. Tighten the bolts evenly, in a criss-cross pattern, to the specified torque setting **(see illustration)**.
49 If removed, install the clutch cover dowels and, on 2004-on models, the steel pin **(see illustration 18.7)**.
50 Fit the new cover gasket, making sure it locates correctly onto the dowels **(see illustration)**. Ensure that the gasket does not block the oil jet in the sealing surface of the crankcase **(see illustration)**.
51 Lubricate the inside of the two cover seals with a smear of grease and install the cover, ensuring that the kickstart shaft is correctly

aligned to avoid damaging the shaft seal **(see illustrations)**.
52 Install the cover screws, ensuring they are in their correct locations **(see illustration 18.5a and b)**. Don't forget to fit the bracket for the brake pedal return spring **(see illustration)**. Tighten the cover screws to the torque setting specified at the beginning of this Chapter.
53 Refill the engine with oil to the correct level (see Chapter 1).
54 Install the kickstart lever. Clean the threads of the retaining bolt and apply a drop of specified locking compound, then tighten the bolt to the specified torque setting **(see illustration)**.
55 Install the brake pedal (see Chapter 7).
56 Check the operation of the clutch and the rear brake before riding the bike.

19 Primary gear, starter motor clutch and starter gears

Note: *This procedure can be carried out with the engine in the frame. If the engine has been removed, ignore the steps which do not apply.* **Special tool:** *A crankshaft holding tool (see Step 3) or gear holding tool (see Step 6), and a gear puller (see Step 8) are required for this procedure.*

Removal

1 Follow the procedure in Section 18 and remove the right-hand engine cover.
2 Withdraw the shaft for the starter motor

18.51d . . . to avoid damaging the seals (arrowed)

18.52 Don't forget the bracket for the brake pedal return spring

18.54 Apply thread lock to the kickstart lever bolt

19.2a Withdraw the shaft . . .

19.2b . . . and lift out the reduction gear

19.3a Ensure the holding tool is correctly engaged in the teeth of the clutch housing and primary gear

reduction gear, then lift out the gear (see illustrations). On 2000 to 2005 models, the gear turns on one needle roller bearing. On later models, two bearings are fitted.

3 Follow the procedure in Section 18 and remove the clutch. Note that at the appropriate stage (Section 18, Step 11) the KTM service tool (Part No. 590.29.003.100) should be used to loosen the primary gear nut (see illustration).

⚠️ Warning: The primary gear nut may be either right or left-hand threaded. A left-hand threaded nut is marked LEFT and should be turned clockwise to loosen it. A conventional right-hand threaded nut is not marked.

4 If the service tool is not available, the primary gear can be held using a proprietary

gear holding tool (see illustration 19.6a). Alternatively, if the piston has been removed, the crankshaft can be held by passing a suitable bolt through the small-end of the connecting rod (see illustration 19.6b).

5 Undo the E-clip and remove the oil pump gear – take care not to loose the gear drive pin (see Section 22).

6 If the primary gear nut was not loosened during clutch removal, hold the gear with a suitable tool to prevent the crankshaft turning and loosen the nut – note Warning above (see illustrations).

7 Remove the primary gear nut.

8 Undo two of the bolts securing the primary gear to the starter clutch assembly (or flywheel on SX models), then thread a two-legged puller

into the bolt holes. KTM provide a service tool (Part No. 590.29.021.044) for this purpose; alternatively, a similar proprietary tool can be used (see illustration).

9 Carefully draw the primary gear and starter clutch assembly (flywheel on SX models) off the crankshaft (see illustration). Note the location of the Woodruff key and remove it for safekeeping if it is loose (see illustration).

Inspection

Note: With the exception of Steps 15 and 16, the inspection procedure applies only to starter motor equipped models.

10 With the assembly face down, check that the driven gear rotates freely in a clockwise direction and locks against the starter clutch housing in an anti-clockwise direction

19.3b Hold the tool firmly while freeing the primary gear nut

19.6a Holding the primary gear with a proprietary tool

19.6b Holding the primary gear with a bolt through the con-rod small-end

19.8 Install a two-legged puller on the primary gear

19.9a Draw off the primary gear

19.9b Note the location of the Woodruff key (arrowed)

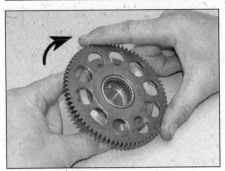

19.10 Driven gear should rotate freely in clockwise direction

19.11 Withdraw the driven gear from the starter clutch

19.12a Check the condition of the starter clutch sprags (arrowed)

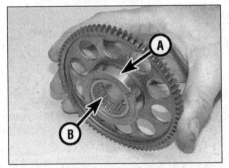

19.12b Check the surface of the hub (A) and the needle bearing (B)

19.13 Circlip (arrowed) secures the sprag assembly

19.15 Check the primary gear teeth for wear and damage

(see illustration). If it doesn't, inspect the components of the starter clutch.

11 Withdraw the driven gear from the starter clutch. If it appears stuck, rotate the gear clockwise as you withdraw it to free it from the clutch sprags (see illustration).

12 Check the condition of the sprags inside the clutch housing, the bearing surface on the hub of the driven gear, and the condition of the driven gear needle bearing (see illustrations). If any components show signs of excessive wear, or the sprags or bearing rollers are damaged, marked or pitted, they should be renewed.

13 Using circlip pliers, remove the circlip securing the sprag assembly inside the starter clutch housing and lift the sprag assembly out (see illustration). Install the new sprag assembly and secure it with the circlip. Make sure that the tabs on the outer edge of the circlip are correctly located in the groove in the housing.

14 Support the driven gear on the worktop with sufficient clearance to drive the old needle bearing out using a suitably-sized socket or driver. Press the new bearing in carefully to avoid damage (see Tools and Workshop Tips in the Reference section).

15 Check the teeth on the primary gear and the corresponding teeth around the outer edge of the clutch housing (see illustration). If any wear or damage is found, renew the primary gear and the clutch housing.

16 To separate the primary gear from the starter clutch housing (flywheel on SX models), hold the gear securely and undo the bolts (see illustration). Prior to reassembly, clean the threads of the bolts and apply a drop of specified locking compound (see illustration). Install the bolts and tighten them evenly, in a criss-cross pattern, to the specified torque setting.

17 Examine the teeth of the starter driven gear and the corresponding teeth of the reduction gear (smaller pinion), and the teeth on the reduction gear (larger pinion) and the corresponding teeth of the starter idler gear. Renew the gears if worn or chipped teeth are discovered on related pinions – note that the starter driven gear and reduction gear are only available as a paired set. If the teeth on the idler gear are damaged, check the starter motor drive shaft (see Chapter 9).

18 Check the condition of the needle roller bearing(s) for the reduction gear. Assemble the bearing(s) and gear on their shaft and ensure that the gear turns smoothly without any lateral play. If the shaft is worn or scored, or if the gear is a loose fit on the bearing(s), renew the shaft and bearing(s).

19 Check that the starter idler gear turns freely on its shaft (see illustration). If the gear

19.16a Undo the bolts to separate the primary gear from the starter clutch housing

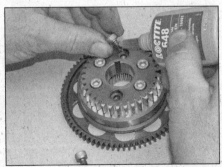

19.16b Apply thread locking compound prior to reassembly

19.19a Check that the starter idler gear turns freely

19.19b Remove the circlip . . .

19.19c . . . and the washer . . .

19.19d . . . and draw the gear off

is stiff, or there is lateral play on the shaft, remove the circlip and washer and draw the gear off **(see illustrations)**. The idler gear turns on a bush which is not available separately – if the surface of the bush is worn or scored, a new gear will have to be fitted. On installation, lubricate the shaft with clean engine oil, then fit the gear and washer and secure them with a new circlip. Ensure that the squared edge of the circlip is facing out.

Installation

20 Lubricate the driven gear needle bearing and the sprags inside the starter clutch housing with clean engine oil, then install the

19.27a Apply locking compound to the threads

driven gear into the clutch, rotating the gear clockwise as you do so to spread the sprags and allow the hub of the gear to enter **(see illustration 19.11)**.
21 If removed, install the Woodruff key in the crankshaft **(see illustration 19.9b)**.
22 Align the slot in the centre of the primary gear with the key and install the primary gear and starter clutch assembly (or flywheel) onto the crankshaft.
23 If the KTM service tool (Part No. 590.29.003.100) is available, the primary gear nut can be installed and tightened once the clutch centre has been secured (see Step 29).
24 If the service tool is not available, the primary gear nut can be installed at this stage as follows.
25 Hold the primary gear securely using a suitable gear holding tool **(see illustration 19.6a)**. Alternatively, if the piston has been removed, the crankshaft can be held by passing a suitable bolt through the small-end eye of the connecting rod **(see illustration 19.6b)**.
26 Clean the threads of the crankshaft and the primary gear nut with suitable solvent.
27 Apply specified locking compound to the threads of the crankshaft, then install the nut and tighten it to the torque setting specified at the beginning of this Chapter **(see illustrations)**.

⚠️ *Warning: The primary gear nut may be either right or left-hand threaded. A left-hand threaded nut is marked LEFT and should be turned anti-clockwise to tighten it. A conventional right-hand threaded nut is not marked.*

28 Install the oil pump gear and secure it with a new E-clip (see Section 22).
29 Follow the procedure in Section 18 and install the clutch. Note that once the clutch centre has been secured, the KTM service tool (Part No. 590.29.003.100) should be used to tighten the primary gear nut – note **Warning** above **(see illustration 19.3b)**. Don't forget to clean the threads of the crankshaft and the primary gear nut and apply specified locking compound to the threads of the crankshaft. Tighten the nut to the specified torque setting.
30 Position the starter motor reduction gear with the small pinion facing inwards and engaged with the starter driven gear. The large pinion should engage with the starter idler gear. Install the needle bearing(s) on the shaft as appropriate, and lubricate them with clean engine oil, then press the shaft and bearings through the centre of the gear **(see illustrations 19.2b and a)**. Ensure that the shaft is pressed fully into its location in the crankcase.
31 Follow the procedure in Section 18 and install the right-hand engine cover.

19.27b Check for any marking on the primary gear nut

19.27c Hold the gear and tighten the nut to the specified torque

20.2a Undo the bolt (arrowed) . . .

20.2b . . . and remove the return spring bracket

20.3 Note the location of the kickstart ratchet spring (arrowed)

20 Kickstart mechanism and gears

Note: *This procedure can be carried out with the engine in the frame. If the engine has been removed, ignore the steps which do not apply.*

Removal

1 Follow the procedure in Section 18 and remove the clutch.
2 The kickstart mechanism is retained in the engine case by the return spring. Hold the spring to relieve tension on the spring bracket, then undo the bolt securing the bracket and release the spring tension **(see illustrations)**. Remove the bracket for safekeeping.
3 Draw the kickstart mechanism out of the case, noting the location of the ratchet spring

(see illustration). A thrust washer is fitted on the inner end of the kickstart shaft – be sure to remove it if it is stuck to the edge of the shaft housing **(see illustration 20.6b)**.
4 Check that the kickstart intermediate gear turns freely on its shaft **(see illustration)**. If the gear is stiff, or there is lateral play on the shaft, remove the circlip and washer and draw the gear off **(see illustrations)**. The intermediate gear turns on a bush which is not available separately – if the surface of the bush is worn or scored, a new gear will have to be fitted. On installation, lubricate the shaft with clean engine oil, then fit the gear and washer and secure them with a new circlip. Ensure that the squared edge of the circlip is facing out.
5 Check that the kickstart stop plate is held securely in the case **(see illustration 20.4a)**. If the plate is badly worn or loose, undo the retaining bolts and lift it off. Prior to

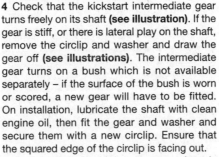

20.4a Check that the kickstart intermediate gear turns freely. Note the stop plate (A)

reassembly, clean the threads of the bolts and apply a drop of specified locking compound, then tighten the bolts to the torque setting specified at the beginning of this Chapter.

20.4b Remove the circlip . . .

20.4c . . . and the washer . . .

20.4d . . . and draw the gear off

20.6a Remove the ratchet spring . . .

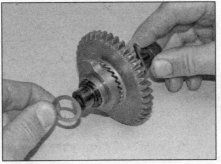

20.6b . . . and thrust washer

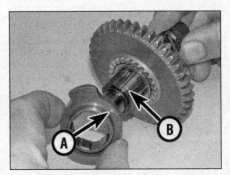

20.7 Note the alignment of the register marks on the gear (A) and the shaft (B)

20.8 Unhook the end of the spring from the hole (arrowed)

20.9 Note the alignment of the slot in the sleeve (A) and the hole in the shaft (B)

Inspection

6 Remove the ratchet spring and thrust washer from the inner end of the kickstart shaft (see illustrations).

20.10a Remove the circlip (arrowed) . . .

7 Slide off the ratchet gear – note the alignment of the register marks on the gear and the shaft (see illustration).
8 Unhook the cranked end of the return spring from the hole in the shaft (see illustration). If the spring is worn or damaged, or if there is insufficient tension in the spring to hold the kickstart lever in the rest position when the bike is in use, fit a new spring on reassembly.
9 Slide off the sleeve – note the alignment of the slot in the sleeve with the hole in the shaft (see illustration).
10 Use circlip pliers to remove the circlip retaining the kickstart gear, then slide off the outer thrust washer (see illustrations).
11 Slide off the kickstart gear, the needle bearing and the inner thrust washer (see illustrations).
12 Clean the components with a suitable

solvent, then inspect the kickstart shaft, the bearing and the inner bearing surface of the kickstart gear for wear and score marks (see illustration). Examine the bearing rollers for pitting and ensure that the bearing cage is not damaged. Renew any components that are worn or damaged.
13 Ensure that the oil hole in the kickstart shaft is clear and check that the splines on the end of the shaft are not damaged. If the shaft splines are damaged, it is likely that the splines on the kickstart lever will also be damaged – renew the shaft and lever as a set.
14 Check the teeth on the ratchet gear and the corresponding teeth on the back of the kickstart gear – renew the gears as a set if the teeth are worn or damaged (see illustration).
15 Examine the teeth of the kickstart gear and the corresponding teeth of the intermediate

20.10b . . . and the outer thrust washer

20.11a Slide off the kickstart gear . . .

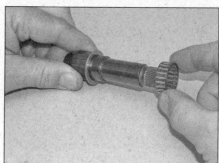

20.11b . . . the needle bearing . . .

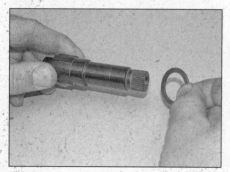

20.11c . . . and the inner thrust washer

20.12 Examine the needle bearing and bearing surface

20.14 Examine the ratchet gears for wear and damage

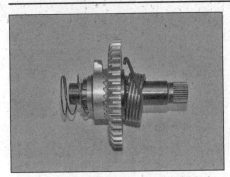

20.20 Arrangement of the assembled kickstart mechanism

gear and renew the gears if worn or chipped teeth are discovered. If the teeth on the intermediate gear are damaged, check the pinion on the back of the clutch housing (see Section 18). If any wear or damage is found, renew the appropriate components as sets.

Installation

16 Slide the inner thrust washer and needle bearing onto the kickstart shaft (see illustrations 20.11c and b). Lubricate the bearing with clean engine oil, then slide on

the kickstart gear with the ratchet teeth facing inwards (see illustration 20.11a).
17 Slide on the outer thrust washer and secure the gear with a new circlip – ensure that the circlip is correctly located in its groove in the shaft (see illustration 20.10a).
18 Install the sleeve with the widest end against the gear; align the slot in the sleeve with the hole in the shaft, then slide on the return spring and locate the cranked end in the hole (see illustrations 20.9 and 20.8).
19 Align the register mark on the ratchet gear with the mark on the shaft and install the gear, then slide on the thrust washer and ratchet spring (see illustrations 20.7, 20.6b and a).
20 The assembled kickstart mechanism should look like this (see illustration).
21 Install the kickstart mechanism in the case – position the arm on the ratchet gear to the rear of the stop plate and press the shaft into its housing so that the kickstart gear and intermediate gear are fully meshed (see illustration).
22 Clean the threads of the return spring bracket bolt and apply a drop of the specified locking compound. Fit the smaller hole in the bracket over the end of the spring, then

tension the spring to align the bracket with its location in the case and install the bolt (see illustrations 20.2b and 2a). Tighten the bolt to the specified torque setting.
23 Position the kickstart return spring equidistant around the kickstart shaft to allow for fitting of the right-hand engine cover (see illustration).
24 Follow the procedure in Section 18 and install the clutch.

21 External gearchange mechanism

Note: *This procedure can be carried out with the engine in the frame. If the engine has been removed, ignore the steps which do not apply.*

Removal

1 Make sure the transmission is in neutral and note the position of the gearchange lever. Undo the bolt securing the lever to the gearchange shaft and draw the lever off (see illustration). Note the arrangement of washers on the lever bolt (see illustration).

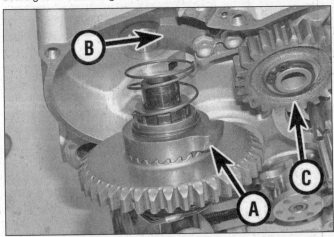

20.21 Position arm (A) to the rear of the stop plate (B). Note location of intermediate gear (C)

20.23 Ensure there is space between the spring (A) and the shaft (B) to allow for fitting of the cover

21.1a Undo the bolt to remove the gearchange lever

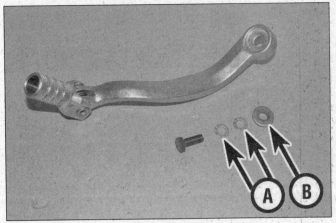

21.1b Note the arrangement of the serrated locking (A) and plain (B) washers

21.4a Note how the gearchange shaft return spring fits either side of the crankcase stop (arrowed)

21.4b Selector arm pawls engage with the pins on the gearchange rotor (arrowed)

2 Follow the procedure in Section 18 and remove the clutch.

3 Undo the E-clip and remove the oil pump gear – take care not to loose the gear drive pin (see Section 22).

4 Note how the ends of the gearchange shaft return spring fit on each side of the crankcase stop, and how the selector arm pawls engage with the pins on the gearchange rotor **(see illustrations)**.

5 Slide back the pawl plate and withdraw the gearchange shaft from the crankcase, noting the thrust washer on the shaft **(see illustrations)**.

6 Note how the stopper arm roller locates in the neutral detent on the gearchange cam **(see illustration)**. Undo the gearchange rotor centre bolt, then pull the stopper arm away from the cam and lift the rotor off **(see illustration)**. Note how the rotor locates on the end of the selector drum.

21.5a Slide back the pawl plate . . .

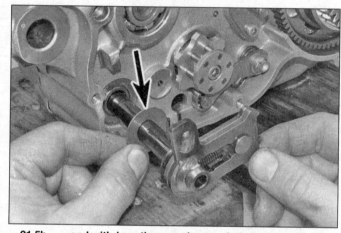

21.5b . . . and withdraw the gearchange shaft. Note the thrust washer (arrowed)

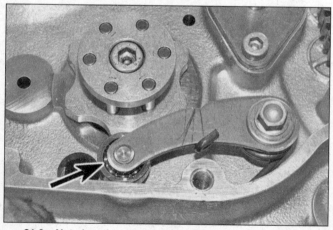

21.6a Note location of stopper arm roller (arrowed) on the gearchange cam

21.6b Note how segments on back of rotor (A) locate on the end of selector drum (B)

21.7a Undo the stopper arm pivot bolt (arrowed)

21.7b Note where the ends of the stopper arm spring (arrowed) locate

7 Undo the stopper arm pivot bolt and remove the stopper arm assembly, noting how the stopper arm spring locates against the inside of the case and the underside of the arm **(see illustrations)**.

Inspection

8 Check the selector arm pawls for wear **(see**

illustration). Check the pawl spring and the gearchange shaft return spring – if they are fatigued, worn or damaged they must be renewed.

9 Using a feeler gauge, measure the pawl assembly sliding clearance and compare the result with the specification at the beginning of this Chapter **(see illustration)**. If the clearance

is outside the specification, disassemble the selector arm assembly as follows and renew any worn components.

10 Note the location of the gearchange shaft return spring, then ease the ends of the spring off the stopper pin and remove the spring **(see illustration 21.8)**. Slide off the spring collar, noting how it locates in the slot in the pawl plate **(see illustration)**.

11 Note the location of the pawl spring, then slide the plate and spring off **(see illustration)**. Note how the guide pin on the pawl plate locates in the slot in the fixed plate.

12 Inspect the gearchange shaft for wear and score marks where it locates in its bearings. If the shaft is damaged it must be renewed, and it is likely that the shaft bearings will be damaged also. The bearings are located in the left and right-hand crankcase halves and require the use of an internal bearing puller to extract them (see *Tools and Workshop Tips* in the *Reference* section). Note that the bearings should only be removed if they are going to be renewed.

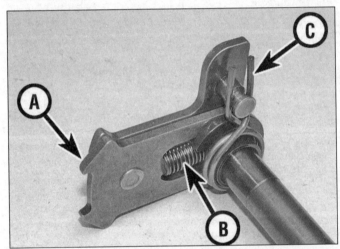

21.8 Check the pawls (A), pawl spring (B) and shaft return spring (C)

21.9 Measure the pawl assembly sliding clearance

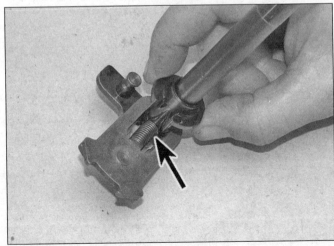

21.10 Slide off the spring collar, noting how it locates in the slot (arrowed)

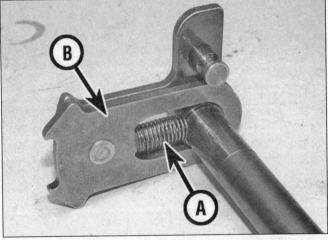

21.11 Note location of pawl spring (A) and pawl plate (B)

21.13 Location of the gearchange shaft seal

21.14 Check the gearchange shaft for straightness and damage to the splines

21.16 Components of the stopper arm assembly

13 A seal is fitted on the outside edge of the left-hand bearing – ease the old seal out carefully with a flat-bladed screwdriver, then press the new seal in using a suitably-sized socket (see illustration).

14 Check the gearchange shaft for straightness and damage to the splines (see illustration). If the shaft is bent you can attempt to straighten it, but if the splines are damaged the shaft must be renewed. If the shaft splines are damaged, it is likely that the splines in the gearchange lever will also be damaged – renew the shaft and lever as a set.

15 Install the selector arm components in the reverse order of removal. Ensure that the tabs on the shaft return spring collar are correctly located in the slot in the pawl plate and that the ends of the spring are located in the groove on either side of the stopper pin (see illustration 21.8).

16 Examine the stopper arm assembly for wear (see illustration). If the spring is fatigued or damaged it must be renewed. Check that the stopper arm roller turns freely.

17 Inspect the lobes on the gearchange cam and the pins on the rotor for wear and renew the rotor if necessary (see illustration).

Installation

18 Clean the threads of the stopper arm pivot

bolt. Slide the washer and stopper arm onto the bolt, then slide on the spacer and fit the shouldered end into the hole in the stopper arm (see illustration 21.16). Fit the spring over the spacer and locate the hooked end under the lower edge of the arm.

19 Apply a drop of the specified thread locking compound to the pivot bolt and install the stopper arm assembly (see illustrations 21.7b and a). Tighten the pivot bolt to the torque setting specified at the beginning of this Chapter, then check the operation of the stopper arm.

20 Press the stopper arm down and install the gearchange rotor onto the end of the selector drum. Release the stopper arm and ensure that the roller locates in the neutral detent on the gearchange cam (see illustration 21.6a). Clean the threads of the gearchange rotor centre bolt and apply a drop of specified thread locking compound. Install the bolt and tighten it to the specified torque setting (see illustration).

21 Check that the thrust washer is on the gearchange shaft. Lubricate the shaft and the left-hand oil seal with clean engine oil, then slide the shaft into place from the right-hand side (see illustration 21.5b).

22 Slide back the pawl plate and engage the pawls with the pins on the gearchange rotor,

and locate the ends of the gearchange shaft return spring on each side of the crankcase stop (see illustrations 21.4b and 4a).

23 Position the gearchange lever on the left-hand end of the shaft as noted on removal. Clean the threads of the lever bolt, slide on the two serrated locking washers and the plain washer, and apply a drop of specified thread locking compound to the bolt. Install the bolt and tighten it to the specified torque setting.

24 Install the remaining components in the reverse order of removal.

22 Oil pumps and pressure relief valve

Note: This procedure can be carried out with the engine in the frame. If the engine has been removed, ignore the steps which do not apply.

Oil pumps

1 Two oil pumps are fitted. One supplies oil to the engine (right-hand pump) and the other supplies oil to the transmission (left-hand pump). The pumps are driven by a common shaft, via the small pinion on the back of the clutch housing.

2 To gain access to the left-hand pump, first

21.17 Gearchange cam lobes (A) and rotor pins (B)

21.20 Thread lock the gearchange rotor centre bolt

22.5a Prise off the E-clip . . .

22.5b . . . remove the washer . . .

22.5c . . . pull off the oil pump gear and remove the drive pin (arrowed)

22.7 Undo the bolts and remove the left-hand cover

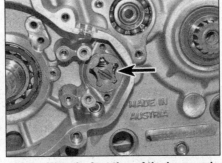

22.8a Note the location of the inner and outer pump rotors and the drive pin

drive shaft and pull the drive pin out of the shaft (see illustrations).

6 Grasp the end of the drive shaft and try to pull it in-and-out; there should be no discernable freeplay. If available, use a dial gauge to measure any axial play and compare the result with the specification at the beginning of this Chapter (see *Tools and Workshop Tips* in the *Reference* section). If play exceeds the specified limit, remove the pump and inspect the components for wear.

Removal

Note: *As the pump components are removed, lay them on a clean work surface in the exact order of disassembly.*

7 Working on the left-hand side of the engine, undo the bolts securing the pump cover and lift the cover off (see illustration).

8 Note the location of the inner and outer pump rotors and the drive pin (see illustration). Both rotors have register marks which should be facing inwards – however, if the marks face outwards, ensure that the rotors are fitted accordingly on reassembly. Draw the outer rotor, drive pin and inner rotor out of the pump housing (see illustrations).

9 Working on the right-hand side of the engine, first mark the end of the pump drive shaft with a dab of paint to aid reassembly, then undo the bolts securing the pump cover and lift the cover off (see illustration).

10 Note the location of the inner and outer pump rotors and the drive pin (see illustration). Both rotors have register marks which should be facing inwards – however,

remove the alternator cover and displace the ignition pick-up coil (see Section 15).

3 To gain access to the right-hand pump, first remove the clutch (see Section 18).

4 Before removing the pumps, check the amount of axial freeplay (end-float) in the pump drive shaft as follows.

5 Working on the right-hand side of the engine, prise off the E-clip and remove the washer, then pull the oil pump gear off the

22.8b Remove the outer rotor . . .

22.8c . . . drive pin . . .

22.8d . . . and inner rotor

22.9 Remove the right-hand pump cover

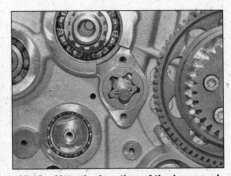

22.10a Note the location of the inner and outer pump rotors and the drive pin

22.10b Draw the rotors out of the pump housing together with the shaft

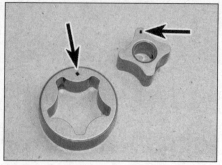

22.16a Note the register marks (arrowed) on the pump rotors

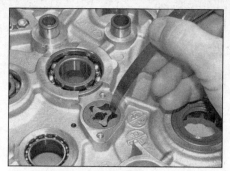

22.16b Measure the clearance between the inner and outer rotors . . .

if the marks face outwards, ensure that the rotors are fitted accordingly on reassembly (see illustration 22.16a). Draw the rotors, drive pin and shaft out of the pump housing (see illustration).

Inspection

11 Clean all the components with a suitable solvent.
12 Inspect the inside surface of both pump covers for score marks and renew them if necessary.
13 Check the drive shaft for wear and check that it is straight by rolling it on a flat surface.
14 Check the teeth on the oil pump gear, and check the slot in the centre of the gear where the drive pin locates. If any wear or damage is found, fit a new gear.
15 Use a clean cloth to wipe any residual oil out of the pump housings, then inspect the surface of the housings for wear or score marks.
16 Inspect the rotors for scoring and wear – keep the paired rotors together, noting the register marks (see illustration). Install the paired rotors in their respective housings with the register marks adjacent to each other, then, using a feeler gauge, measure the clearance between the inner and outer rotors, and the clearance between the outer rotor and pump housing (see illustrations). Compare the results with the specifications at the beginning of this Chapter. If any damage, scoring or uneven or excessive wear is evident, renew the rotors as sets.

Installation

17 Clean the threads of the oil pump cover bolts.

18 Make sure all the pump internal components are clean and lubricate them with clean engine oil prior to installation.
19 Working on the right-hand side of the engine, insert the drive shaft part way into the cases – the previously made paint mark should be facing out (see Step 9).
20 Slide the inner and outer right-hand rotors onto the shaft – the register marks should be adjacent to each other and, unless noted differently on removal, facing the inside of the pump housing. Install the drive pin, then carefully slide the assembly into the housing (see illustration).
21 With the pump components seated inside the housing, install the right-hand cover (see illustrations 22.10a and 9). Apply a drop of the specified thread locking compound to the cover bolts and tighten them to the torque setting specified at the beginning of this Chapter.
22 Working on the left-hand side of the engine, install the inner rotor, drive pin and outer rotor (see illustrations 22.8d, c and b). Don't forget that the register marks should be adjacent to each other and, unless noted differently on removal, facing the inside of the pump housing.
23 With the pump components seated inside the housing, install the left-hand cover (see illustrations 22.8a and 7). Apply a drop of the specified thread locking compound to the cover bolts and tighten them to the torque setting specified at the beginning of this Chapter.
24 Check that the drive shaft rotates freely.
25 Install the pump gear drive pin in the right-hand end of the shaft (see illustration). Install the gear and washer and secure them with a new E-clip (see illustrations 22.5c and 5b). Ensure that the E-clip is located fully into the groove on the end of the drive shaft (see illustration).
26 Once again, check that the drive shaft rotates freely.

Oil pressure relief valve

27 The oil pressure relief valve is located at the rear of the crankcase (see illustration). If excess pressure builds-up in the oil supply from the filters to the crankshaft and the

22.16c . . . and the outer rotor and pump housing

22.20 Slide the assembled components into the right-hand housing

22.25a Install the pump gear drive pin (arrowed) in the right-hand end of the shaft

22.25b Ensure the E-clip is installed securely in its groove

22.27 Location of the oil pressure relief valve (arrowed)

22.29 Clean the area around the relief valve thoroughly

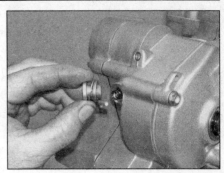

22.30a Note the two washers on the plug

nozzle which sprays oil onto the underside of the piston, the valve opens and directs oil back into the crankcase. A weakened valve spring or damaged valve piston will result in loss of oil pressure.

28 To access the pressure relief valve, first remove the rear wheel (see Chapter 7) and the rear shock absorber (see Chapter 6).

29 Displace the carburettor breather hoses and wash the rear of the engine thoroughly to prevent any dirt getting into the valve assembly or engine lubrication system **(see illustration)**.

30 Unscrew the plug, noting the two sealing washers **(see illustration)**, then draw out the spring and valve piston **(see illustration)**.

31 Clean the components with a suitable solvent **(see illustration)**. Inspect the piston for wear, score marks and pitting. If there is any damage to the surface of the piston it must be renewed.

32 Using a Vernier gauge, measure the free length of the valve spring and compare it to that listed in the specifications. If the spring is shorter than specified it must be renewed.

33 Prior to installation, lubricate the spring and piston with clean engine oil. Fit new sealing washers onto the plug, then tighten the plug securely.

34 Install the remaining components in the reverse order of removal.

23 Crankcase halves and main bearings

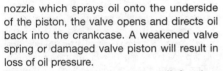

Note: *To separate the crankcase halves, the engine must be removed from the frame (see Section 4).*
Special tools: *An external bearing puller is required to draw the inner main bearing races off the crankshaft.*

Separation

1 To access the crankshaft assembly, engine main bearings, balancer shaft and transmission components, the crankcase halves must be separated.

2 Before the crankcase halves can be separated, the following components must be removed:

● Engine oil filters and strainers (see Chapter 1)
● Final drive front sprocket (see Chapter 7)
● Cylinder head (see Section 10)
● Cylinder (see Section 12)
● Starter motor (see Chapter 9)
● Alternator rotor (see Section 15)
● Cam chain drive sprocket, tensioner blade and guide (see Section 16)
● Clutch (see Section 18)
● Primary gear (see Section 19)
● Kickstart mechanism (see Section 20)
● External gearchange mechanism (see Section 21)
● Oil pumps (see Section 22)

3 If not already done, tape some clean rag around the connecting rod to prevent it knocking against the cases. Although not essential, it is a good idea to remove the piston to avoid damaging it (see Section 13). Ensure the transmission is in neutral. If not already done, remove the crankshaft position screw.

4 Lay the crankcase assembly on the work surface on its right-hand side, making sure it is properly supported using blocks of wood **(see illustration)**.

5 Before separating the crankcase halves, measure the amount of crankshaft axial clearance (end-float) using a dial gauge (see *Tools and Workshop Tips* in the *Reference* section). Mount the dial gauge with its pointer contacting the end of the crankshaft. Zero the gauge, then pull the crankshaft out of the casing and record the end-float. Compare the result to the specifications at the beginning of this Chapter. If the end-float exceeds the service limit, it will have to be adjusted by fitting shims between the inner race of the left-hand crankshaft main bearing and the balancer shaft drive gear once the crankshaft has been removed from the cases (see Steps 27 to 29). **Note:** *If new main bearings are to be fitted, measure the end-float once the new bearings are in place.*

6 Follow the same procedure to measure the transmission output shaft end-float, then support the crankcase assembly on its left-hand side and measure the transmission input shaft end-float. If the end-float on either of the

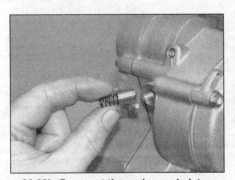

22.30b Draw out the spring and piston

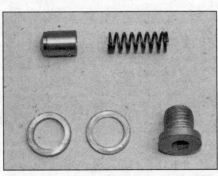

22.31 Inspect the piston and measure the spring length

23.4 Support the right-hand side of the crankcase on blocks of wood

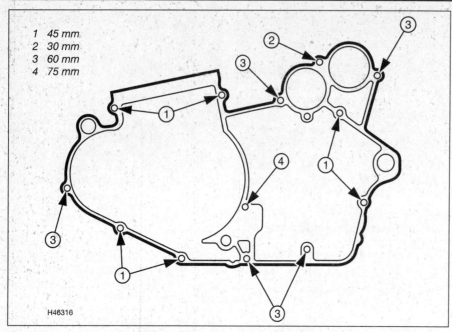

1 45 mm
2 30 mm
3 60 mm
4 75 mm

H46316

23.7 Location of the crankcase bolts

transmission shafts exceeds the service limit, it will have to be adjusted by fitting shims between the appropriate bearing and its

housing in the left-hand crankcase half (see Section 27).
7 To separate the crankcase halves, support

the assembly on its right-hand side and undo the thirteen crankcase bolts evenly, a little at a time. Note the location of the bolts as they are of different lengths **(see illustration)**.

> **HAYNES HiNT** *Make a cardboard template of the crankcase and punch a hole for each bolt location. As each bolt is removed, store it in its relative position in the template. This will ensure all bolts are installed correctly on reassembly.*

8 Carefully lift the left-hand crankcase half off the right-hand half, tapping around the joint face between the two halves with a soft-faced mallet to free them – don't attempt to lever them apart with a screwdriver, you'll damage the sealing surfaces **(see illustration)**.
9 The crankshaft assembly, transmission components and balancer shaft should remain in the right-hand crankcase half.
10 Note the location of the thrust washer on the left-hand end of the transmission input shaft and either remove it for safekeeping or, if the shaft is not going to be disassembled, secure it in place with a dab of grease **(see illustration)**. Note that the thrust washer sometimes sticks to the shaft bearing in the crankcase, so check inside the left-hand crankcase half if the washer is not on the shaft.
11 Note the location of the O-ring on the end of the transmission output shaft **(see illustration 23.10)**. If the shaft is not going to be disassembled, don't forget to fit a new O-ring before the crankcase halves are reassembled.
12 Lift the sleeve out of the output shaft seal in the left-hand crankcase half **(see illustration)**.
13 Follow the procedure in the appropriate Sections to remove the balancer shaft, crankshaft assembly, selector drum and forks

23.8a Tap around the joint between the crankcase halves . . .

23.8b . . . then lift the left-hand half off

23.10 Note the thrust washer (A) on the input shaft and the O-ring (B) on the output shaft

23.12 Remove the output shaft sleeve

23.14 Location of the crankcase dowels

23.15a Location of the crankshaft oil seal

23.15b Drive the seal out from the inside of the case

and transmission shafts from the right-hand crankcase half.

14 Note the location of the two dowels in the right-hand crankcase half and remove them for safekeeping if they are loose **(see illustration)**.

15 Note the position of the crankshaft oil seal in the right-hand crankcase half **(see illustration)**. Support the case on wood blocks and drive the seal out from the inside **(see illustration)**.

16 Follow the same procedure to remove the transmission output shaft oil seal **(see illustration)**. The gearchange shaft oil seal can be removed by levering it out carefully with a flat-bladed screwdriver **(see illustration)**.

17 Discard the old seals as new ones must be fitted on reassembly.

Inspection

18 If the main bearings have failed, excessive rumbling and vibration will be felt when the

engine is running. Check the condition of the bearings – they should spin freely and smoothly without any rough spots. Inspect the rollers for pitting and check the inner races on the crankshaft assembly for score marks and pitting **(see illustrations)**. Renew the bearings if there is any doubt about their condition and always renew both main bearings at the same time (see Steps 24 to 29).

19 Remove all traces of old gasket from the crankcase sealing surfaces, taking care not to nick or gouge the soft aluminium if a scraper is used. Wash all the components in a suitable solvent and dry them with compressed air.

20 If not already done, remove the oil pressure relief valve (see Section 22). Unscrew the oil jet that supplies lubrication for the underside of the piston and the jet that meters the oil supply to the connecting rod big-end bearing, noting their locations **(see illustrations)**. Use compressed air to blow through the oil galleries

in the cases between the oil pump housings, filter housings and jets to ensure that they are clear. Prior to installation, clean the threads of the oil jets and apply a drop of Loctite 243, then install the jets and tighten them securely.

21 Check both crankcase halves very carefully for cracks and damaged threads. Small cracks or holes in aluminium castings may be repaired with an epoxy resin adhesive as a temporary measure. Permanent repairs can only be effected by welding, and only a specialist in this process is in a position to advise on the economy or practical aspect of such a repair. Note, however, that there are low-temperature welding kits available for small repair jobs. If any damage is found that can't be repaired, renew both crankcase halves as a set.

22 Damaged threads can be reclaimed with a thread insert, which is fitted after drilling and re-tapping the affected thread (see *Tools and*

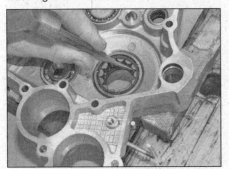

23.16a Drive out the transmission output shaft oil seal

23.16b Lever out the gearchange shaft oil seal

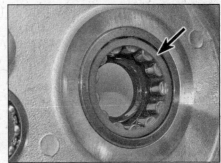

23.18a Inspect the main bearing rollers . . .

23.18b . . . and the inner races (arrowed) on the crankshaft

23.20a Location of piston oil jet on inside of right-hand case

23.20b Location of big-end oil jet on outside of right-hand case

23.25a Use a suitably-sized socket . . .

23.25b . . . to drive out the main bearings

23.27 Note any shims fitted between the bearing race (A) and the balancer shaft gear (B)

Workshop Tips in the *Reference* section). Most motorcycle dealers and small engineering firms offer a service of this kind. Sheared screws and studs can usually be removed with screw extractors which consist of a tapered, left thread screw of very hard steel. These are inserted into a pre-drilled hole in the broken fixing, and usually succeed in dislodging the most stubborn stud or screw (see *Tools and Workshop Tips* in the *Reference* section). If you are in any doubt about removing a sheared screw, consult a KTM dealer or automotive engineer.

23 Always wash the crankcases thoroughly after any repair work to ensure no dirt or metal swarf is trapped inside when the engine is rebuilt.

24 Before removing the main bearings, note which way round they are fitted. **Note:** *Before attempting to remove any of the bearings in the crankcase halves, the cases must be heated in an oven to approximately 150ºC. Ensure all oil*

seals have been removed prior to heating, and that the cases have been washed to remove any residual oil. Refer to the appropriate Sections and check the condition of the transmission and balancer shaft bearings so that all the necessary bearings can be renewed at the same time.

> **HAYNES HINT** *If any of the bearings are loose in their housings, or have seized and damaged their housings, have the condition of the casing assessed by a KTM dealer. A loose bearing can often be secured using a suitable bearing lock compound.*

25 To remove the main bearings, heat the appropriate casing, then support the case on wood blocks and drive the bearing out from the outside towards the inside using a suitably-sized socket **(see illustrations)**.

⚠ *Warning: Be careful when handling the crankcases and wear protective gloves – when heated, the cases could cause severe burns.*

26 Turn the casing over and drive the new bearing in from the inside towards the outside – make sure that the bearing is fitted the correct way round and locate the driver against the bearing outer race only (see *Tools and Workshop Tips*). Note that it may be necessary to re-heat the casing before the bearing can be driven in.

27 To remove the main bearing inner races from the crankshaft assembly, use a hot air gun to heat the races and draw them off using an external bearing puller (see *Tools and Workshop Tips*). Note the location of any shims fitted between the inner race of the left-hand main bearing and the balancer shaft drive gear – these are used to adjust the crankshaft end-float **(see illustration)**.

28 Refer to the measurements made before the crankcase halves were separated (see Step 5). If the end-float is too large, add a suitably sized shim to correct it. If the end-float is too small, remove a shim or substitute a thinner shim to correct it. Three thicknesses of shim are available, from 0.10 to 0.30 mm – consult your KTM dealer for details. **Note:** *If new main bearings are being fitted, follow the procedure in Step 5 to measure the crankshaft end-float once the new bearings are in place, then adjust the shimming as necessary.*

29 Before installing the new inner races, support the crankshaft assembly securely on the work surface. Heat the inner races to approximately 150°C and press them into position over the shafts using a suitable length of tubing (see *Tools and Workshop Tips*).

Reassembly

30 Locate the new crankshaft oil seal in position in the right-hand crankcase half, ensuring that it is the correct way round **(see illustration)**. Drive the seal in carefully to ensure that it enters the case squarely and use a block of wood to ensure that it is fitted level with the outside edge of the case **(see illustration)**. Lubricate the inside of the seal with a smear of clean engine oil. Follow the same procedure to install the new transmission output shaft oil seal in the left-hand crankcase half **(see illustrations)**.

23.30a Install the new crankshaft oil seal . . .

23.30b . . . and ensure that it is fitted level with the case

23.30c Install the new transmission output shaft oil seal . . .

23.30d . . . and ensure that it is fitted level with the case

23.31a Install the new gearchange shaft oil seal . . .

23.31b . . . and ensure that it is fitted level with the case

23.33 Lubricate all the bearings prior to reassembly

31 Install the new gearchange shaft oil seal, using a block of wood to ensure that it is fitted level with the outside edge of the case **(see illustrations)**.

32 If removed, ensure that the oil jets for piston lubrication and big-end oil supply are installed correctly (see Step 20). The jet for piston lubrication is numbered 60, the jet for big-end lubrication is numbered 100.

33 Support the right-hand crankcase half on wooden blocks on the work surface and lubricate all the bearings in the case with clean engine oil **(see illustration)**.

34 Follow the procedure in the appropriate Sections to install the crankshaft assembly, balancer shaft, transmission shafts and the selector drum and forks.

35 Ensure that the thrust washer is installed on the end of the transmission input shaft and that a new O-ring has been fitted on the end of the transmission output shaft **(see illustration 23.10)**.

36 If removed, install the two dowels in the right-hand crankcase half **(see illustration 23.14)**.

37 Wipe the sealing surfaces of both crankcase halves with a rag soaked in a suitable solvent. Apply a smear of non-permanent sealant to the crankcase mating surfaces around the oil filter housings, then fit the new gasket **(see illustrations)**.

38 Lubricate all the bearings in the left-hand crankcase half, then carefully lower the case onto the right-hand half, ensuring that the crankshaft, balancer shaft and transmission

shafts are correctly aligned **(see illustration)**. If necessary, tap around the left-hand half with a soft-faced mallet **(see illustration)**. Do not force the halves together – if they are not fitting, lift the left-hand half off and find out why. **Note:** *Do not attempt to pull the crankcase halves together using the crankcase bolts as the casing will crack and be ruined.*

39 Check that the crankcase halves are seated all the way round, then smear the threads of the crankcase bolts with grease and install them finger-tight **(see illustration 23.7)**. Ensure that the bolts are fitted in their correct locations. Tighten the bolts evenly, a little at a time in a criss-cross sequence, to the torque setting specified at the beginning of this Chapter.

40 Check that the crankshaft and transmission shafts are free to rotate – if there are any signs of stiffness, tap the end of the appropriate shaft with a soft-faced mallet and check again. If the problem persists, it must be rectified before proceeding further.

41 Install the gearchange mechanism (see Section 21) and check that all the gears can be selected and that the transmission shafts rotate freely in every gear. If there are any signs of stiffness, rough spots, or of any other problem, the fault must be rectified before proceeding further.

42 Trim off the excess gasket across the crankcase mouth with a craft knife, taking care not to gouge the sealing surface **(see illustration)**.

43 Lubricate the transmission output shaft

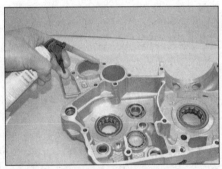

23.37a Apply sealant around the oil filter housings . . .

23.37b . . . then fit the new gasket

23.38a Ensure that all the shafts are correctly aligned when fitting the left-hand case

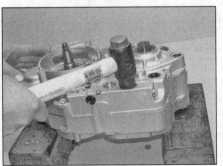

23.38b Tap around the upper case to seat the two halves

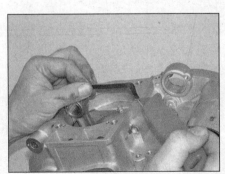

23.42 Trim off the excess gasket

sleeve with clean engine oil and press it carefully into the shaft seal **(see illustration)**.
44 Install the remaining components in the reverse order of removal.

24 Balancer shaft

23.43 Lubricate and install the output shaft sleeve

24.2a Align the register marks on the gears (arrowed) . . .

Note: *To remove the balancer shaft, the engine must be removed from the frame (see Section 4).*
Special tools: *An knife-edged bearing puller is required to draw the balancer shaft bearings out of the crankcase.*

Removal

1 To access the balancer shaft and shaft bearings, follow the procedure in Section 23 and separate the crankcase halves.
2 Rotate the crankshaft carefully until the register marks on the balancer shaft drive gear and the balancer shaft gear are aligned, then lift out the balancer shaft **(see illustrations)**.

Inspection

3 Check the condition of both bearings – they should spin freely and smoothly without any rough spots or excessive noise – and only remove them if they need renewing **(see illustration)**.
4 To renew the bearings, first follow the procedure in the appropriate Sections to remove the crankshaft assembly, selector drum and forks and transmission shafts from the right-hand crankcase half.
5 Using a knife-edged bearing puller and slide-hammer attachment, draw the old bearings out from their housings – note that bearing removal is made a lot easier if the casings are heated first (see Section 23, Step 24).
6 An oil seal is located behind the bearing in the right-hand crankcase half **(see**

24.2b . . . then lift the balancer shaft out

24.3 Inspect the balancer shaft bearings – left-hand side shown

illustration). Draw the seal out with the bearing puller.
7 Ensure that the seal and bearing housings are clean, then install the new seal with its open side facing down. Press the seal all the way in, using a suitably-sized socket. Lubricate the inside of the seal with clean engine oil.
8 Press the new bearings in using a driver that locates against the bearing outer race only (see *Tools and Workshop Tips*). When installed, the outer races of the bearings should be level with the edges of the crankcase housings.
9 Check the teeth on the balancer shaft gear

and the drive gear – renew the balancer shaft and the drive gear as a set if the teeth are worn or damaged. Note that the balancer shaft and gear are not available separately.
10 To renew the drive gear, first remove the left-hand main bearing inner race, noting the location of any shims fitted between the race and the drive gear (see Section 23).
11 Note the location of the two threaded holes in the drive gear, then undo the screws securing the drive gear to the crankshaft assembly **(see illustration)**.
12 Thread two M6 bolts into the threaded holes, then tighten the bolts evenly, a little

24.6 A seal is fitted behind the right-hand balancer shaft bearing

24.11 Balancer shaft drive gear threaded holes (A), mounting screws (B), register mark (C) and crankpin (D)

at a time, and draw the drive gear off **(see illustration)**.

13 Before installing the new drive gear, note the register mark on the gear – when the mounting screw holes are aligned, the register mark must be adjacent to the crank pin **(see illustration 24.11)**.

14 Support the crankshaft assembly securely on the work surface. Heat the drive gear to approximately 100°C and press it into position over the shaft using a suitable length of tubing – ensure that the mounting screw holes and register mark are correctly positioned.

15 Clean the threads of the mounting screws and apply a drop of the specified locking compound, then install the screws and tighten them to the torque setting specified at the beginning of this Chapter.

16 Follow the procedure in Section 23 and install the shims (if fitted) and left-hand main bearing inner race.

Installation

17 Ensure that the balancer shaft bearings are lubricated with clean engine oil.

18 Align the register marks on the balancer shaft gear and the drive gear and install the balancer shaft **(see illustration 24.2b and a)**.

19 Follow the procedure in Section 23 and reassemble the crankcase halves.

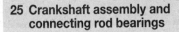

25 Crankshaft assembly and connecting rod bearings

Note: *To remove the crankshaft assembly and big-end bearing, the engine must be removed from the frame (see Section 4).*

Removal

1 To access the crankshaft and the big-end bearing, follow the procedure in Section 23 and separate the crankcase halves.

2 Follow the procedure in Section 24 and remove the balancer shaft, then lift out the crankshaft assembly.

Inspection

3 A worn big-end bearing will produce a

24.12 Tighten the M6 bolts to draw the drive gear off

25.4 Check the connecting rod for up-and-down freeplay

pronounced knocking noise, most audible when the engine is under load, and increasing as engine speed rises. This should not be confused with small-end bearing wear, which produces a lighter, metallic rattle.

4 To assess the condition of the big-end bearing, hold the crankshaft assembly firmly and push and pull on the connecting rod, checking for any up-and-down freeplay between the two **(see illustration)**. If suitable measuring equipment is available, the radial clearance (up-and-down freeplay) between the big-end bearing and the connecting rod can be assessed accurately and the result compared with the Specifications at the beginning of this Chapter – in practice, any freeplay is an indication that the bearing is worn.

5 If the big-end bearing is worn a new connecting rod assembly, comprising of a new rod, crankpin and bearing, must be fitted – however, this is a specialist task that should only be undertaken by a KTM dealer or automotive engineer. **Note:** *Although thrust washers are included in all rod assembly kits, they are only fitted to year 2000 models.*

6 Use feeler gauges to measure the axial clearance between the connecting rod big-end and the flywheels – note that on year 2000 models, a thrust washer is fitted on both sides of the big-end **(see illustration)**. Compare the result with the Specification; if the big-end bearing axial clearance is beyond the service

limit, the connecting rod assembly will have to be replaced with a new one (see Step 5).

7 To check the rod small-end, lubricate the piston pin with clean engine oil, then insert it in the rod and check for any freeplay between the two. There should be no discernable freeplay.

8 Measure the pin external diameter in the centre where it bears in the small-end, and at both ends, to determine if the pin has worn unevenly **(see illustration)**. If necessary, fit a new piston pin.

9 Using a small-bore gauge and a micrometer (see *Tools and Workshop Tips* in the *Reference* section), measure the diameter of the small-end bore, both in-line with the con-rod and at 90° to it **(see illustration)**. If the small-end has worn unevenly, a new connecting rod assembly will have to be fitted (see Step 5).

10 The main bearing inner races should be a tight fit on the crankshaft. If there is evidence that the bearings have over-heated or seized, blueing or scoring the races, or if the races are loose, remove them and inspect the crankshaft journals for damage – if necessary, follow the procedure in Section 23 to remove the bearing races. **Note:** *Evidence of extreme heat indicates that lubrication failure has occurred. Be sure to check the oil pump and bearing oil galleries before reassembling the engine (see Section 22).*

11 If available, place the crankshaft assembly on V-blocks and check the runout at the

25.6 Measuring big-end bearing axial clearance

25.8 Measuring the external diameter of the piston pin

25.9 Measuring the internal diameter of the small-end

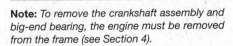

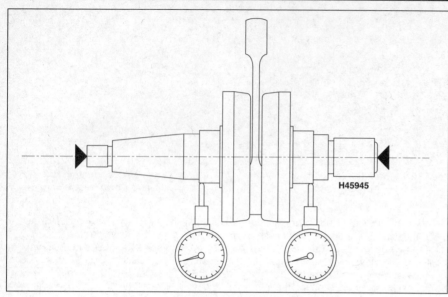

25.11 Checking the crankshaft runout

journals using a dial gauge (see illustration). If the crankshaft is out-of-true it will cause excessive engine vibration. If there is any doubt about the condition of the crankshaft have it checked by a KTM dealer or automotive engineer.

12 Use a Vernier gauge to measure the distance between the outer faces of the left and right-hand flywheels (see illustration). If the crankshaft width differs from the specification, have the assembly and crankcases assessed by a KTM dealer. Note: *Discrepancies in the crankshaft assembly width are only likely to occur if the assembly has been damaged, or incorrectly assembled after fitting a new big-end bearing.*

13 Inspect the threads on the end of the crankshaft and ensure that the retaining nuts for the alternator rotor and the primary gear are a good fit. Inspect the keyways in the left-hand side of the shaft for the alternator rotor and cam chain drive sprocket Woodruff keys, and the keyway in the right-hand side for the primary gear key – damage or wear that prevents the keys from being fitted securely will require a new crankshaft assembly.

14 If required, follow the procedure in Section 24 to remove the balancer shaft drive gear.

Installation

15 Ensure that the crankshaft bearings and the right-hand crankshaft oil seal are lubricated with clean engine oil.

16 Align the right-hand end of the crankshaft with the bearing in the crankcase and lower it carefully into position to avoid damaging the oil seal (see illustration).

17 Install the balancer shaft (see Section 24), then follow the procedure in Section 23 and reassemble the crankcase halves.

26 Selector drum and forks

Note: *To remove the selector drum and forks, the engine must be removed from the frame (see Section 4).*

1 To access the selector drum and forks, follow the procedure in Section 23 and separate the crankcase halves.

Removal

Four-speed transmission

Note: *The four and six-speed transmissions use components that are visually similar. However, in the four-speed transmission, there are no 5th and 6th gear pinions on the input shaft and the 3/4th gear pinion is fixed on the shaft by two spacers (see Section 27). Consequently, only one selector fork shaft is fitted, and the forks on that shaft locate in the grooves on the left and right-hand sliding pinions on the output shaft. For the purpose of identification, and when ordering spare parts, the left-hand sliding pinion is referred to as the 6th gear pinion, and the right-hand sliding pinion as the 5th gear pinion.*

2 Note the location of the spring in the left-hand end of the selector fork shaft (see illustration 26.8).

3 Note how the selector forks locate in the grooves on the 6th and 5th gear pinions on the output shaft (see illustration 26.9).

4 Note how the guide pins on the forks locate in the grooves in the selector drum and note which grooves the pins locate in as an aid for installation. The selector drum should be in the neutral position.

5 Lift out the selector forks shaft, noting the location of the spring in the right-hand end (see illustration 26.11).

6 Displace the selector forks from the selector drum and the 6th and 5th gear pinions and lift them out (see illustrations 26.12a, b and c). Note: *The selector forks are different but they may not be marked – to aid identification, mark each fork with a dab of paint before removing it. Note the location of the rollers on the selector fork guide pins. Slide the forks back onto the shaft in the correct order and the right way round.*

7 Note the position of the selector drum as an aid for installation, then lift the selector drum out.

Six-speed transmission

8 Note the location of the springs in the left-hand ends of the selector fork shafts (see illustration).

9 Note how the input shaft selector fork locates in the groove on the 3/4th gear pinion

25.12 Measuring the crankshaft width

25.16 Take care not to damage the right-hand oil seal when installing the crankshaft

26.8 Note the location of the springs (arrowed)

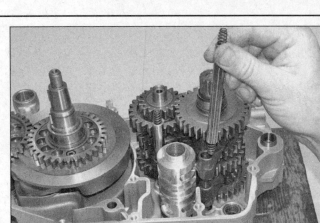

26.9 Input shaft selector fork (A) and output shaft selector forks (B)

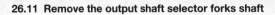

26.11 Remove the output shaft selector forks shaft

and how the output shaft selector forks locate in the grooves on the 6th and 5th gear pinions **(see illustration)**.

10 Note how the guide pins on the forks locate in the grooves in the selector drum and note which grooves the pins locate in as an aid for installation. The selector drum should be in the neutral position.

11 Lift out the output shaft selector forks shaft, noting the location of the spring in the right-hand end **(see illustration)**.

12 Displace the output shaft selector forks from the selector drum and the 6th and 5th gear pinions and lift them out **(see illustrations)**. **Note:** *The selector forks are different but they may not be marked – to aid identification, mark each fork with a dab of paint before removing it.* Note the location of the rollers on the selector fork guide pins. Slide the forks back onto the shaft in the correct order and the right way round **(see illustration)**.

13 Lift out the input shaft selector fork shaft, noting the location of the spring in the right-hand end **(see illustration)**.

14 Displace the input shaft selector fork from the selector drum, then lift the drum out **(see illustration)**.

15 Displace the input shaft selector fork from the 3rd/4th gear pinion and lift it out **(see illustration)**. Note the location of the roller on the selector fork guide pin.

26.12a Displace the selector forks from the drum (arrowed)

26.12b Upper fork locates in the 6th gear pinion

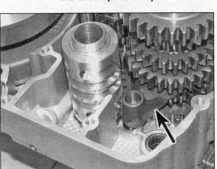

26.12c Lower fork (arrowed) locates in the 5th gear pinion

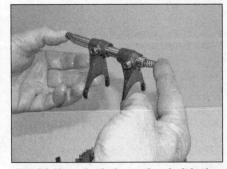

26.12d Keep the forks on the shaft in the correct order

26.13 Remove the input shaft selector fork shaft

26.14 Displace the selector fork (arrowed) from the drum

26.15 Lift out the input shaft selector fork (arrowed)

26.16 Inspect the components in the order of disassembly

26.17 Measure the ends of the selector forks

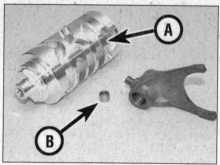

26.21 Check the grooves in the selector drum (A) and the guide pin rollers (B)

Inspection

16 Clean all the components with a suitable solvent, then lay them on a clean work surface in the exact order of disassembly (see illustration).

17 Inspect the selector forks for any signs of wear or damage, especially around the fork ends where they engage with the grooves in the pinions. Using a micrometer, measure the ends of the forks and compare the results with the specifications at the beginning of this Chapter (see illustration). Check that each fork fits correctly in its pinion groove. Check closely to see if the forks are bent. If the forks are worn or damaged in any way they must be replaced with new ones.

18 Check that the forks fit correctly on their shafts – they should move freely with a light fit but no appreciable freeplay. Check that the fork shaft holes in the casing are not worn or damaged.

19 Check that the selector fork shafts are straight by rolling them on a flat surface such as a sheet of glass. A bent shaft will cause difficulty in selecting gears and make the gearchange action heavy and should be replaced with a new one.

20 A spring should be fitted in both ends of each shaft. If a spring appears to be missing, check for it in the fork shaft hole in the casing. Renew any springs that are shortened or damaged.

21 Inspect the selector drum grooves and selector fork guide pin rollers for signs of wear or damage (see illustration). If either show signs of wear or damage they must be replaced with new ones.

22 The selector drum turns on two bearings (see illustrations). Check the condition of the bearings – they should spin freely and smoothly without any rough spots or excessive noise – and only remove them if they are unserviceable and need to be renewed.

23 To renew the bearings, first follow the procedure in the appropriate Sections to remove the balancer shaft, crankshaft assembly and transmission shafts from the right-hand crankcase half.

24 Before removing the bearings, note which way round they are fitted. Undo the screw securing the right-hand bearing (see illustration 26.22a).

25 Bearing removal is made a lot easier if the casings are heated first (see Section 23, Step 24). At the recommended temperature, tap the case down onto a flat wooden surface and the bearing should fall out. Alternatively, drive the right-hand bearing out from the outside towards the inside using a suitably-sized socket. To remove the left-hand bearing, use a knife-edged bearing puller and slide-hammer attachment (see Tools and Workshop Tips in the Reference section).

26 Ensure that the bearing housings are clean, then press the new bearings in using a driver that locates against the bearing outer race only. When installed, the outer races of the bearings should be level with the edges of the crankcase housings. Clean the threads of the right-hand bearing retaining screw, then apply a drop of the specified locking compound and tighten the screw to the specified torque setting.

Installation

27 If removed, follow the procedure in the appropriate Sections to install the crankshaft assembly, balancer shaft and transmission shafts in the right-hand crankcase half.

28 Ensure that the selector drum bearings are lubricated with clean engine oil.

Four-speed transmission

29 Install the selector drum and position it as noted on removal.

30 Apply a dab of grease to the selector fork guide pins to hold the rollers in place during installation, then slide the forks into the grooves on the 5th and 6th pinions on the output shaft (see illustrations 26.12c and b). Use the marks made on removal to ensure the forks are fitted correctly. Engage the guide pins in the appropriate grooves in the selector drum and align the fork bores with the shaft hole in the right-hand casing.

31 Apply a dab of grease to the springs to hold them in place in the ends of the forks shaft, then install the shaft ensuring it passes through both fork bores and engages fully in the shaft hole (see illustration 26.11).

32 Ensure the selector drum is in the neutral position and check the alignment of the gear pinions on the transmission shafts – both shafts should be free to rotate independently.

Six-speed transmission

33 Apply a dab of grease to the selector fork guide pins to hold the rollers in place during installation (see illustration). Apply a dab of

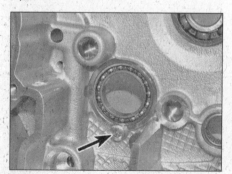

26.22a Right-hand selector drum bearing. Note the screw (arrowed)

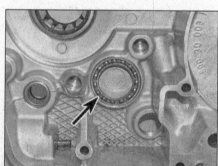

26.22b Left-hand selector drum bearing

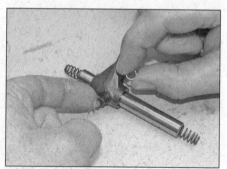

26.33 Hold the guide pin rollers in place with grease

26.36 Ensure the components are correctly aligned

27.3 Lift the transmission shafts out as an assembly

27.4 Lay the input (A) and output (B) shafts on a clean surface

grease to the springs to hold them in place in the ends of the forks shafts.

34 Slide the input shaft selector fork into the groove on the 3rd/4th gear pinion **(see illustration 26.15)**.

35 Install the selector drum, ensuring it locates fully into the bearing in the right-hand casing, and position it as noted on removal **(see illustration 26.14)**. Engage the guide pin on the input shaft selector fork in the appropriate groove in the selector drum and align the fork bore with the shaft hole in the right-hand casing.

36 Install the input shaft selector fork shaft ensuring it passes through the fork bore and engages fully in the shaft hole **(see illustration 26.13)**. Jiggle the input shaft and selector drum backwards and forwards to ensure that the fork is correctly engaged in both **(see illustration)**.

37 Follow the procedure in Step 30 to install the forks into the grooves on the 5th and 6th pinions on the output shaft. Secure the forks with the shaft (see Step 31).

38 Check the alignment of the selector drum and forks **(see illustration 26.9)**.

39 Ensure the selector drum is in the neutral position and check the alignment of the gear pinions on the transmission shafts – both shafts should be free to rotate independently.

40 Follow the procedure in Section 23 and reassemble the crankcase halves.

27 Transmission shafts and bearings – removal and installation

Note: *To remove the transmission shafts, the engine must be removed from the frame (see Section 4).*

1 To access the transmission shafts, follow the procedure in Section 23 and separate the crankcase halves.

2 Follow the procedure in Section 26 and remove the selector drum and forks.

Removal

3 Note the relative positions of the two transmission shafts and how they fit together, then lift the shafts out as an assembly **(see illustration)**. Don't try to pull the shafts out individually. If necessary, have an assistant support the right-hand crankcase half and tap the right-hand end of the input shaft with a soft-faced mallet to aid disassembly.

4 Lay the transmission shafts on a clean work surface **(see illustration)**.

5 Note the location of the thrust washer on the right-hand end of the output shaft and secure it in place with a dab of grease for

27.5 The thrust washer (arrowed) may stick to the bearing in the crankcase

safekeeping. The thrust washer sometimes sticks to the shaft bearing in the crankcase, so check inside the right-hand crankcase half if the washer is not on the shaft **(see illustration)**.

6 If necessary, the shafts can be disassembled and the components inspected for wear or damage (see Section 28).

7 If not already done, remove the transmission output shaft oil seal from the crankcase (see Section 23).

8 Check the transmission shaft caged ball bearings – they should spin freely and smoothly without any rough spots or excessive noise **(see illustrations)**. If required, flush the

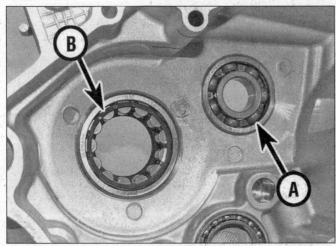

27.8a Input shaft ball bearing (A) and output shaft roller bearing (B) – left-hand side

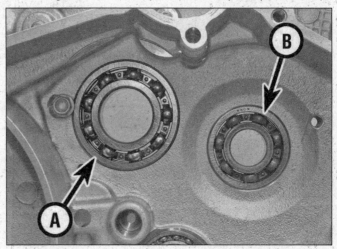

27.8b Input shaft bearing (A) and output shaft bearing (B) – right-hand side

27.17a Remove the output shaft O-ring . . .

27.17b . . . then remove the inner bearing race as described

27.24 Install the assembled transmission shafts in the right-hand crankcase half

bearings with a suitable solvent then dry them thoroughly – use low pressure compressed air if it is available. Lubricate the bearings lightly with clean engine oil, then check them as described.

9 The left-hand output shaft bearing is a roller bearing – inspect the rollers for pitting and check the inner race on the output shaft for score marks and pitting **(see illustration 27.17b)**.

10 To renew the bearings, first follow the procedure in the appropriate Sections to remove the balancer shaft and crankshaft assembly from the right-hand crankcase half. **Note:** *Only remove the bearings from the crankcases if they are unserviceable and need to be renewed.*

11 Before removing the bearings, note which way round they are fitted. On 2003-on models, undo the screw securing the right-hand input shaft bearing **(see illustration 27.8b)**. **Note:** *Before attempting to remove any of the bearings in the crankcase halves, the cases must be heated in an oven to approximately 150°C. Ensure all oil seals have been removed prior to heating, and that the cases have been washed to remove any residual oil. Refer to the appropriate Sections and check the condition of the crankshaft and balancer shaft bearings so that all the necessary bearings can be renewed at the same time.*

 If any of the bearings are loose in their housings, or have seized and damaged their housings, have the condition of the casing assessed by a KTM dealer. A loose bearing can often be secured using a suitable bearing lock compound.

12 To remove the transmission bearings, heat the appropriate casing, then support the case on wood blocks and drive the bearings out from the outside towards the inside using a suitably-sized socket **(see illustrations 23.25a and b).**

 Warning: Be careful when handling the crankcases and wear protective gloves – when heated, the cases could cause severe burns.

13 Note the location of any shims fitted between the bearings and their housings in the left-hand crankcase half – these are used to adjust the transmission shaft end-float **(see illustration 27.8a)**.

14 Refer to the measurements made before the crankcase halves were separated (see Section 23). If the end-float is too large, add a suitably sized shim to correct it. If the end-float is too small, remove a shim or substitute a thinner shim to correct it. Two thicknesses of shim are available – consult your KTM dealer for details.

15 Turn the casing over and drive the new bearings in from the inside towards the outside – make sure that the bearings are fitted the correct way round and locate the driver against the bearing outer race only (see *Tools and Workshop Tips*). Note that it may be necessary to re-heat the casing before the bearings can be driven in. When installed, the outer races of the bearings should be level with the edges of the crankcase housings.

16 If applicable, clean the threads of the right-hand input shaft bearing retaining screw, then apply a drop of the specified locking compound and tighten the screw to the specified torque setting **(see illustration 27.8b)**.

17 To remove the output shaft bearing inner race from the shaft, first follow the procedure in Section 28 to remove the gear pinions. Remove the shaft O-ring, then use a hot air gun to heat the race and slide it off **(see illustrations)**. If the race is a tight fit, draw it off using an external bearing puller (see *Tools and Workshop Tips*).

18 Before installing the new inner race, support the output shaft upright in a vice fitted with soft jaws so as not to damage the surface of the shaft. Heat the inner race to approximately 150°C and press it into position over the shaft using a suitable length of tubing (see *Tools and Workshop Tips*).

19 When the inner race has cooled, fit a new O-ring and lubricate it with clean engine oil.

Installation

20 If not already done, fit a new transmission output shaft oil seal (see Section 23).

21 Lubricate the transmission shaft bearings with clean engine oil.

22 Ensure that the thrust washer is installed on the right-hand end of the output shaft and secure it in place with a dab of grease.

23 Place the shafts side-by-side on the work surface and align the gear pinions **(see illustration 27.4)**.

24 Grasp the shafts assembly, align the right-hand ends of the shafts with the bearings in the right-hand casing and install the shafts **(see illustration)**.

25 Follow the procedure in Section 26 and install the selector drum and forks.

26 Follow the procedure in Section 23 and reassemble the crankcase halves.

28 Transmission shafts – overhaul

Note: *To remove the transmission shafts, the engine must be removed from the frame (see Section 4).*

1 To access the transmission shafts, follow the procedure in Section 23 and separate the crankcase halves.

2 Follow the procedure in Section 26 and remove the selector drum and forks, then remove the transmission shafts (see Section 27).

3 Always disassemble the transmission shafts separately to avoid mixing up the components.

 When disassembling the transmission shafts, place the parts on a long rod or thread a wire through them to keep them in order and facing the proper direction.

Input shaft

Note: *The four and six-speed transmissions use components that are visually similar. However, in the four-speed transmission, there are no 5th and 6th gear pinions on the input shaft and the 3/4th gear pinion is fixed on the shaft by two spacers.*

Disassembly – four-speed transmission

4 Remove the thrust washer from the left-hand end of the shaft, then slide off

28.8a Remove the thrust washer . . .

28.8b . . . then slide off the 2nd gear pinion

28.9 Slide off the 6th gear pinion

28.10 Ease off the needle bearing

28.11 Slide off the splined washer

28.12a Remove the circlip . . .

the 2nd gear pinion **(see illustrations 28.8a and b)**.
5 Slide off the spacer.
6 Slide the combined 3rd/4th gear pinion off, noting which way round it fits **(see illustration 28.12b)**.
7 Slide off the spacer. The 1st gear pinion is integral with the shaft **(see illustration 28.16)**.

Disassembly – six-speed transmission

Note: *The gear pinions are secured by circlips – fit new circlips on reassembly, never re-use the old circlips.*
8 Remove the thrust washer from the left-hand end of the shaft, then slide off the 2nd gear pinion **(see illustrations)**.

9 Slide the 6th gear pinion off the shaft **(see illustration)**.
10 The 6th gear pinion needle roller bearing has a split cage – locate the join in the cage, then prise the ends apart and ease the bearing off carefully **(see illustration)**.
11 Slide off the splined washer **(see illustration)**.
12 Remove the circlip securing the combined 3rd/4th gear pinion, then slide the pinion off, noting which way round it fits **(see illustrations)**.
13 Remove the circlip securing the 5th gear pinion, then slide off the thrust washer **(see illustrations)**.
14 Slide the 5th gear pinion off the shaft **(see illustration)**.
15 The 5th gear pinion needle roller bearing has a split cage – locate the join in the cage, then prise the ends apart and ease the bearing off along the shaft carefully **(see illustration)**.

28.12b . . . then slide off the combined 3rd/4th gear pinion

28.13a Remove the circlip . . .

28.13b . . . then slide off the thrust washer

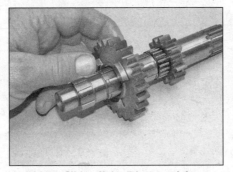

28.14 Slide off the 5th gear pinion

28.15 Ease the needle bearing off the length of the shaft

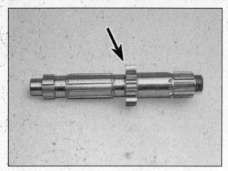

28.16 The 1st gear pinion (arrowed) is integral with the shaft

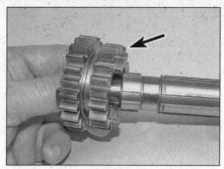

28.26 3rd gear pinion (arrowed) should face the 1st gear pinion

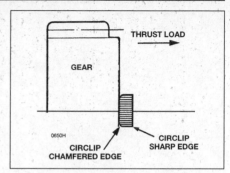

28.29 Correct fitting of a stamped circlip

16 The 1st gear pinion is integral with the shaft (see illustration).

Inspection

17 Wash all the components in suitable solvent and dry them off.

18 Check the gear teeth for cracking, chipping, pitting and other obvious wear or damage. Any pinion that is damaged must be renewed. Note: *If a pinion on the input shaft is damaged, check the corresponding pinion on the output shaft. Transmission pinions should be renewed in matched pairs.*

19 Check for signs of scoring or blueing on the pinions and shaft. This could be caused by overheating due to inadequate lubrication. Replace any worn or damaged parts with new ones.

20 The shaft is unlikely to sustain damage unless the engine has seized, placing an unusually high loading on the transmission, or the machine has covered a very high mileage. Check the surface of the shaft, especially where a pinion turns on it, and replace the shaft with a new one if it has scored or picked up, or if there are any cracks. If available, check the shaft runout using V-blocks and a dial gauge and replace the shaft with a new one if it is bent.

21 On four-speed transmissions, check the ends of the spacers for burring. Later machines were fitted with steel spacers – these can be used to replace the aluminium spacers used in early models.

22 On six-speed transmissions, inspect the dogs and the dog holes in the gears for cracks, chips, and excessive wear especially in the form of rounded edges. Make sure mating gears engage properly. Renew mating gears as a set if necessary. Also, inspect the needle roller bearings. There should be no flat spots or pitting on the bearing rollers. If the needle rollers are damage, it is likely that the internal bearing surface of the corresponding gear pinion is worn also.

23 Check the shaft bearings in the crankcase halves (see Section 27).

Reassembly – four-speed transmission

24 During reassembly, lubricate the mating surfaces of the shaft and pinions with clean engine oil.

25 Slide the spacer on from the left-hand end of the shaft.

26 Slide on the combined 3rd/4th gear pinion with the smaller 3rd gear pinion facing the integral 1st gear pinion (see illustration).

27 Slide on the spacer.

28 Fit the 2nd gear pinion and thrust washer onto the end of the shaft.

Reassembly – six-speed transmission

29 During reassembly, lubricate the surfaces of the shaft, pinions and bearings with clean engine oil. When installing the **new** circlips, do not expand their ends any further than is necessary to slide them along the shaft. Install them so that their chamfered side faces the pinion they secure (see illustration).

30 Slide the needle roller bearing for the 5th gear pinion onto the shaft from the left-hand end and install it against the integral 1st gear (see illustration).

31 Slide the 5th gear pinion onto the shaft with its dogs facing away from the integral 1st gear (see illustration 28.14). Position the pinion on its bearing, then slide on the thrust washer and secure it with a new circlip (see illustrations 28.13b and a). Make sure the circlip locates correctly in the groove in the shaft (see illustration).

32 Slide on the combined 3rd/4th gear pinion with the smaller 3rd gear pinion facing the 5th gear pinion (see illustration 28.12b). Secure the 3rd/4th gear pinion with a new circlip

33 Slide on the splined washer (see illustration 28.11).

34 Install the needle roller bearing for the 6th gear pinion, then slide the pinion onto the shaft with its dogs facing the larger 4th gear

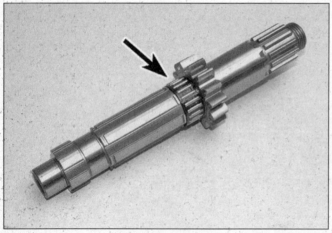

28.30 Install the needle bearing (arrowed) against the integral 1st gear

28.31 Note the position of the circlip ends (arrowed)

28.34 6th gear pinion dogs (A) should face 4th gear pinion (B)

28.36 Assembled transmission input shaft

pinion of the combined 3rd/4th gear (see illustration).

35 Fit the 2nd gear pinion (with washer recess outwards) and thrust washer onto the end of the shaft (see illustration 28.8b and a).

36 Check that all components have been correctly installed. The assembled shaft should look like this (see illustration).

Output shaft

Note: *The four and six-speed transmissions use components that are visually similar. Although there are no 5th and 6th gear pinions on the four-speed transmission input shaft, 5th and 6th gear pinions are fitted on the four-speed transmission output shaft.*

Disassembly

Note: *The gear pinions are secured by circlips – fit new circlips on reassembly, never re-use the old circlips.*

37 Remove the thrust washer from the right-hand end of the shaft, then slide off the 1st gear pinion, noting which way round it fits (see illustrations).

38 Slide off the needle roller bearing and the thrust washer (see illustrations).

39 Slide the 5th gear pinion off the shaft, noting which way round it fits (see illustration).

40 Remove the circlip and the splined washer, then slide off the 3rd gear pinion (see illustrations).

28.37a Remove the thrust washer . . .

28.37b . . . then slide off the 1st gear pinion

28.38a Slide off the needle bearing . . .

28.38b . . . and the thrust washer

28.39 Slide off the 5th gear pinion

28.40a Remove the circlip . . .

28.40b . . . and the splined washer . . .

28.40c . . . then slide off the 3rd gear pinion

28.41 Ease the needle bearing off the length of the shaft

28.42 Slide off the 4th gear pinion

28.43a Slide off the splined washer . . .

41 The 3rd gear pinion needle roller bearing has a split cage – locate the join in the cage, then prise the ends apart and slide the bearing along the shaft carefully **(see illustration)**.

42 Slide the 4th gear pinion off the shaft **(see illustration)**. The 4th gear pinion needle roller bearing has a split cage – locate the join in the cage, then prise the ends apart and slide the bearing off carefully.

43 Remove the splined washer and the circlip, then slide off the 6th gear pinion, noting which way round it fits **(see illustrations)**.

44 Remove the circlip and the splined washer securing the 2nd gear pinion, then slide the gear off **(see illustrations)**.

45 The 2nd gear pinion needle roller bearing has a split cage – locate the join in the cage, then prise the ends apart and slide the bearing along the shaft carefully **(see illustration)**.

Inspection

46 Refer to Steps 17 to 23 above – note that Step 22 applies to both four and six-speed transmission output shafts.

Reassembly

47 During reassembly, lubricate the surfaces of the shaft, pinions and bearings with clean engine oil. When installing the new circlips, do not expand their ends any further than is necessary to slide them along the shaft. Install them so that their chamfered side faces the pinion they secure **(see illustration 28.29)**.

48 Slide the needle roller bearing for the 2nd gear pinion onto the shaft from the right-hand end and install it against the stop for the shaft bearing inner race **(see illustration 28.45)**.

49 Slide the 2nd gear pinion onto the shaft with its dog holes facing the right-hand end **(see illustration 28.44c)**. Position the pinion on its bearing, then slide on the thrust washer and secure it with a new circlip **(see illustrations 28.44b and a)**. Make sure the circlip locates correctly in the groove in the shaft **(see illustration 28.31)**.

50 Slide on the 6th gear pinion with its selector fork groove facing the right-hand end of the shaft **(see illustration 28.43c)**.

51 Secure the 6th gear pinion with a new circlip, then slide on the splined washer **(see illustrations 28.43b and a)**.

52 Slide on the needle roller bearing for the 4th gear pinion and install it against the splined washer.

53 Slide the 4th gear pinion onto the shaft with its dog holes facing the 6th gear pinion

28.43b . . . then remove the circlip . . .

28.43c . . . and slide off the 6th gear pinion

28.44a Remove the circlip . . .

28.44b . . . and splined washer . . .

28.44c . . . and slide off the 2nd gear pinion

28.45 Ease the needle bearing off the length of the shaft

28.60 Assembled transmission output shaft

(see illustration 28.42). Position the pinion on its bearing.
54 Slide on the needle roller bearing for the 3rd gear pinion **(see illustration 28.41).**
55 Slide the 3rd gear pinion onto the shaft with its dog holes facing the right-hand end of the shaft **(see illustration 28.40c).** Position the pinion on its bearing.
56 Slide on the splined washer and secure it with a new circlip **(see illustration 28.40b and a).**
57 Slide on the 5th gear pinion with its selector fork groove facing the 3rd gear pinion **(see illustration 28.39).**
58 Fit the thrust washer and needle roller bearing for the 1st gear pinion **(see illustration 28.38b and a).**
59 Fit the 1st gear pinion with its dog

holes facing the 5th gear pinion, then fit the thrust washer onto the end of the shaft **(see illustration 28.37b and a).**
60 Check that all components have been correctly installed. The assembled shaft should look like this **(see illustration).**

29 Initial start-up after overhaul/running-in

1 Make sure the engine oil and coolant levels are correct (see *Pre-ride checks*).
2 Make sure the lubricating system has been primed (see Chapter 1, Section 13).
3 Make sure there is fuel in the tank, then turn the fuel tap to the 'ON' position, and set the choke.
4 Check that the transmission is in neutral and that the kill switch (if fitted) is OFF.
5 Start the engine, then allow it to run at a moderately fast idle until it reaches normal operating temperature. Do not be alarmed if there is a little smoke from the exhaust – this will be due to the oil used to lubricate the piston and bore during assembly being burnt off and should subside after a while.
6 Check carefully that there are no oil or coolant leaks and make sure the transmission and controls, especially the brakes and clutch, work properly before riding the machine.
7 Upon completion of the test ride, and after the engine has cooled down completely,

recheck the engine oil and coolant levels (see *Pre-ride checks*).

Recommended running-in procedure

8 Treat the machine gently for the first few hours to allow the oil to circulate throughout the engine and transmission and for any new parts installed to seat.
9 Great care is necessary if the engine has been extensively overhauled – the bike will have to be run-in as when new. This means more use of the transmission and a restraining hand on the throttle for the first 3 hours of riding time. Avoid labouring the engine and to gradually increase performance up to, but not exceeding, 7000 rpm.
10 During the next 12 hours, continue the running-in procedure by varying engine speed and gradually increasing the load on the engine to 75% of its maximum performance.
11 These recommendations apply less when only a partial overhaul has been done, though it does depend to an extent on the nature of the work carried out and which components have been renewed. Experience is the best guide, since it is easy to tell when an engine is running freely. If in any doubt, consult a KTM dealer.
12 If a lubrication failure is suspected, stop the engine immediately and try to find the cause. If an engine is run without oil, even for a short period of time, severe damage will occur.

Notes

Chapter 3
Cooling system

Contents

Degrees of difficulty

Easy, suitable for novice with little experience	**Fairly easy,** suitable for beginner with some experience 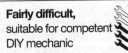	**Fairly difficult,** suitable for competent DIY mechanic	**Difficult,** suitable for experienced DIY mechanic 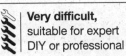	**Very difficult,** suitable for expert DIY or professional

Specifications

Coolant
Coolant
  Type . . . . 60% distilled water, 40% corrosion inhibited ethylene glycol anti-freeze
  Capacity . . . . 1 litre

Thermostat
Opening temperature. . . . . 70°C approx

Torque settings
Cooling fan switch . . . . 20 Nm
Radiator mounting bolts. . . . . 25 Nm
Water pump cover bolts
  2000 to 2005. . . . . 8 Nm
  2006 and 2007 . . . . 10 Nm

1 General information

The cooling system uses a mixture of water and antifreeze to carry away excess energy in the form of heat. The cylinder is surrounded by a water jacket from which the heated coolant is circulated by a water pump, driven off the camshaft. The hot coolant passes upwards to the radiators, where it is cooled by the passing air, and then back to the engine where the cycle is repeated.

A thermostat is fitted in the system to prevent the coolant flowing through the radiator when the engine is cold, therefore accelerating the speed at which the engine reaches normal operating temperature.

A thermostatically-controlled cooling fan is fitted behind the radiator on certain models to aid cooling in extreme conditions. The cooling fan assembly can be retro-fitted to all 2001 to 2007 models fitted with an electric starter.

The complete cooling system is partially sealed and pressurised, the pressure being controlled by a spring-loaded valve contained in the pressure cap. By pressurising the coolant the boiling point is raised, preventing premature boiling in adverse conditions. An overflow hose is connected to the filler cap neck through which excess coolant is discharged under pressure if the system is overfilled or overheats.

Warning: Do not remove the pressure cap from the filler neck when the engine is hot. Scalding hot coolant and steam may be blown out under pressure, which could cause serious injury. When the engine has cooled, place *a thick rag, like a towel, over the pressure cap; slowly rotate the cap anti-clockwise to the first stop. This procedure allows any residual pressure to escape. When the steam has stopped escaping, press down on the cap while turning it anti-clockwise and remove it.*

Do not allow antifreeze to come in contact with your skin or painted surfaces of the motorcycle. Rinse off any spills immediately with plenty of water. Antifreeze is highly toxic if ingested. Never leave antifreeze lying around in an open container or in puddles on the floor; children and pets are attracted by its sweet smell and may drink it. Check with the local authorities about disposing of used antifreeze. Many communities will have collection centres which will see that antifreeze is disposed of safely.

Caution: At all times use the specified type of antifreeze, and always mix it with distilled water in the correct proportion. The antifreeze contains corrosion inhibitors which are essential to avoid damage to the cooling system. A lack of these inhibitors could lead to a build-up of corrosion which would block the coolant passages, resulting in overheating and severe engine damage. Distilled water must be used as opposed to tap water to avoid a build-up of scale which would also block the passages.

2 Coolant change

⚠ *Warning: Allow the engine to cool completely before performing this maintenance operation. Also, don't allow antifreeze to come into contact with your skin or the painted surfaces of the motorcycle. Rinse off spills immediately with plenty of water. Antifreeze is highly toxic if ingested. Never leave antifreeze lying around in an open container or in puddles on the floor; children and pets are attracted by its sweet smell and may drink it. Check with local authorities (councils) about disposing of antifreeze. Many communities have collection centres where antifreeze can be disposed of safely. Antifreeze is also combustible, so don't store it near open flames.*

Drain

1 Support the motorcycle securely in an upright position using an auxiliary stand.
2 Remove the pressure cap from the left-hand radiator **(see illustration)**.
3 Position a suitable container beneath the radiators. Loosen the clips securing the bottom hoses to left and right-hand radiators, then pull the hoses off and drain the coolant **(see illustrations)**.
Caution: The radiator unions are fragile. Do not use excessive force when attempting to remove the hoses.
4 Remove the drain bolt from the bottom of the cylinder and allow the coolant to completely drain from the system. Note the sealing washer on the bolt and retain it for use during flushing **(see illustration)**.

Flush

5 Reconnect the radiator bottom hoses and tighten the clips.
6 Flush the system with clean tap water by inserting a garden hose in the coolant filler neck. Allow the water to run through the system until it is clear when it flows out of the cylinder drain hole. If there is a lot of sediment in the water, remove the radiators and have them cleaned at a radiator shop (see Section 3). If the drain hole appears to be clogged with sediment, use compressed air to clear the blockage.
7 Install the drain bolt using the old sealing washer, then fill the system via the filler neck with clean water mixed with a flushing

compound. Make sure the flushing compound is compatible with aluminium components, and follow the manufacturer's instructions carefully. Loosen the bleed screws on the cylinder head and the top of the right-hand radiator to vent any trapped air, then tighten them again **(see illustrations)**. Install the pressure cap.
8 Start the engine and allow it to reach normal operating temperature. Let it run for about ten minutes.
9 Stop the engine. Let it cool for a while, then cover the pressure cap with a heavy rag and unscrew it slowly, releasing any pressure that may be present in the system.
10 Drain the system as described above.
11 Fill the system with clean water and repeat the procedure in Steps 8 to 10.

Refill

12 Fit a new sealing washer onto the drain bolt and thread the drain bolt into the cylinder.
13 Fill the system via the filler neck with the proper coolant mixture (see this Chapter's Specifications). **Note:** *Pour the coolant in slowly to minimise the amount of air entering the system.* Don't forget to release any trapped air via the bleed screws, then tighten the screws **(see illustrations 2.7a and b)**.
14 When the system appears full, move the bike off its stand and shake it slightly to dissipate the coolant, then place the bike back on the auxiliary stand and, if required, top the system up. The coolant level should be 10 mm above the top of the radiator fins (see *Pre-ride checks*). Install the pressure cap.

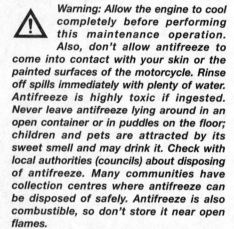

2.2 Remove the coolant pressure cap

2.3a Disconnect the left-hand . . .

2.3b . . . and right-hand radiator bottom hoses

2.4 Location of the drain bolt (arrowed) at the bottom of the cylinder

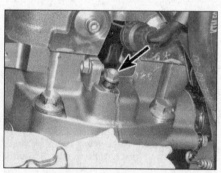

2.7a Cylinder head bleed screw (arrowed)

2.7b Bleed screw at top of right-hand radiator

15 Start the engine and allow it to run for several minutes. Flick the throttle open 3 or 4 times, then stop the engine. Wait a few minutes for the coolant to settle, then check the level; if it has fallen, top-up with the specified mixture.

16 Check the system for leaks.

17 Do not dispose of the old coolant by pouring it down the drain. Instead pour it into a heavy plastic container, cap it tightly and take it into an authorised disposal site or service station – see **Warning** at the beginning of this Section.

3 Radiators

Removal

 Warning: The engine must be completely cool before carrying out this procedure.

1 Remove the fuel tank (see Chapter 4).

2 Undo the bolts securing the radiator panels and lift them off **(see illustrations)**. Where fitted, disconnect the horn wiring connectors and remove the horn with the right-hand panel.

3 If fitted, remove the cooling fan assembly (see Section 7).

4 Drain the cooling system (see Section 2). Leave the bottom hoses disconnected.

5 Loosen the clips securing the radiator top hoses and detach both hoses **(see illustrations)**.

Caution: The radiator unions are fragile. Do not use excessive force when attempting to remove the hoses.

6 Loosen the clip and detach the hose between the thermostat housing and the right-hand radiator from the radiator.

7 Disconnect the overflow hose from the pressure cap neck **(see illustration)**.

8 Unscrew the upper and lower mounting bolts, noting the arrangement of the washers and rubber bushes, and lift the radiators off their mountings **(see illustrations)**.

Check

9 Check the radiator mounting bushes, and replace them with new ones if necessary.

10 Inspect the radiator for signs of damage and clear any dirt or debris that might obstruct airflow and inhibit cooling (see Chapter 1, Section 2).

11 If there was a lot of sediment in the radiators when they were drained, reverse flush them with clean tap water. If it is likely that a radiator is blocked internally, have it assessed by a KTM dealer.

12 If problems such as overheating or loss of coolant occur, and no apparent damage to the radiators can be found, have the radiator pressure cap tested by a KTM dealer. The cap's valve should hold pressurised coolant in the system up to a temperature of approximately 120°C. If the valve is defective, renew the cap. Also check the thermostat (see Section 4) and the water pump impeller (see Section 5). If a cooling fan is fitted, check the operation of the fan switch (see Section 7).

Installation

13 Installation is the reverse of removal, noting the following:
● Make sure the rubber bushes are correctly installed in the brackets.

3.2a Undo the bolts . . .

3.2b . . . and lift the radiator panels off

3.5a Disconnect the left-hand (arrowed) . . .

3.5b . . . and right-hand radiator top hoses (arrowed)

3.7 Disconnect the overflow hose

3.8a Undo the mounting bolts (arrowed) . . .

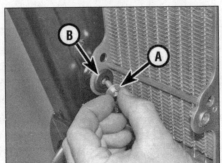
3.8b . . . noting the washers (A) and bushes (B)

3.8c Lift the radiator off its mountings (arrowed)

4.2 Location of the thermostat housing (arrowed)

4.5 Detach the hose to the water pump housing (arrowed)

4.7a Lift off the thermostat housing and hoses

● Tighten the bolts to the torque setting specified at the beginning of this Chapter.
● Ensure the coolant hoses are in good condition and are securely retained by their clips, using new ones if necessary (see Section 6).
● Refill the cooling system (see Section 2).

4 Thermostat

1 The thermostat is automatic in operation and should give long and reliable service without requiring attention. In the event of a failure, the valve will probably jam open, in which case the engine will take much longer than normal to warm up. Conversely, if the valve jams shut, the coolant will be unable to circulate and the engine will quickly overheat.

Removal

 Warning: The engine must be completely cool before carrying out this procedure.

2 The thermostat is located inside its housing at the junction of the coolant hoses behind the radiators (see illustration). To gain access, first remove the fuel tank (see Chapter 4).
3 Drain the cooling system (see Section 2).
4 Loosen the clips securing the radiator top hoses and detach both hoses (see illustrations 3.5a and b).
5 Loosen the clip securing the hose to the water pump housing and detach the hose (see illustration).
6 Loosen the clip and detach the hose between the thermostat housing and the

right-hand radiator from the radiator.
7 Lift the thermostat housing and coolant hose assembly off (see illustration). If the hoses are going to be removed, note their positions and mark them as an aid to reassembly (see illustration).
8 Undo the screws securing the two halves of the thermostat housing together, then lift the top half off carefully, noting the location of the thermostat (see illustrations).
9 Remove the housing O-ring, then lift out the thermostat (see illustrations). Discard the O-ring as a new one must be fitted.

Check

10 Examine the thermostat visually before carrying out the test. If the thermostat remains in the open position at room temperature, it should be replaced with a new one (see illustration).

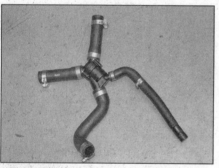

4.7b Note the position of the hoses if they are going to be removed

4.8a Undo the screws (arrowed) . . .

4.8b . . . and separate the halves of the housing

4.9a Remove the housing O-ring . . .

4.9b . . . then lift out the thermostat

4.10 The thermostat should be closed when cold

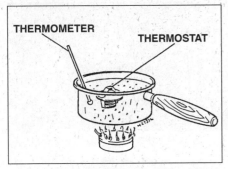

4.11 Set-up for testing the thermostat

11 Suspend the thermostat in a container of cold water. Place a thermometer capable of reading temperatures up to 100°C in the water so that the bulb is close to the thermostat **(see illustration)**. Heat the water, noting the temperature at which the thermostat opens, and compare the result with the specification given at the beginning of this Chapter. If the result obtained differs from the specification, the thermostat is faulty and must be replaced with a new one.

12 In the event of the thermostat jamming closed, *as an emergency measure only*, it can be removed and the machine used without it. **Note:** *Take care when starting the engine from cold, as it will take much longer than usual to warm up.* Ensure that a new thermostat is installed as soon as possible.

Installation

13 Installation is the reverse of removal, noting the following:

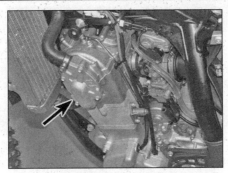

5.1 Location of the water pump (arrowed)

● Ensure that the thermostat is correctly seated in its housing.
● Fit a new housing O-ring.
● Tighten the housing screws evenly.
● If removed, assemble the coolant hoses on the housing before installation **(see illustration 4.7b)**.
● Tighten the hose clips securely, using new ones if necessary (see Section 6).
● Refill the cooling system (see Section 2).

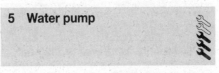

5 Water pump

1 The water pump is located on the left-hand side of the cylinder head **(see illustration)**.
2 If the pump is thought to be faulty, or if there is evidence that the internal seals have failed, remove the pump as follows.

Removal

Note: *On models from 2002-on the pump seal carrier can be removed with the camshaft in position in the engine. On earlier models, to access the seal carrier, the camshaft must be removed first.*

3 On 2000 and 2001 models, follow the procedure in Chapter 2, Section 9, and remove the camshaft. Now go to Step 6 below.
4 On 2002-on models, drain the cooling system (see Section 2), then remove the fuel tank (see Chapter 4).
5 Undo the bolts securing the pump cover and lift the cover off, being prepared to catch any residual coolant **(see illustrations)**. Discard the cover gasket as a new one must be fitted.
6 Remove the circlip securing the impeller on the shaft, then lift the impeller off, noting the location of the drive pin **(see illustrations)**. **Note:** *For the purpose of this manual, the procedure is illustrated with the camshaft removed.*
7 Pull the drive pin out of the shaft **(see illustration)**.
8 On 2002-on models, if the camshaft is in position, thread two M3 screws into the holes in the outer face of the seal carrier, then carefully draw the carrier out. If the camshaft has been removed, pull the seal carrier off the shaft. Note the location of the stop washer behind the seal carrier **(see illustration)**.
9 On 2000 and 2001 models, pull the seal carrier off the shaft, noting which way round it fits.
10 Remove the O-rings from the carrier and discard them as new ones must be fitted

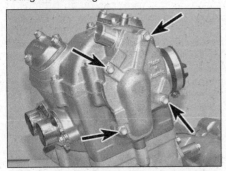

5.5a Undo the water pump cover bolts (arrowed) . . .

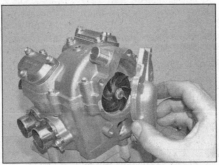

5.5b . . . and lift the cover off

5.6a Remove the circlip . . .

5.6b . . . and lift the pump impeller off

5.7 Pull out the drive pin

5.8 Note the location of the stop washer (arrowed)

5.13a Drive out the internal seals as described

5.13b Install the seals with the open side (arrowed) facing out

5.13c Outer edge of the seal should be level with the face of the carrier. Note the thick flange (arrowed)

5.14 Install the O-rings in the outside grooves

5.15 Fit a plastic sleeve over the shaft

5.16 Install the stop washer – 2002 to 2007 models

Inspection

11 Check the blades on the pump impeller, and check the slot in the centre of the impeller where the drive pin locates. If any wear or damage is found, fit a new impeller. **Note:** *From 2001 models, a longer drive pin was fitted with a corresponding longer slot in the impeller. On 2000 models, if a later-type impeller is fitted, ensure that a longer drive pin is fitted also.*

12 Inspect the seal carrier for pitting and corrosion. If the surface of the carrier is damaged, fit a new one.

13 Support the seal carrier on two blocks of wood and drive the internal seals out using a suitably-sized socket **(see illustration)**. Press the new seals in with their open sides facing out **(see illustration)**. Use a driver that bears on the outer edge of the seals only. When

installed, the outer edge of each seal should be level with the face of the carrier **(see illustration)**. Lubricate the lips of the seals with water pump grease.

14 Lubricate the new seal carrier O-rings with a smear of grease and install them in the grooves on the carrier **(see illustration)**. Note that on 2002-on models, two sizes of O-ring are fitted – the smaller O-ring fits in the outer groove next to the pump impeller.

Installation

15 Slide a suitable plastic sleeve over the shaft to prevent the edges of the circlip groove and drive pin hole damaging the inside of the shaft seals – electrical heat shrink sleeving is ideal. If a suitable sleeve is not available, take great care when installing the seal carrier **(see illustration)**.

16 On 2002-on models, if the camshaft has

been removed, ensure that the stop washer is in place **(see illustration)**.

17 Slide the seal carrier onto the shaft **(see illustration)**. Ensure that the thick flange is facing inwards **(see illustration 5.13c)**. On 2002-on models, the two M3 screw holes should face outwards. From 2003 models, the seal carrier has a drain hole located between the two inner seals **(see illustration)**. The drain hole must face up when the carrier is installed – the position of the hole is indicated by a punch mark on the outside face of the carrier. If the camshaft has not been removed, ensure the O-rings are greased and ease the carrier in carefully to avoid damaging the O-rings.

18 Pull the plastic sleeve off the shaft.

19 Install the drive pin and the impeller, then secure the impeller with a new circlip **(see illustrations 5.7, 5.6b and a)**.

20 If applicable, follow the procedure in Chapter 2 and install the camshaft.

21 Remove all traces of old gasket from the mating surfaces of the camshaft cover, cylinder head and pump cover. If a scraper must be used, be very careful not to nick or gouge the soft aluminium or oil leaks will result.

22 Fit a new gasket, holding it in position with a dab of grease if necessary, then install the pump cover and tighten the screws to the torque setting specified at the beginning of this Chapter.

23 Refill the cooling system (see Section 2).

24 If removed, install the fuel tank (see Chapter 4).

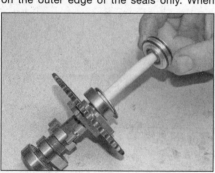

5.17a Slide on the seal carrier

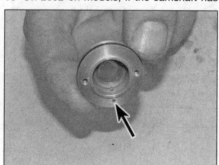

5.17b Punch mark (arrowed) indicates position of drain hole

6 Coolant hoses and unions

Removal

1 Before removing a hose, drain the coolant (see Section 2). **Note:** *When removing components of the cooling system, be prepared to catch any residual fluid.*
2 Use a small, flat-bladed screwdriver to loosen the hose clips, then slide them back along the hose and clear of the union.
Caution: The radiator unions are fragile. Do not use excessive force when attempting to remove the hoses.
3 If a hose proves stubborn, release it by rotating it on its union before working it off – a squirt of dry-film lubricant often helps. If all else fails, cut the hose with a sharp knife then slit it at each union so that it can be peeled off in two pieces. Whilst this means renewing the hose, it is preferable to buying a new radiator.

Installation

4 Slide the clip onto the hose and then work the hose all the way onto its union.
5 Rotate the hose on its union to settle it in position before sliding the clip into place and tightening it securely.

 HAYNES HINT *If the hose is difficult to push onto its union, it can be softened by soaking it in very hot water, or alternatively a little soapy water can be used as a lubricant.*

7 Cooling fan switch and cooling fan

Note: *The cooling fan and switch assembly can be retro-fitted to all 2001 to 2007 models fitted with an electric starter. It is fitted as standard to MXC and XC models.*
1 If the engine is overheating and the cooling fan isn't coming on, first check the coolant level (see *Pre-ride checks*). If the level is correct, remove the fuel tank (see Chapter 4) and locate the cooling fan circuit fuse in the fan sub-loom **(see illustration)**. Follow the procedure in Chapter 9 to check the fuse. If the fuse is blown, check the fan circuit for a short to earth (see *Wiring Diagrams* at the end of Chapter 9).
2 If the fuse is good, check that the terminals in the fan sub-loom wiring connectors are clean and that the connectors are secure. Spray the terminals in the connectors with electrical contact cleaner prior to reconnection.

Cooling fan switch

3 If the fan still isn't coming on, check the operation of the fan switch as follows.
4 Using a multimeter set to the ohms scale, back-probe the switch terminals and test for continuity with the engine cold. The switch should be OFF and there should be no continuity (infinite resistance).
5 Now start the engine and bring it up to operating temperature. The fan switch should turn ON between 80 and 85°C. With the switch ON the meter should show continuity (no resistance).
6 If the switch does not perform as described it is faulty and should be renewed. Drain the cooling system (see Section 2), then disconnect the switch wiring connector and unscrew the switch from the radiator **(see illustration)**. Discard the sealing washer as a new one must be fitted.
7 Fit a new sealing washer onto the new switch, then install the switch in the radiator and tighten it to the torque setting specified at the beginning of this Chapter. Take care not to over-tighten the switch. Reconnect the switch wiring connector, then refill the cooling system (see Section 2).
8 If the fan stays on all the time, disconnect the fan switch wiring connector. If the fan stops, the switch is defective and must be renewed. If it doesn't, check the wiring between the switch and the fan motor for a short to earth.

Cooling fan

9 If the engine is overheating and fan isn't coming on, and the fan switch is good, test the fan motor as follows.
10 Disconnect the fan motor from the sub-loom wiring connector. Using a fully-charged 12 volt battery and two jumper wires, connect the battery positive (+ve) terminal to the red wire terminal and the battery negative (-ve) terminal to the black wire terminal on the fan side of the wiring connector **(see illustration)**. Once connected the fan motor should operate. If it does not, the motor is faulty and must be renewed.
11 Release the clips securing the sub-loom to the fan assembly. Unscrew the bolts securing the fan assembly to the radiator and remove the fan.
12 Install the new fan assembly and tighten the mounting bolts securely. Connect the fan motor to the sub-loom and secure the wiring to the assembly with cable-ties as noted on removal.

Cooling fan and switch installation

13 The cooling fan kit consists of a cooling fan assembly, thermostatic switch and wiring sub-loom. The kit is available from KTM dealerships and comes complete with fitting instructions.
14 Provision is made in the wiring looms of all 2001-on models equipped with an electric starter for the fitment of the cooling fan. Remove the fuel tank (see Chapter 4) and identify the wiring connector for the fan sub-loom (see *Wiring Diagrams* at the end of Chapter 9).
15 Ensure the right-hand radiator is clean and free of obstructions. If necessary, clean the threads of the mounting brackets on the back of the radiator, then install the fan assembly and tighten the mounting bolts securely.
16 Drain the cooling system (see Section 2) and unscrew the plug from the lower edge of the radiator. On 2001 and 2002 models, the plug is located on the left-hand radiator; on 2003 to 2007 models, the plug is located on the right-hand radiator. Discard the sealing washer.
17 Follow the procedure in Step 7 to install the fan switch.
18 Connect the cooling fan sub-loom to the main wiring harness, the terminals on the thermostatic switch and the fan motor wiring connector. Secure the wiring with cable-ties.
19 Install the fuel tank (see Chapter 4).

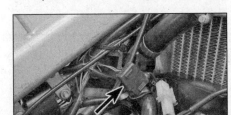
7.1 Unclip fuseholder lid to access cooling fan 5A fuse

7.6 Fan switch is screwed into base of right-hand radiator

7.10 Disconnect the fan wire connector (arrowed)

Chapter 4
Fuel and exhaust systems

Contents

Degrees of difficulty

Easy, suitable for novice with little experience	Fairly easy, suitable for beginner with some experience	Fairly difficult, suitable for competent DIY mechanic	Difficult, suitable for experienced DIY mechanic	Very difficult, suitable for expert DIY or professional

Specifications

Fuel

Grade	Unleaded, minimum 95 RON (Research Octane Number)
Fuel tank capacity (total)	
400/520 EXC (2000)	9.0 litres
250/400/520 EXC (2001 and 2002)	8.5 litres
250/450/525 EXC (2003)	8.0 litres
250/450/525 EXC (2004 and 2005)	8.5 litres
450 EXC-G and XC-G (2006-on)	9.5 litres
400/520 SX (2000 to 2002)	7.5 litres
450/525 SX (2003-on)	7.0 litres
450/525/560 SMR and 450/540 SXS	7.0 litres
400/520 MXC and 450/525 MXC (inc. Desert)	13.0 litres
Fuel tank capacity (reserve)	
MXC models	2.0 litres
EXC models	1.0 litres

Carburettor

250 EXC (2002 to 2004), 250 EXC-G (2004)

Type	
2002	Keihin CR35
2003 and 2004	Keihin FCR-MX37
Mixture screw setting	
250 EXC (2002 to 2004)	1.25 turns out
250 EXC-G (USA) (2004)	0.75 turn out
Slide	15
Main jet	160
Main air jet	200
Idle jet	
2002	48
2003 and 2004	42
Idle air jet	100
Starter jet	85
Jet needle	
2002	OBEVP
2003 and 2004	OBETP
250 EXC-G (USA) (2004)	OBEKT
Needle position	
2002	6th from top
2003 and 2004	3rd from top
Idle speed	1400 to 1500 rpm

Carburettor (continued)

250 EXC (2005 and 2006)

Type
  2005 . . . . Keihin FCR-MX3700A
  2006 . . . . Keihin FCR-MX3700B
Mixture screw setting . . . . 3/4 turn out
Slide 15
Main jet 160
Main air jet 200
Idle jet 42
Idle air jet 100
Starter jet 85
Jet needle . . . . OBEKT
Needle position . . . . 3rd from top
Idle speed . . . . 1400 to 1500 rpm

400 EXC and SX (2000 and 2001), 520 EXC and SX (2000 and 2001)

Type . . . . Keihin FCR-MX 39
Mixture screw setting
  400 EXC and 520 SX (2000) . . . . 2 turns out
  400 SX (2000) . . . . 2 1/4 turns out
  400 EXC, MXC and SX (2001) . . . . 1 turn out
  520 EXC and MXC (2000 and 2001) . . . . 2 1/2 turns out
  520 SX (2001) . . . . 1 turn out
Slide 15
Main jet 175
Main air jet 200
Idle jet
  400 EXC and 520 SX (2000) 52
  400 SX and 520 EXC (2000) 48
  400/520 EXC, MXC and SX (2001) 48
Idle air jet 100
Starter jet 85
Jet needle . . . . OBDTM
Needle position
  400 EXC and 520 EXC and SX (2000) . . . . 2nd from top
  400 SX (2000 and 2001) . . . . 4th from top
  400 EXC and MXC (2001) . . . . 4th from top
  520 EXC and MXC (2001) . . . . 2nd from top
  520 SX (2001) . . . . 3rd from top
Idle speed . . . . 1400 to 1500 rpm

400 EXC, MXC and SX (2002), 520 EXC/MXC/SX (2002)

Type . . . . Keihin CR39
Mixture screw setting
  400 EXC and MXC, and 400/520 SX . . . . 1 turn out
  520 EXC and MXC . . . . 2 1/2 turns out
Slide 15
Main jet 175
Main air jet 200
Idle jet 48
Idle air jet 100
Starter jet 85
Jet needle . . . . OBDTM
Needle position
  400 EXC and MXC, and 400 SX . . . . 4th from top
  520 EXC and MXC . . . . 2nd from top
  520 SX . . . . 3rd from top
Idle speed . . . . 1400 to 1500 rpm

400 EXC (2004)

Type . . . . Keihin FCR-MX 39
Mixture screw setting . . . . 1 1/4 turns out
Slide 15
Main jet 178

Carburettor (continued)

400 EXC (2004) (continued)

Main air jet	200
Idle jet	42
Idle air jet	100
Starter jet	85
Jet needle	OBDVR
Needle position	1st from top
Idle speed	1400 to 1500 rpm

400 EXC, EXC-G and XC (2005 to 2007)

Type	
2005	Keihin FCR-MX 3900C
2006 EXC and EXC-G and 2007 XC	Keihin FCR-MX 3900D
2007 EXC	Keihin FCR-MX 3900E
Mixture screw setting	1 1/4 turns out
Slide	15
Main jet	178
Main air jet	200
Idle jet	42
Idle air jet	100
Starter jet	85
Jet needle	OBDVR
Needle position	1st from top
Idle speed	1400 to 1500 rpm

450 EXC (2003 and 2004), 525 EXC (2003 and 2004)

Type	Keihin FCR-MX 39
Mixture screw setting	
450 EXC (2003)	1 1/4 turns out
450 EXC (2004)	1 1/2 turns out
525 EXC (2003 and 2004)	1 1/2 turns out
Slide	15
Main jet	178
Main air jet	200
Idle jet	42
Idle air jet	100
Starter jet	85
Jet needle	
450 EXC (2003)	OBDVR
450 EXC (2004)	OBDTN
525 EXC (2003 and 2004)	OBDTN
Needle position	
450 EXC (2003)	3rd from top
450 EXC (2004)	2nd from top
525 EXC (2003 and 2004)	2nd from top
Idle speed	1400 to 1500 rpm

450 EXC (2005 to 2006), 525 EXC (2005 to 2006)

Type	
450 EXC (2005)	Keihin FCR-MX 3900A
450 EXC (2006)	Keihin FCR-MX 3900E
525 EXC (2005)	Keihin FCR-MX 3900B
525 EXC (2006)	Keihin FCR-MX 3900F
Mixture screw setting	2 turns out
Slide	15
Main jet	
2005	178
2006	182
Main air jet	200
Idle jet	42
Idle air jet	100
Starter jet	85
Jet needle	OBDTR
Needle position	
450 EXC	4th from top
525 EXC	5th from top
Idle speed	1400 to 1500 rpm

Carburettor (continued)

450 EXC and 450 XC (2007) and 450 EXC Six Days (2007)

Type . . . . Keihin FCR-MX 3900E
Mixture screw setting
  450 EXC and XC . . . . 1 1/4 turns out
  450 Six Days . . . . 2 turns out
Slide 15
Main jet
  450 EXC and XC 178
  450 Six Days 182
Main air jet 200
Idle jet 42
Idle air jet 100
Starter jet 85
Jet needle
  450 EXC and XC . . . . OBDVR
  450 Six Days . . . . OBDTR
Needle position
  450 EXC and XC . . . . 3rd from top
  450 Six Days . . . . 4th from top
Idle speed . . . . 1400 to 1500 rpm

525 EXC and 525 XC (2007)

Type . . . . Keihin FCR-MX 3900F
Mixture screw setting
  525 EXC and 525 XC . . . . 1 1/4 turns out
  525 Six Days . . . . 2 turns out
Slide 15
Main jet
  525 EXC and 525 XC 178
  525 Six Days 182
Main air jet 200
Idle jet 42
Idle air jet 100
Starter jet 85
Jet needle
  525 EXC and 525 XC . . . . OBDVT
  525 Six Days . . . . OBDTR
Needle position
  525 EXC and 525 XC . . . . 3rd from top
  525 Six Days . . . . 5th from top
Idle speed . . . . 1400 to 1500 rpm

450/525 EXC-G and MXC-G (2004)

Type . . . . Keihin FCR-MX 39
Mixture screw setting . . . . 1 1/4 turns out
Slide 15
Main jet 178
Main air jet 200
Idle jet 42
Idle air jet 100
Starter jet 85
Jet needle
  450 EXC-G and MXC-G . . . . OBDVR
  525 EXC-G and MXC-G . . . . OBDVT
Needle position . . . . 3rd from top
Idle speed . . . . 1400 to 1500 rpm

450/525 EXC-G and MXC-G (2005), 450/525 EXC-G and XC-G (2006)

Type
  450 EXC-G and MXC-G (2005) . . . . Keihin FCR-MX 3900A
  450 EXC-G and XC-G (2006) . . . . Keihin FCR-MX 3900E
  525 EXC-G and MXC-G . . . . Keihin FCR-MX 3900B
  525 EXC-G and XC-G . . . . Keihin FCR-MX 3900F
Mixture screw setting . . . . 1 1/4 turns out
Slide 15
Main jet 178
Main air jet 200
Idle jet 42

Carburettor (continued)

450/525 EXC-G and MXC-G (2005), 450/525 EXC-G and XC-G (2006) (continued)
Idle air jet 100
Starter jet 85
Jet needle
   450 EXC-G, MXC-G and XC-G . . . . OBDVR
   525 EXC-G, MXC-G and XC-G . . . . OBDVT
Needle position . . . . 3rd from top
Idle speed . . . . 1400 to 1500 rpm

450/525 SX (2003 and 2004)
Type . . . . Keihin FCR-MX 41
Mixture screw setting
   450 SX . . . . 1 turn out
   525 SX . . . . 1 1/2 turns out
Slide 15
Main jet 185
Main air jet 200
Idle jet
   450 SX 40
   525 SX 42
Idle air jet 100
Starter jet 85
Jet needle . . . . OBDTP
Needle position . . . . 4th from top
Idle speed . . . . 1400 to 1500 rpm

450 SX and SXS (2005 and 2006), 525 SX (2005 and 2006)
Type
   450 SX and SXS (2005) . . . . Keihin FCR-MX 4122A
   450 SX and SXS (2006) . . . . Keihin FCR-MX 4122B
   525 SX (2005) . . . . Keihin FCR-MX 4125A
   525 SX (2006) . . . . Keihin FCR-MX 4125C
Mixture screw setting
   450 SX and SXS (2005) . . . . 1 turn out
   450 SX and SXS (2006) . . . . 1 1/2 turn out
   525 SX . . . . 1 1/2 turns out
Slide 15
Main jet
   450/525 SX and SXS (2005) 185
   450/525 SX (2006) 185
   450 SXS (2006) 190
Main air jet 200
Idle jet
   450 SX and SXS (2005 and 2006) 40
   525 SX 42
Idle air jet 100
Starter jet 85
Jet needle . . . . OBDTP
Needle position . . . . 4th from top
Idle speed . . . . 1400 to 1500 rpm

450/525 SMR (2004), 450/540 SXS (2004)
Type . . . . Keihin FCR-MX 41
Mixture screw setting
   450 SMR and SXS . . . . 1 turn out
   525 SMR and 540 SXS . . . . 1 1/2 turns out
Slide 15
Main jet
   450/525 SMR and 450 SXS 185
   540 SXS 190
Main air jet 200
Idle jet
   450 SMR and SXS 40
   525 SMR and 540 SXS 42
Idle air jet 100
Starter jet 85
Jet needle . . . . OBDTP
Needle position . . . . 4th from top
Idle speed . . . . 1400 to 1500 rpm

Carburettor (continued)

450/525 SMR (2005), 450 SMR (2006), 560 SMR (2006), 540 SXS (2005)

Type
  450 SMR and 540 SXS (2005) .... Keihin FCR-MX 4122A
  450 SMR (2006) .... Keihin FCR-MX 4122B
  525 SMR... Keihin FCR-MX 4125A
  560 SMR... Keihin FCR-MX 4125E
Mixture screw setting
  450 SMR (2005) .... 1 turn out
  450 SMR (2006) .... 1 1/2 turn out
  525/560 SMR and 525 SXS .... 1 1/2 turns out
Slide 15
Main jet
  560 SMR.. 190
  All other models 185
Main air jet 200
Idle jet
  450 SMR.. 40
  525/560 SMR and 540 SXS 42
Idle air jet 100
Starter jet 85
Jet needle.. OBDTP
Needle position
  560 SMR.. 5th from top
  All other models .... 4th from top
Idle speed.. 1400 to 1500 rpm

Torque settings

Exhaust manifold bolts..................................... 10 Nm*
Exhaust pipe mounting bolt .... 25 Nm
Silencer mounting bolts .... 10 Nm
*Use thread locking compound Loctite 243

1 General information and precautions

General information

The fuel system consists of the fuel tank, fuel tap, filter, carburettor, fuel hose and control cables.

The fuel filter is part of the tap and is fitted inside the fuel tank.

The carburettor used on all models is a cable-operated, flat slide type Keihin, of which two variants are used.

For cold starting, a choke knob is mounted on the carburettor. In addition, SX and SXS models are equipped with a hot start knob. A throttle position sensor is mounted on the carburettor of 2004-on models – see Chapter 5 for details.

Air is drawn into the carburettor through an air filter element which is housed behind the left-hand side panel.

The exhaust system is either a two or three-piece assembly, depending upon year of manufacture, consisting of two-into-one header pipes and silencer.

Several fuel system service procedures are considered routine maintenance items and for that reason are included in Chapter 1.

Precautions

⚠ Warning: Petrol (gasoline) is extremely flammable, so take extra precautions when you work on any part of the fuel system. Don't smoke or allow open flames or bare light bulbs near the work area, and don't work in a garage where a natural gas-type appliance is present. If you spill any fuel on your skin, rinse it off immediately with soap and water. When you perform any kind of work on the fuel system, wear safety glasses and have a fire extinguisher suitable for a class B type fire (flammable liquids) on hand.

Always perform service procedures in a well-ventilated area to prevent a build-up of fumes.

Never work in a building containing a gas appliance with a pilot light, or any other form of naked flame. Ensure that there are no naked light bulbs or any sources of flame or sparks nearby.

Do not smoke (or allow anyone else to smoke) while in the vicinity of petrol (gasoline) or of components containing it. Remember the possible presence of vapour from these sources and move well clear before smoking.

Check all electrical equipment belonging to the house, garage or workshop where work is being undertaken (see the Safety first! section of this manual). Remember that certain electrical appliances such as drills, cutters etc. create sparks in the normal course of operation and must not be used near petrol (gasoline) or any component containing it. Again, remember the possible presence of fumes before using electrical equipment.

Always mop up any spilt fuel and safely dispose of the rag used.

Any stored fuel that is drained off during servicing work must be kept in sealed containers that are suitable for holding petrol (gasoline), and clearly marked as such; the containers themselves should be kept in a safe place. Note that this last point applies equally to the fuel tank if it is removed from the machine; also remember to keep its filler cap closed at all times.

Read the Safety first! section of this manual carefully before starting work.

2 Fuel tank and fuel tap

⚠ Warning: Refer to the precautions given in Section 1 before starting work.

Fuel tank

Removal

1 Make sure the fuel filler cap is secure and fuel tap is in the OFF position.

2.4 Disconnect the fuel tank breather hose

2.5 Fuel hose is secured by clip (arrowed)

2.6a Undo the tank mounting bolt (arrowed) . . .

2 Remove the seat (see Chapter 8).
3 Remove the radiator/fuel tank side panels (see Chapter 8).
4 Disconnect the breather hose from the filler cap **(see illustration)**.
5 Place a rag under the fuel tap to catch any residual fuel as the hose is detached, then release the clip securing the fuel hose to the tap and detach the hose **(see illustration)**.
6 Undo the tank mounting bolt, then ease the tank back off the support brackets and lift it off **(see illustrations)**.
7 Note the location of the rubber bushes on the central mounting bolt and the support brackets **(see illustration)**. If the bushes show signs of damage or deterioration, renew them **(see illustration)**.

Repair

8 All repairs to the fuel tank should be carried out by a professional who has experience in

2.6b . . . then ease the tank back off the support brackets . . .

2.6c . . . and lift it off

this critical and potentially dangerous work. Even after cleaning and flushing of the fuel system, explosive fumes can remain and ignite during repair of the tank.

Installation

9 Check that the tank mounting bushes are fitted, then carefully lower the tank into position, taking care not to obstruct the run of the throttle cables **(see illustration)**. Ensure that the tank locates onto the support brackets **(see illustration 2.6b)**.
10 Tighten the mounting bolt securely.
11 Connect the breather hose to the filler cap, ensuring the hose is routed inboard of the throttle cables **(see illustration)**.
12 Fit the fuel hose onto its union on the tap and secure it with the clip. Turn the tap ON and check for fuel leaks **(see illustration)**.
13 Install the remaining components in the reverse order of removal.

Fuel tap

14 The fuel tap is located on the underside of the fuel tank on the left-hand side **(see illustration 2.12)**. The tap has two positions on

2.7a Check the condition of the mounting bushes (arrowed)

2.7b Unscrew the bolts to remove the tank brackets

2.9 Take care not to trap the throttle cables (arrowed)

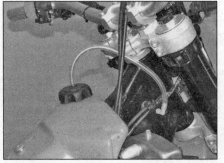

2.11 Note the routing of the breather hose

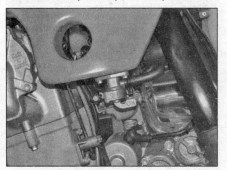

2.12 Check the operation of the fuel tap

SX models – OFF and ON. The tap has three positions – OFF, ON and RES (reserve) on EXC models. Only use the RES position when the main fuel supply has been used – the reserve range is extremely limited. Turn the tap to the ON position as soon as the tank is refilled.

15 The tap should not be removed from the tank unnecessarily to avoid the possibility of damaging the tap body O-ring or the filter. If the fuel tap-to-tank joint is leaking, first ensure that the tap retaining screws are tight. If leakage persists, drain the tank, remove the tap and fit a new O-ring (see below).

16 If fuel flow problems are experienced, first check that the breather hose in the tank cap is clear **(see illustration 2.11)**, then remove the tap and check the tap filter as follows.

17 Remove the fuel tank (see Steps 1 to 6). Drain any residual fuel into a suitable container, then undo the screws securing the tap and withdraw the tap assembly. Note which way round the tap is fitted.

18 Note the location of the tap O-ring and discard it as a new one must be fitted.

19 Allow the filter gauze to dry, then clean it with a soft brush or compressed air to remove all traces of dirt and sediment. Check the gauze for holes. If any are found, a new tap must be fitted as the filter is not available as a separate item. **Note:** *A damaged filter will allow dirt and sediment to block the tap internally and/or block the carburettor jets.*

20 Installation is the reverse of removal, noting the following:
- Fit a new O-ring to the tap body.
- Ensure that the tap is fitted the right way round **(see illustration 2.12)**.
- Take care not to over-tighten the tap mounting screws.

3 Throttle cables

⚠️ *Warning: Refer to the precautions given in Section 1 before proceeding.*

Removal

1 Remove the fuel tank (see Section 2).

2 Before removing the cables, make a careful note of their routing to ensure correct installation.

3 Pull back the boots on the adjusters at the carburettor end of both cables **(see illustration)**. The lower cable is the opening cable and the upper cable is the closing cable.

4 Undo the screw securing the cable pulley cover and lift the cover off **(see illustration)**. Note how the inner cable ends locate on the throttle pulley and how the nuts on the adjusters locate in the pulley housing **(see illustration)**.

5 Working on one cable at a time, loosen the adjuster locknut, then draw the adjuster out of the housing. Disconnect the inner cable end from the pulley.

6 To detach the cables from the throttle twistgrip, first pull back the boot on the twistgrip housing **(see illustration)**.

7 Undo the two bolts on the twistgrip

3.3 Pull back the boots on the cable adjusters

3.4a Remove the cable pulley cover

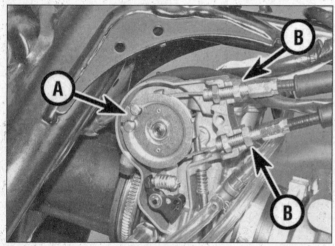

3.4b Note the location of the cable ends (A) and the adjuster locknuts (B)

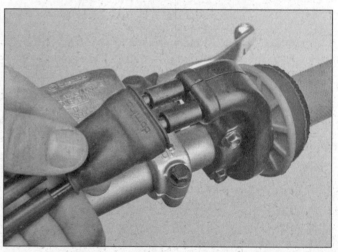

3.6 Pull back the boot on the twistgrip housing

3.7a Undo the two bolts . . .

housing and lift the rear half of the housing off **(see illustrations)**. Note how the inner cables locate on the twistgrip pulley **(see illustration)**. Remove the front half of the twistgrip housing.

8 Note how the cable elbows are locked together, then separate the elbows and detach the inner cable ends from the twistgrip pulley **(see illustrations)**.

9 Release the cables from any clips or ties and lift them off.

Installation

10 Installation is the reverse of removal, noting the following:
- The cables are nylon-lined so shouldn't require lubrication – however, if required, use a suitable lubricant (see Chapter 1).
- Make sure the cables are correctly routed. They must not interfere with any other component and should not be kinked or bent sharply. Turn the handlebars back and forth to make sure the cables don't cause the steering to bind.
- Operate the throttle to check that it opens and closes smoothly and freely.
- Check and adjust the cable freeplay (see Chapter 1).
- Start the engine and check that the idle speed does not rise as the handlebars are turned. If it does, a cable is routed incorrectly. Correct the problem before riding the machine.

4 Carburettor overhaul information

1 Poor engine performance, difficult starting, stalling, flooding and backfiring are all signs that carburettor maintenance may be required.
2 Keep in mind that many so-called carburettor problems can often be traced to mechanical faults within the engine or ignition system malfunctions. Check the air filter, fuel tap and filter, the intake manifold joints, and the ignition system and spark plug before assuming that the carburettor is at fault.
3 Most carburettor problems are caused by dirt particles, varnish and other deposits which build up in and eventually block the fuel jets and air passages inside the carburettor. Also, unless the carburettor is serviced at the specified intervals, gaskets and O-rings deteriorate and cause fuel and air leaks which lead to poor performance.

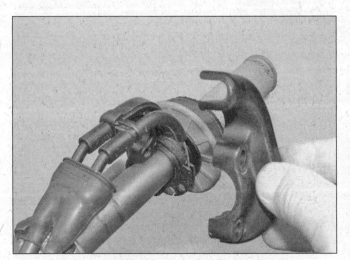

3.7b . . . and lift the rear half of the housing off

3.7c Note how the inner cables (arrowed) locate on the twistgrip pulley

3.8a Separate the cable elbows (arrowed) . . .

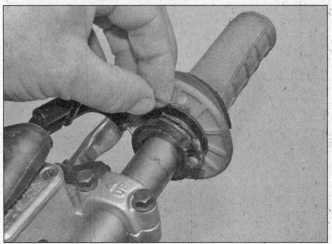

3.8b . . . and detach the cable ends form the pulley

5.2 Drain residual fuel from the float chamber

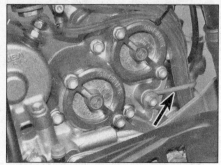

5.3a Note the location of the guide (arrowed)

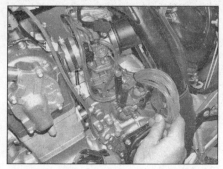

5.3b Draw the hoses out from behind the crankcases

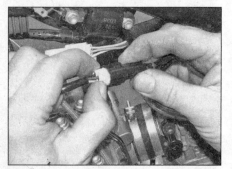

5.4 Disconnect the throttle position sensor connector

5.5 Disconnect the crankcase breather hose from the carburettor

4 When overhauling the carburettor, disassemble it completely and clean the parts thoroughly with a carburettor cleaning solvent. If available, blow through the fuel jets and air passages with compressed air to ensure they are clear. Once the cleaning process is complete, reassemble the carburettor using new gaskets and O-rings.

5 Before disassembling the carburettor, make sure you have the correct carburettor gasket set, some carburettor cleaner, a supply of clean rags, some means of blowing out the carburettor passages and a clean place to work.

5 Carburettor removal and installation

 Warning: Refer to the precautions given in Section 1 before starting work.

Removal

1 Remove the fuel tank (see Section 2).
2 Position a suitable container underneath the open end of the carburettor float chamber drain hose, then loosen the drain screw and drain out any residual fuel **(see illustration)**. Tighten the drain screw.
3 Note how the carburettor drain and breather hoses are routed behind the crankcase, then draw them free of the guide **(see illustrations)**.
4 Where fitted, trace the wiring from the throttle position sensor on the left-hand side of the carburettor body and disconnect it at the connector **(see illustration)**. Release the wiring from any ties.
5 Release the clip securing the crankcase breather hose to the union on the carburettor and pull the hose off **(see illustration)**.
6 If the carburettor is just being displaced and not removed from the machine completely, the throttle cables can be left attached. If the carburettor is being removed, follow the procedure in Section 3 and disconnect the cables from the throttle pulley and housing.
7 Loosen the clip securing the carburettor to the air filter housing **(see illustration)**.
8 Note how the peg on the carburettor body engages with the intake manifold, then loosen the clip securing the carburettor to the manifold **(see illustration)**.
9 Press the carburettor back into the air filter housing and disengage it from the intake manifold, then twist the carburettor body to the left and draw it away from the filter housing

5.7 Clip (arrowed) secures carburettor to the air filter housing

5.8 Note location of peg (A). Clip (B) secures carburettor to the intake manifold

5.9a Press the carburettor back (arrowed) . . .

5.9b . . . to disengage it from the intake manifold . . .

5.9c . . . then draw it off the air filter housing

(see illustrations). If the carburettor is just being displaced, secure it to the machine with a cable-tie to avoid it being damaged.
Caution: Stuff clean rag into the intake after removing the carburettor to prevent anything from falling inside.

Installation

10 Installation is the reverse of removal, noting the following:
● Make sure the carburettor is fully engaged with the air filter housing and intake manifold – it is important that there are no air leaks at these joints.
● Tighten the manifold and filter housing clips securely.
● Make sure all hoses are correctly routed and secured and not trapped or kinked.
● If applicable, ensure that the throttle position sensor wiring connector is secure.

● Refer to Section 3 for installation of the throttle cables. Check the operation of the cables and adjust them as necessary (see Chapter 1).
● Check the idle speed and adjust as necessary (see Chapter 1).

6 Carburettor overhaul

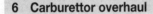

 Warning: Refer to the precautions given in Section 1 before starting work.
Note: *Two variants of Keihin carburettor are fitted to the machines covered in this manual – the FCR 35/39 (CR 35/39 early type) and the FCR-MX 37/39/41. An FCR-MX carburettor*

is used to illustrate the following procedures with any differences between the two variants detailed in the text.

Disassembly

1 Remove the carburettor (see Section 5).
2 Note the location of the drain hose and breather hoses on the carburettor body, and the hose guides that are secured by two of the float chamber screws **(see illustrations).** Release the clips securing the hoses and pull them off their unions **(see illustration).**
3 Release the clip securing the fuel hose and remove the hose **(see illustration).**
4 Undo the screws securing the carburettor top cover and lift the cover off, noting the location of the cover gasket **(see illustrations).**

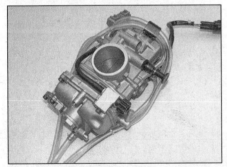

6.2a Note the location of the hoses on the carburettor body

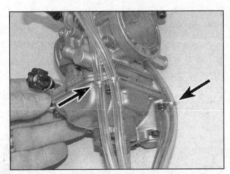

6.2b Note the location of the hose guides (arrowed)

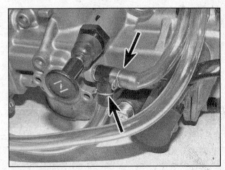

6.2c Release the clips securing the hoses

6.3 Disconnect the fuel hose from its union

6.4a Undo the screws (arrowed) . . .

6.4b . . . and lift off the top cover

6.5 Note the location of the plug (arrowed)

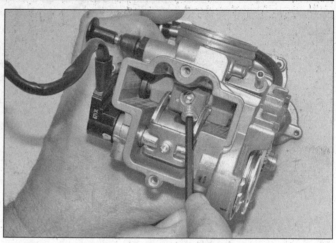

6.6a Unscrew the plug . . .

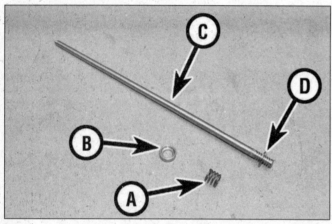

6.6b . . . and remove the spring (A), spring cup (B) and needle (C).
Note the position of the clip (D)

6.7 Undo the screw on the throttle slide arm

5 Note the location of the plug in the top of the throttle slide (see illustration).

6 On FCR carbs, unscrew the plug and carefully remove the needle; on FCR-MX carbs, carefully remove the spring, spring cup and needle (see illustrations). Note the location of the clip on the upper end of the needle but do not remove it.

7 Undo the screw securing the throttle slide arm to the shaft of the cable pulley see illustration).

8 On FCR carbs, pull the cable pulley away from the body and turn it to allow the slide to be lifted out. Note how the two small rollers on the ends of the throttle slide arm locate in the top of the slide.

9 On FCR-MX carbs, turn the cable pulley to allow the slide to be lifted out see illustration). Note how the two small rollers on the ends of the throttle slide arm locate in the top of the slide (see illustration).

10 Undo the screws securing the accelerator pump cover and lift the cover off, noting the location of the spring (see

6.9a Lift out the throttle slide

6.9b Note the small rollers (arrowed) on the throttle slide arm

6.10a Undo the screws (arrowed) . . .

6.10b . . . and lift the cover off, noting the location of the spring

6.10c Note the O-ring in the cover (arrowed) . . .

6.10d . . . and in the float chamber body (arrowed)

illustrations). Note the location of the O-ring in the cover and the O-ring in the body of the float chamber **(see illustrations).** Lift out the accelerator pump diaphragm **(see illustration).**

11 Note how the support bracket for the idle speed adjuster is retained by the float chamber screw(s) **(see illustration).** Undo the screws securing the float chamber and lift it off **(see illustration).** On FCR carbs, detach the upper end of the accelerator pump rod from the actuating arm and keep the rod with the float chamber – the rod should be retained by its boot. On FCR-MX carbs,

the accelerator pump rod should stay in the carburettor body.

12 On FCR carbs, lift out the plastic guard from around the main jet. Undo the screw securing the float pin, then lift out the float and pin together with the float valve.

13 On FCR-MX carbs, press out the float pin,

6.10e Lift out the accelerator pump diaphragm

6.11a Note how the bracket (arrowed) is attached

6.11b Lift off the float chamber. Note the accelerator pump rod (arrowed)

6.13a Press out the float pin . . .

6.13b . . . then lift out the float together
with the float valve (arrowed)

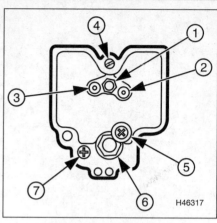

6.14 Component location –
FCR carburettor

1 Main jet and needle jet
2 Idle jet
3 Starter jet
4 Mixture screw
5 Float valve retaining screw
6 Float valve
7 Float pin retaining screw

then lift out the float together with the float valve **(see illustrations)**.

14 On FCR carbs, unscrew the main jet from the needle jet, then unscrew the idle jet, starter jet and needle jet **(see illustration)**.

15 On FCR-MX carbs, unscrew the main jet from the needle jet, then unscrew the idle jet, starter jet and needle jet **(see illustrations)**. Lift out the plastic guard **(see illustration)**.

16 Carefully turn the mixture screw in all

the way and note the number of turns **(see illustration)**. **Note:** *This should be the same as the base setting shown in the specifications at the beginning of this Chapter, although it may have been altered to suit specific riding conditions – if in doubt, consult a KTM dealer.* Now unscrew the mixture screw and remove it together with the O-ring, washer and spring **(see illustration)**.

6.15a Unscrew the main jet . . .

6.15b . . . the idle jet . . .

6.15c . . . the starter jet . . .

6.15d . . . and the needle jet

> **HAYNES HiNT** To record the mixture screw's current setting, turn the screw in until it seats lightly, counting the number of turns necessary to achieve this, then unscrew it fully. On installation, turn the screw in until it seats, then back it out the number of turns you've recorded.

17 On an FCR carb equipped with a throttle position sensor (TPS), undo the single screw securing the sensor's mounting plate to the

6.15e Lift out the plastic guard

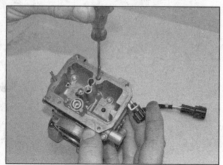

6.16a Note the mixture screw setting

6.16b Note the O-ring, washer and spring
on the mixture screw

6.18a Location of the throttle position sensor – FCR-MX shown (arrowed)

6.18b Undo the screw to remove the fuel union

carburettor body and lift the TPS off, noting the location of the spacer behind the plate. Do not loosen the two screws securing the TPS to the mounting plate, otherwise the TPS will require adjusting after reassembly (see Chapter 5). Undo the screw securing the fuel union keeper, noting the location of the spacer behind the keeper. Draw the union out of the carburettor body, noting the location of the O-ring.

18 On an FCR-MX carb equipped with a throttle position sensor (TPS), do not remove the sensor unless it is faulty and a new one is going to be fitted. If required, undo the screws securing the TPS and lift it off **(see illustration)**. Undo the screw securing the fuel union, then draw the union out of the carburettor body, noting the location of the O-rings **(see illustration)**.

19 Unscrew the choke mechanism from the carburettor body **(see illustration)**. If fitted, unscrew the hot start mechanism from the carburettor body.

20 Before removing the idle speed adjuster, note the location of the end of the adjuster against the stop on the throttle cable pulley

6.19 Unscrew the choke mechanism

6.20 Pulley stop (arrowed) rests against end of idle speed adjuster

(see illustration). Unscrew the idle speed adjuster, noting the position of the washer and spring.

Cleaning

Caution: Use only a petroleum-based solvent for carburettor cleaning. Don't use caustic cleaners. If a cleaning solvent is going to be used, fit new O-rings after the cleaning process.

21 Submerge the metal components in carburettor cleaning solvent for approximately thirty minutes, or longer if the directions recommend it **(see illustration)**.

22 After the carburettor body has soaked long enough for the cleaner to loosen and dissolve most of the varnish and other deposits, use a nylon-bristled brush to remove the stubborn deposits. Rinse it again, then dry it with compressed air **(see illustrations)**.

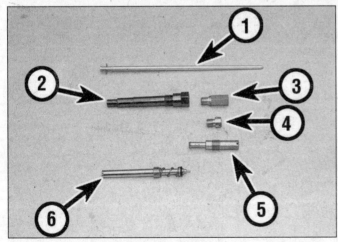

6.21 Carburettor components
1 Needle 2 Needle jet 3 Main jet 4 Starter jet 5 Idle jet 6 Mixture screw

6.22 Clean deposits off thoroughly, particularly in the float chamber and the gasket groove (arrowed)

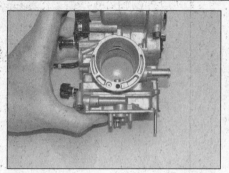

6.23 Blow air through the passages in the carburettor body

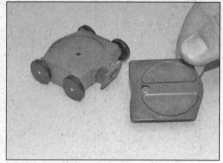

6.25 Inspect the throttle slide and slide plate

6.26 Ensure the throttle slide moves freely in the carburettor body

23 If available, use compressed air to blow out all the fuel jets and the air passages in the carburettor body, not forgetting the passages in the carburettor intake and accelerator pump cover **(see illustration)**.
Caution: Never clean the jets or passages with a piece of wire or a drill bit, as they will be enlarged, causing the fuel and air metering rates to be upset.

Inspection

24 Check the carburettor body, float chamber and top cover for cracks, distorted sealing surfaces and other damage. If any defects are found, renew the faulty component.
25 Check the throttle slide and slide plate for wear and score marks **(see illustration)**. Check that the rollers turn freely and have not worn flat on the edge. Note that a new slide and plate should be fitted at the specified service interval.

26 Insert the throttle slide in the carburettor body and check that it moves up-and-down smoothly without binding. Ensure that the small rollers on the throttle slide arm turn freely **(see illustration)**.
27 Check the needle for straightness by rolling it on a flat surface such as a piece of glass. Fit a new needle if it's bent or if the tip is worn. Note the position of the clip on the old needle and fit a new clip to the new needle. Note that a new needle and needle jet should be fitted at the specified service interval on 2006-on models.
28 Check the tip of the mixture screw and the spring for wear or damage. Fit a new O-ring and renew the screw or spring if necessary **(see illustration 6.16b)**.
29 Inspect the tip of the float valve and the valve seat in the carburettor body **(see illustration)**. If either has grooves or scratches in it, or is in any way worn, they

must be renewed as a set. **Note:** *A worn float needle valve or valve seat will not be able to shut off the fuel supply sufficiently to prevent carburettor flooding and excessive use of fuel.* On some carburettors, the valve seat is retained by a screw, on others it is a press fit in the carburettor body **(see illustration)**. Pull the old seat out carefully with needle nosed pliers, then press the new seat in until it is level with its housing – if an O-ring is fitted to the seat, don't forget to renew it. If fitted, don't forget to tighten the retaining screw securely.
30 Check the float for damage. This will usually be apparent by the presence of fuel inside the float. If the float is damaged, it must be renewed.
31 Inspect the accelerator pump diaphragm for cracking and splits, and ensure that the spring is not damaged **(see illustration)**. Fit new components if necessary.
32 Check the operation of the choke and hot start mechanisms **(see illustration)**. Ensure that the spring is not broken and that the plunger is neither worn or scored.
33 Check that the throttle cable pulley turns smoothly and snaps shut under spring pressure. To renew the spring, first note how the ends of the spring locate, then draw the pulley shaft out of the carburettor body. Install the new spring, making sure it is fitted the correct way round, then insert the pulley shaft and locate the spring between the carburettor body and the pulley. Note that if a TPS is fitted, the peg on the left-hand end of the shaft locates in the groove inside the TPS.

Reassembly and float level check

Note: *New O-rings and gaskets are all included in the carburettor rebuild kit. Use all of the new parts, regardless of the apparent condition of the old ones. Do not over-tighten the carburettor jets and screws as they are easily damaged.*
34 Fit the spring and washer to the end of the idle speed adjuster and install the adjuster. Ensure that the end of the adjuster aligns with the stop on the cable pulley as noted on disassembly **(see illustration 6.20)**.
35 Screw the choke mechanism and, if fitted, the hot start mechanism into the carburettor body **(see illustration 6.19)**. Check that the

6.29a Inspect the tip of the float valve carefully . . .

6.29b . . . and the valve seat (arrowed) in the carburettor body

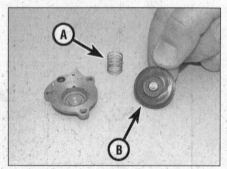

6.31 Inspect the accelerator pump spring (A) and diaphragm (B)

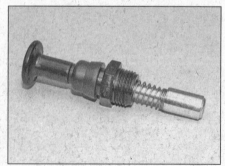

6.32 Check the choke and hot start mechanisms for wear and damage

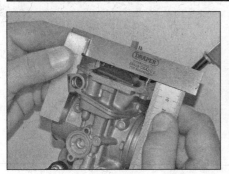

6.45 Checking the float height – FCR carbs

6.54a Insert the needle into the throttle slide . . .

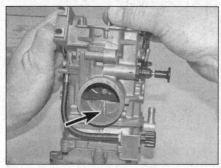

6.54b . . . and check that it enters the needle jet (arrowed)

plungers move smoothly and lock in the ON position.

36 On FCR carbs, fit a new O-ring onto the fuel union. Lubricate the O-ring with a smear of clean oil, then press the union into place and secure it with the keeper and screw.

37 On FCR-MX carbs, fit three new O-rings onto the fuel union. Lubricate the O-rings with a smear of clean oil, then press the union into place and secure it with the screw **(see illustration 6.18b)**.

38 Assemble the spring, washer and new O-ring on the mixture screw, then install the screw and adjust it to the setting as noted on removal (see Step 16).

39 If not already done, install the float valve seat (see Step 29).

40 On FCR-MX carbs, install the plastic guard **(see illustration 6.15e)**.

41 Install the needle jet, starter jet and idle jet, then install the main jet (see Steps 14 and 15 as appropriate).

42 On FCR carbs, install the float pin, then hook the float valve onto the float tab. Position the float assembly in the carburettor, making sure the valve enters its seat, and secure it with the screw.

43 On FCR-MX carbs, hook the float valve onto the float tab, then position the float assembly in the carburettor and secure it with the pin **(see illustration 6.13a)**.

44 The carburettor float height should be checked at this point. Hold the carburettor upside down, then tilt it so that the float tab is just resting on the end of the needle, but not compressing it.

45 On FCR carbs, use a set-square and ruler to measure the distance between the bottom of the float and the float chamber gasket face **(see illustration)**. The float height should be 9 mm. If the height differs from the specification, check that the needle is not worn and that the seat is clean. If the needle and seat are good, adjust the height by carefully bending the tab.

46 On FCR-MX carbs, check the alignment of the float chamber gasket face and the moulding line on the side of the float – they should be parallel. If the height differs from the specification, check that the needle is not worn and that the seat is clean. If the needle and seat are good, adjust the height by carefully bending the tab.

47 On FCR carbs, fit the plastic guard around the main jet.

48 Fit a new gasket onto the float chamber, making sure it is seated properly in its groove **(see illustration 6.22)**.

49 On FCR carbs, ensure that the boot for the accelerator pump rod is installed on the float chamber. Attach the upper end of the rod to the actuating arm, then align the float chamber with the carburettor body, ensuring that rod enters the boot. Check that the float chamber is correctly seated all the way round. Align the bracket for the idle speed adjuster with the carburettor body and install the float chamber fixing screws

50 On FCR-MX carbs, align the float chamber with the carburettor body and the accelerator pump rod **(see illustration 6.11b)**. Check that the float chamber is correctly seated all the way round. Align the bracket for the idle speed adjuster with the carburettor body and install the float chamber fixing screws **(see illustration 6.11a)**.

51 Install new O-rings in the accelerator pump cover and the carburettor body **(see illustrations 6.10c and d)**. Install the accelerator pump diaphragm with the writing facing outwards, and the spring, then fit the cover and secure it with the screws **(see illustrations 6.10b and a)**

52 On FCR carbs, turn the throttle slide arm to allow the throttle slide to be inserted into the carburettor body – note that the slide plate should face the engine side of the carburettor. Locate the rollers on the throttle slide arm in the slots at the top of the slide, then check that the slide moves freely up and down inside the carburettor body. Align the screw hole in the cable pulley shaft with the slot in the centre of the slide arm. Apply a drop of Loctite243 to the screw and install it finger-tight. Push the cable pulley towards the body and push the slide arm towards the pulley, then tighten the screw – the screw should be in the centre of the slot in the slide arm. Turn the cable pulley to check that the slide moves freely up and down inside the carburettor body.

53 On FCR-MX carbs, turn the throttle slide arm to allow the throttle slide to be inserted into the carburettor body – note that the slide plate should face the engine side of the

carburettor **(see illustration 6.9a)**. Locate the rollers on the throttle slide arm in the slots at the top of the slide, then check that the slide moves freely up and down inside the carburettor body. Align the screw hole in the cable pulley shaft with the slot in the centre of the slide arm. Apply a drop of Loctite 243 to the screw and tighten it securely **(see illustration 6.7)**. Turn the cable pulley to check that the slide moves freely up and down inside the carburettor body.

54 Check that the clip is secure on the upper end of the needle. The clip should be located in the appropriate groove in the needle (see Specifications at the beginning of this Chapter). Insert the needle into the throttle slide, ensuring that it enters the top of the needle jet **(see illustrations)**. On FCR carbs, install the plug and tighten it securely; on FCR-MX carbs, install the spring cup and spring, then tighten the plug securely **(see illustration 6.6a)**.

55 Fit a new gasket onto the top cover, making sure it is correctly seated, then install the cover and tighten the screws securely **(see illustrations 6.4b and a)**.

56 Install the fuel hose and secure it with its clip **(see illustration 6.3)**.

57 Install the drain and breather hoses and the hose guides, then secure the hoses with the clips **(see illustrations 6.2a, b and c)**.

58 On FCR carbs, align the throttle position sensor (TPS) with the carburettor body so that the peg on the end of the cable pulley shaft engages in the slot in the centre of the TPS. Fit the spacer behind the mounting plate, then install the screw and tighten it securely. If required, follow the procedure in Chapter 5 to check and adjust the TPS after the carburettor has been installed on the bike.

59 On FCR-MX carbs, if the throttle position sensor (TPS) has been removed, align the TPS with the carburettor body so that the peg on the end of the cable pulley shaft engages in the slot in the centre of the TPS. Install the mounting screws and tighten them temporarily – the TPS must be adjusted after the carburettor has been installed on the bike (see Chapter 5).

60 Install the carburettor (see Section 5).

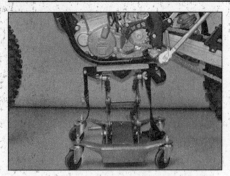

7.1 Supporting the motorcycle on an auxiliary stand

7.4a Spring secures silencer to the header pipe (arrowed)

7.4b Considerable force is required to unhook the spring

7.5a Silencer is retained by two screws (arrowed)

7.5b Note the location of the screw clips (arrowed)

7 Exhaust system

Silencer

1 Support the motorcycle securely in an upright position using an auxiliary stand (see illustration).

2 On 2000 to 2003 models, first remove the right-hand number plate panel (see Chapter 8).

3 On later models, if required, remove the seat and rear mudguard unit (see Chapter 8).

4 The silencer is secured to the exhaust header pipe by springs – there are two springs on 2000 to 2003 models and one spring on later models (see illustration). If necessary, have an assistant steady the bike, then unhook the springs carefully (see illustration).

 Warning: Considerable force is required to unhook the springs – use either an exhaust spring puller or the method shown to avoid damaging components or causing injury to yourself.

5 Loosen the two bolts securing the silencer to the rear sub-frame, noting the location of the clips on the rear of the frame brackets (see illustrations).

6 Support the silencer, then remove the bolts and draw the silencer off the end of the header pipe.

7 Note the location of the mounting bush and two large shouldered washers on both of the silencer mounting brackets (see illustration). If the bushes are worn or deteriorated, renew them.

8 If required, follow the procedure in Steps 31 to 45 to renew the silencer packing.

9 Check that the spring loops are firmly attached to the silencer and header pipe, and that the loops have not been worn by the springs. Check that the springs are neither stretched nor sprained – if a spring is not a tight fit, use a new one on reassembly.

10 Prior to installation, ensure that the screw clips are in position on the frame brackets (see illustration 7.5b).

11 Fit the silencer over the end of the header pipe. Ensure that the shouldered washers are in place on both the silencer mounting bushes, then install the mounting bolts finger-tight (see illustration).

12 Using the method employed on removal,

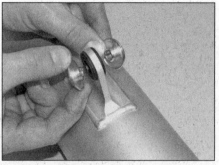

7.7 Note the mounting bush and two large shouldered washers on the mounting brackets

7.11 Install the bolts and shouldered washers

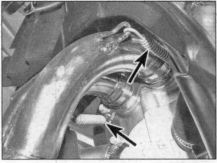

7.16a Bolt (arrowed) secures header pipes to frame at front

7.16b Springs (arrowed) secure pipes to manifold

7.16c Springs (arrowed) secure front to rear exhaust sections

install the silencer-to-pipe springs **(see illustration 7.4b)**.

13 Tighten the mounting bolts to the torque setting specified at the beginning of this Chapter.

14 Install the remaining components in the reverse order of removal, then run the engine and check that there are no exhaust gas leaks.

Header pipe(s)

15 Remove the silencer (see Steps 1 to 6).
16 On 2000 to 2003 models, the header pipe is in two sections – remove the front section first. Undo the mounting bolt securing the front section to the frame, then note the above and unhook the springs securing the pipes to the exhaust manifold **(see illustrations)**. Next, unhook the springs securing the front section to the rear section and draw the front section off **(see illustration)**. Undo the mounting bolt securing the rear pipe section to the frame and lift it off **(see illustration 7.17)**.
17 On 2004 to 2007 models, first undo the mounting bolt securing the header pipe to the frame **(see illustration)**. Next, note the above and unhook the springs securing the pipes to the exhaust manifold and draw the header pipe off **(see illustration 7.16b)**. Note: *On the machine used to illustrate this procedure, there was insufficient clearance for the rear end of the header pipe to pass between the rear shock absorber and the frame. Consequently, it was necessary to remove the rear wheel (see Chapter 7) and rear shock (see Chapter 6) before the pipe could be lifted off* .
18 If required, undo the bolts securing

7.17 Mounting bolt (arrowed) secures header pipe to the frame at rear

7.18 Undo the bolts (arrowed) to remove the exhaust manifold

the exhaust manifold to the cylinder head and remove the manifold and gasket **(see illustration)**. Discard the gasket as a new one must be fitted.
19 Ensure the mating surfaces of the manifold and cylinder head are clean, and scrape any carbon deposits from the inside of the manifold
20 Note the location of the mounting bush and two large shouldered washers on the header pipe mounting brackets **(see illustration 7.25b)**. If the bushes are worn or deteriorated, renew them.
21 Follow the procedure in Step 9 and check the springs and spring loops.
22 On installation, fit a new gasket onto the manifold. Clean the threads of the mounting bolts and apply a drop of the specified locking compound, then tighten the bolts to the torque setting specified at the beginning of this Chapter.

23 Ensure that the screw clips are in position on the frame brackets. Ensure that the shouldered washers are in place on the mounting bushes.
24 On 2000 to 2003 models, install the rear header pipe section and tighten the mounting bolt section finger-tight. Align the front pipe section with the rear section and the manifold, then push it firmly into place – ensure that both front pipes are pushed as far into the manifold as possible, then install the front mounting bolt finger-tight **(see illustration 7.16a)**.
25 On 2004 to 2007 models, align the header pipe with the manifold and the mounting bracket, then push the pipes as far into the manifold as possible **(see illustration)**. Install the mounting bolt finger-tight **(see illustration)**.
26 Using the method employed on removal, install the pipe-to-manifold springs **(see illustration)**.

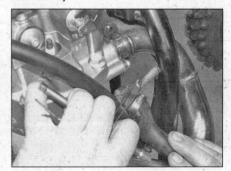

7.25a Push the pipes as far into the manifold as possible

7.25b Don't forget to fit the large washer on the pipe-to-frame bolt

7.26 Installing the pipe-to-manifold springs

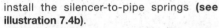
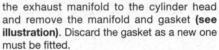

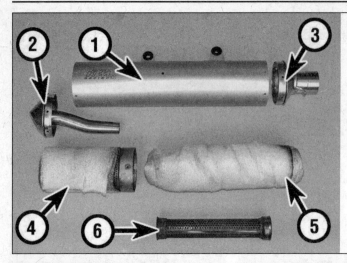

7.31 Silencer components

1 Silencer body
2 End cap
3 Front cap
4 Rear mat and baffle
5 Glass fibre packing
6 Inner pipe

27 On 2000 to 2003 models, tighten the front mounting bolt to the torque setting specified at the beginning of this Chapter.
28 On 2004 to 2007 models, tighten the mounting bolt to the torque setting specified at the beginning of this Chapter.
29 On 2000 to 2003 models, ensure that the front and rear pipe sections are pushed firmly together. Install the springs joining the two sections together, then tighten the rear mounting bolt to the specified torque setting.
30 Install the silencer (see Steps 11 to 14).

Silencer packing and spark arrester

Special tool: *A riveting gun is required for this procedure.*

Removal

31 The silencer packing should be renewed at the specified service interval, or if it becomes saturated with water. KTM advise that the main glass fibre packing requires renewal more often than the rear mat **(see illustration)**. **Note:** *The silencers fitted to SX and XC models contain the main glass fibre packing only.*
32 Remove the silencer (see above).
33 Wrap adhesive tape around the front end of the silencer body to avoid damaging the surface during this procedure **(see illustration)**.
34 Note the alignment between the spring loop(s) on the front cap and the silencer body, then drill out the heads of the rivets securing the front cap and pull it off **(see illustrations)**. Note the O-ring fitted to the front cap and discard it as a new one must be fitted.
35 Pull out the packing together with the inner pipe **(see illustration)**. Note which way round the inner pipe is fitted – a slot in the rear rim of the pipe locates on a tab on the baffle plate.
36 To remove the rear mat, note the alignment between the end cap and silencer body, then drill out the heads of the rivets securing the end cap and pull it off **(see illustration)**. Note the O-ring fitted to the end cap and discard it as a new one must be fitted **(see illustration)**.
37 Undo the screw securing the baffle, then

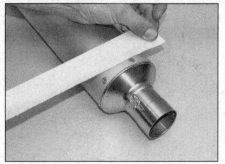

7.33 Protect the silencer body with adhesive tape

7.34a Drill out the rivets . . .

7.34b . . . and pull the front cap off

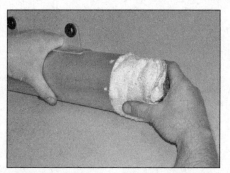

7.35 Pull out the packing and inner pipe

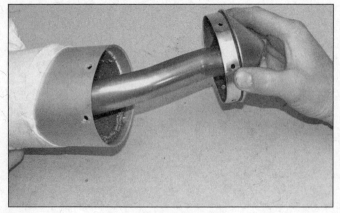

7.36a Pull off the end cap . . .

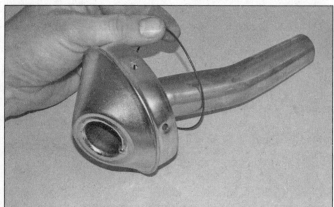

7.36b . . . and discard the old O-ring

7.37a Undo the screw . . .

7.37b . . . to remove the baffle and rear mat

draw the baffle out – the rear mat is wrapped around the baffle **(see illustrations)**.

Installation

38 Use a stiff wire brush to remove the carbon from the inside of the silencer and from the surface of the inner pipe. If removed, clean the carbon off the baffle. On some American market models, a spark arrester is fitted inside the silencer end cap – if not already done, follow the procedure in Step 36 to remove the end cap and scrape out any carbon deposits. Follow the procedure in Step 40 to install the end cap.

39 To install the rear mat, first wrap a fresh piece of mat around the baffle **(see illustration 7.37b)**. Align the screw hole in the baffle with the corresponding hole in the silencer, then insert the baffle into the rear end of the silencer **(see illustration)**. Using a suitable length of wood (a piece of broom handle is ideal), push the baffle into the silencer until the screw holes align. Tighten the fixing screw **(see illustration 7.37a)**.

40 Fit a new O-ring onto the end cap, then install it in the silencer, noting how the pipe on the cap is offset from the hole in the baffle plate **(see illustration)**. Ensure that the O-ring is located against the shoulder on the end cap and press the cap in until the rivet holes align **(see illustration)**. Secure the end cap with a new set of rivets **(see illustration)**.

41 Before the new packing can be fitted, the inner pipe must be pushed up inside it. To facilitate this, make up a tool that will prevent the front edge of the pipe catching on the inside of the packing (see **Tool Tip** overleaf).

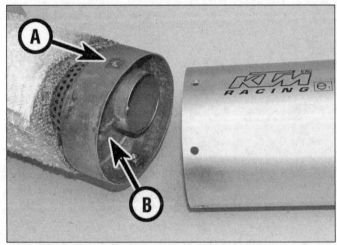

7.39 Insert the baffle into the rear of the silencer. Note the screw hole (A) and tab (B)

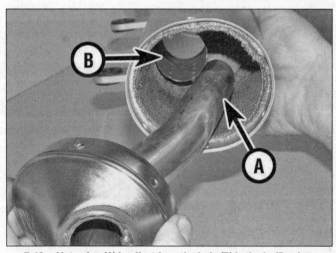

7.40a Note pipe (A) is offset from the hole (B) in the baffle plate

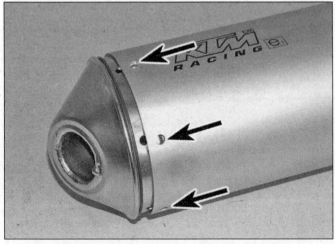

7.40b Install end cap so that rivet holes (arrowed) align

7.40c Secure the end cap with a new set of rivets

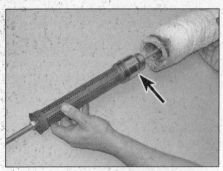

7.42a Insert the inner pipe into the roll of packing. The large socket (arrowed) prevents the pipe catching inside the packing

7.42b Once the inner pipe is in place, remove the installation tool

7.43 Align the inner pipe with the hole in the baffle plate

TOOL TiP *A suitable tool for installing the inner pipe in the packing can be made from a length of threaded bar, a large flat washer, two nuts and a suitably-sized socket. See illustrations 7.42a and b.*

42 Open up the roll of packing and carefully insert the inner pipe in from one end **(see illustration)**. Ease the inner pipe all the way in, then remove the installation tool **(see illustration)**.

43 Insert the inner pipe and packing into the silencer, slotted rear end of the inner pipe first – don't forget to align the slot with the tab on the baffle plate – then carefully ease the packing in **(see illustration 7.39)**. The hole in the baffle plate is offset from the centre of the silencer – when the inner pipe contacts the baffle plate, lever the inner pipe into alignment with the hole, then push the pipe all the way in **(see illustration)**.

44 Press the packing down around the front end of the inner pipe, fit a new O-ring to the front cap and install the front cap **(see illustrations)**.

45 Make sure that the alignment between the spring loop(s) on the front cap and the silencer body is correct and that the rivet holes align, then secure the cap with a new set of rivets **(see illustration)**.

7.44a Press the packing down around the front end of the inner pipe . . .

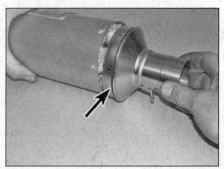

7.44b . . . then install the front cap. Note the O-ring (arrowed)

7.45 Secure the front cap with a new set of rivets

Chapter 5
Ignition system

Contents

Degrees of difficulty

| Easy, suitable for novice with little experience | 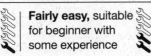 | Fairly easy, suitable for beginner with some experience | | Fairly difficult, suitable for competent DIY mechanic | | Difficult, suitable for experienced DIY mechanic | | Very difficult, suitable for expert DIY or professional | |

Specifications

Spark plug
Type and gap .... see Chapter 1

Ignition source coil
Coil resistance
  4K-3A stator.................................... 26 ± 5.2 ohms
  4K-3B stator.................................... 15 ± 3.0 ohms

Ignition pick-up coil
Coil resistance .... 100 ± 20.0 ohms
Air gap .... 0.75 mm

Ignition HT coil
Primary circuit resistance............................. 0.30 ± 0.05 ohms
Secondary circuit resistance .... 6.3 ± 1.25 K-ohms

Throttle position sensor
Resistance .... 4.0 to 6.0 K-ohms at 20°C
Resistance range .... Zero to 5.0 ± 1.0 K-ohms

Torque settings
Alternator stator mounting bolts
  4K-3A stator.................................... 6 Nm*
  4K-3B stator.................................... 10 Nm*
Pick-up coil bolts .... 10 Nm
Alternator cover screws .... 10 Nm
*Use thread locking compound Loctite 234

1 General information

All models covered in this manual are fitted with a fully transistorised capacitor discharge ignition (CDI) system which, due to its lack of mechanical parts is totally maintenance-free. The system comprises a source coil, rotor, pick-up coil, CDI unit and ignition HT coil (refer to the *Wiring Diagrams* at the end of Chapter 9 for details).

The ignition source coil is integral with the alternator stator. Two types of stator are fitted to the machines covered in this manual. Early SX models have the 4K-3A stator and all other models have the 4K-3B type. The 4K-3A stator does not feature charging coils (see *Wiring Diagrams*).

On 2000 and 2001 400/520 EXC models, the system includes a capacitor. A throttle position sensor is fitted to 2004-on models.

The ignition trigger, which is on the alternator rotor, magnetically operates the pick-up coil as the crankshaft rotates. The pick-up coil sends a signal to the CDI unit which then supplies the HT coil with the power necessary to produce a spark at the plug.

The CDI unit incorporates an electronic advance system controlled by signals generated by the trigger, the pick-up coil, and where fitted, the throttle position sensor. There is no provision for adjusting the ignition timing on these machines.

Because of their nature, the individual ignition system components can be checked but not repaired. If ignition system troubles occur, and the faulty component can be isolated, the only cure for the problem is to replace the part with a new one.

Note: Keep in mind that most electrical parts, once purchased, cannot be returned. To avoid unnecessary expense, make very sure the faulty component has been positively identified before buying a replacement part and, if possible, have a suspect component checked by a KTM dealer.

2 Ignition system fault finding

⚠️ *Warning: The energy levels in electronic systems can be very high. On no account should the ignition be switched on whilst the plug or plug cap is being held – shocks from the HT circuit can be most unpleasant. Secondly, it is vital that the engine is not turned over with the plug cap removed, and that the plug is soundly earthed when the system is checked for sparking. The ignition system components can be seriously damaged if the HT circuit becomes isolated.*

1 As no means of adjustment is available, any failure of the system can be traced either to the failure of a system component or to a simple wiring fault. Of the two possibilities, the latter is by far the most likely. In the event of failure, check the system in a logical fashion.

2 On EXC models, before checking that the ignition system is producing a good spark at the plug, ensure that the battery is fully charged and that the main fuse is good (see Chapter 9). On 2000 and 2001 400/520 EXC models, the capacitor should provide sufficient power for the ignition system in the event of a discharged battery (see Section 4).

3 Follow the procedure in Chapter 1, Section 7, and check the spark plug and the spark plug cap.

4 If the ignition system fails to produce a satisfactory spark, refer to the following check list.

5 Ignition faults can be divided into two categories, namely those where the ignition system has failed completely, and those which are due to a partial failure. The likely faults are listed below, starting with the most probable source of failure. Work through the list systematically, referring to the subsequent sections for full details of the necessary checks and tests.

- Loose, corroded or damaged wiring connections; broken or shorted wiring between any of the component parts of the ignition system (see Wiring Diagrams, Chapter 9).
- Faulty ignition kill switch (see Chapter 9).
- Faulty ignition HT coil.
- Faulty capacitor.
- Faulty ignition source coil.
- Faulty pick-up coil.
- Faulty CDI unit.

If the above checks don't reveal the cause of the problem, have the ignition system tested by a KTM dealer.

3 Ignition HT coil

Check

1 Remove the fuel tank (see Chapter 4). Disconnect the battery negative (-ve) lead (see Chapter 9).

2 The HT coil is located underneath the frame top tube (see illustration).

3 Check the HT coil, HT lead and spark plug cap for cracks, abrasion and other damage. Make sure the plug cap is screwed firmly onto the HT lead. Make sure the wiring connections to the HT coil are clean and secure. **Note:** *The HT lead is integral with the coil and cannot be renewed separately.*

4 The primary and secondary circuit resistance should be measured with a multimeter. **Note:** *KTM advise that the specified resistance values are standard values, and that the actual resistance readings obtained need only match these approximately for the coil to be in good working order.*

5 Pull the cap off the spark plug and disconnect the primary circuit electrical connector.

6 To check the condition of the primary windings, set the meter to the ohms x 1 scale. Measure the resistance between the blue/white wire terminal on the coil and the coil mounting which goes to earth (see illustration).

3.2 Location of the ignition HT coil (arrowed)

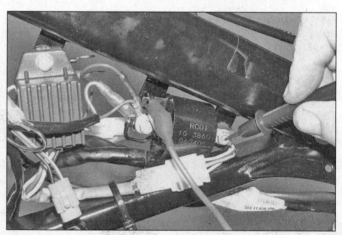

3.6 Checking the coil primary windings

3.8 Checking the coil secondary windings

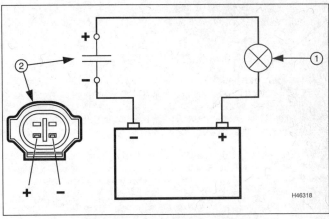

4.7 Test connections for the capacitor

1 Test light   2 Capacitor wiring connector

7 If the reading obtained differs significantly from the range shown in the Specifications at the beginning of this Chapter, it is likely that the coil is defective and must be renewed.

8 To check the condition of the secondary windings, set the meter to the K-ohms scale. Measure the resistance between the plug terminal inside the spark plug cap and the blue/white wire terminal on the coil **(see illustration)**.

9 If the reading obtained differs significantly from the range shown in the Specifications, unscrew the plug cap from the HT lead and measure the resistance between the core wire of the HT lead and the blue/white wire terminal. If the reading obtained is still not within the specified range, it is likely that the coil is defective and must be renewed. If the reading is good, check the resistance of the plug cap and fit a new plug cap if necessary (see Chapter 1, Section 7).

Removal and installation

10 Remove the fuel tank (see Chapter 4). Disconnect the battery negative (-ve) lead (see Chapter 9).

11 Disconnect the electrical connector(s) from the coil and disconnect the HT lead from the spark plug.

12 Unscrew the bolts securing the coil and remove it. Note the location of the earth wire secured by the mounting bolt. Note that the plug cap is a separate item and may not be supplied with the new coil.

13 Installation is the reverse of removal. Make sure that the wiring connector(s), including the earth wire, are clean and securely connected. Make sure the plug cap is screwed firmly onto the HT lead.

4 Capacitor

1 On 2000 and 2001 400/520 EXC models, the capacitor provides power for the ignition system when the battery is discharged or when the battery has been removed.

2 Remove the fuel tank (see Chapter 4). Disconnect the battery negative (-ve) lead (see Chapter 9).

3 The capacitor is located underneath the frame top tube, forward of the ignition coil.

4 Check the capacitor for signs of damage. Make sure the terminals inside the wiring connection are clean and secure.

5 Disconnect the capacitor wiring connector. Using an insulated jumper wire, bridge the terminals inside the capacitor side of the connector to discharge the capacitor.

6 Unscrew the bolts securing the capacitor and remove it.

7 Test the capacitor using insulated jumper wires, a test light and a fully charged 12 V battery **(see illustration)**.

8 Connect the negative (-ve) battery terminal to the negative (brown) wire terminal inside the connector. Connect the positive (+ve) battery terminal to the test light, then connect the test light to the positive (yellow/red) wire terminal inside the connector. When the connection is made, the test light should come on briefly – for one second or less. If the light does not come on, or if it stays on, the capacitor is faulty and a new one must be fitted.

9 Installation is the reverse of removal. Make sure that capacitor is in place and that the wiring connector is secure before connecting the battery negative (-ve) terminal.

5 Source coil and pick-up coil

Check

1 Remove the fuel tank (see Chapter 4). Disconnect the battery negative (-ve) lead (see Chapter 9).

2 The ignition source coil and pick-up coil resistance should be measured with a multimeter.

3 Trace the wiring from the left-hand engine cover and disconnect the black/red and red/white wire connector (source coil), and the red and green wire connector (pick-up coil) **(see illustrations)**.

5.3a Source coil (A) and pick-up coil (B) wiring

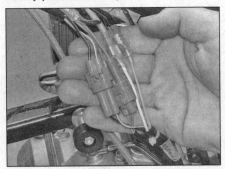

5.3b Trace the wiring to the connectors

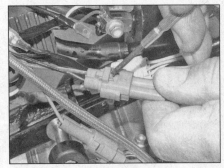

5.3c Release the catch to disconnect the connectors

5.11 Pick-up coil is secured by two bolts (arrowed)

5.12 Align the ignition trigger (arrowed) with the pick-up coil

4 Set the meter to the ohms x100 scale.
5 To test the source coil, measure the resistance between the black/red and red/white wire terminals on the engine side of the connector.
6 To test the pick-up coil, measure the resistance between the red and green wire terminals on the engine side of the connector.
7 Compare the readings obtained with those given in the Specifications at the beginning of this Chapter. If the readings differ greatly from those given, particularly if the meter indicates a short circuit (no measurable resistance) or an open circuit (infinite, or very high resistance), the alternator stator (ignition source coil) and/or the pick-up coil must be renewed. **Note:** *Always check that the fault is not due to a damaged or broken wire between the alternator and/or pick-up coil and the connector, and the connector and the CDI unit (see Wiring Diagrams at the end of Chapter 9). Pinched or broken wires can usually be repaired. Note also, that on 2005-on EXC models, a separate wiring sub-loom is fitted to the CDI unit (on all other machines, the wiring is encapsulated in the unit). Check that the sub-loom connections and the terminals in the CDI multi-pin connector are clean and secure, and check the individual wires in the sub-loom for continuity.*

Removal

8 The source coil is integral with the alternator stator. Refer to the relevant Section of Chapter 9 for the removal and installation procedure.
9 To remove the pick-up coil, first follow the procedure in Chapter 2, Section 15, and remove the left-hand engine cover.
10 If not already done, free the wiring from any clips or ties and disconnect the pick-up coil wiring connector **(see illustrations 5.3a, b and c)**.
11 Undo the two bolts securing the pick-up coil and lift it off **(see illustration)**.

Installation

12 Note the location of the ignition trigger (raised section) on the outside of the alternator rotor. If necessary, turn the engine slowly to bring the trigger into position opposite the pick-up coil **(see illustration)**.
13 Tighten the pick-up coil bolts finger-tight. Using a feeler gauge, check that the gap between the trigger and the pick-up is within the specification shown at the beginning of this Chapter – if the gap is too small, the pick-up will be damaged, if the gap is too large, the ignition signal will be weak and erratic.
14 If necessary, loosen the pick-up mounting bolts and adjust the gap, then tighten the bolts to the specified torque setting and

check the gap once again to ensure that it is still correct.
15 Follow the procedure in Chapter 2, Section 15, and install the left-hand engine cover.

6 CDI unit

1 The CDI unit is located on the left-hand side of the steering head **(see illustration)**.
2 KTM provide no test specifications for this unit. In order to determine conclusively that the unit is defective, it should be substituted with a known good one. If the fault is rectified, the original unit is faulty. Alternatively, have the unit tested by a KTM dealer.
3 Remove the fuel tank (see Chapter 4). Disconnect the battery negative (-ve) lead (see Chapter 9).
4 If required, remove the left-hand radiator for access to the unit (see Chapter 3).
5 Undo the mounting bolts and displace the unit. On 2005-on EXC models, unclip the multi-pin wiring connector. On all other models, trace the wiring from the unit and disconnect it at the connectors. Free the wiring from any clips or ties.
6 Installation is the reverse of removal. Ensure that the terminals inside the wiring connectors are clean and undamaged and tighten the mounting bolts securely. Ensure that all the ignition wiring is connected before reconnecting the battery.

7 Throttle position sensor

Note: *The TPS is fitted to 2004-on models.*
1 The throttle position sensor (TPS) is mounted on the left-hand side of the carburettor and is keyed to the throttle pulley shaft **(see illustration)**. The sensor provides the CDI unit

6.1 Location of the CDI unit (arrowed)

7.1 Location of the throttle position sensor (arrowed)

7.3 Disconnect the TPS wiring connector

with information on throttle position and rate of opening or closing.

Check

2 Remove the fuel tank (see Chapter 4). Disconnect the battery negative (-ve) lead (see Chapter 9).
3 Trace the wiring from the sensor and disconnect it at the connector **(see illustration)**.
4 Using a multimeter set to the K-ohms scale, measure the sensor's resistance by connecting the positive (+ve) meter probe to the blue wire terminal and the negative (-ve) probe to the black terminal on the sensor side of the connector. Compare the reading obtained with that given in the Specifications at the beginning of this Chapter; if it differs greatly, replace the sensor with a new one.
5 Now measure the sensor's resistance range by connecting the positive (+ve) meter probe to the yellow wire terminal and the negative (-ve) probe to the black terminal, and slowly opening the throttle from fully closed to fully open. If the readings obtained differ greatly from those specified at the beginning of this Chapter, replace the sensor with a new one.
Note: *When checking the resistance range, it is more important that there is a smooth and constant change in the resistance as the throttle is opened, than that the figures themselves are exactly as specified.*
6 If the test results are as specified, check the wiring between the connector and the CDI unit. On 2005-on EXC models, check the individual wires in the sub-loom between the connector and the CDI unit for continuity.

Renewal

7 Follow the procedure in Chapter 4, Section 6, to remove and install the TPS. Note it is not necessary to remove the carburettor from the bike. If not already done, remove the fuel tank for access (see Chapter 4).
8 If a new sensor has been fitted, or if the sensor has been removed during carburettor overhaul, it must be adjusted as follows.

Adjustment

9 Before adjusting the sensor, check the engine idle speed (see Chapter 1).

10 Remove the fuel tank (see Chapter 4). Disconnect the battery negative (-ve) lead (see Chapter 9).
11 Follow the procedure in Steps 3 and 4 and measure the sensor's resistance. Note the reading, then multiply this by 0.15. The result (± 50 ohms) is the sensor's adjustment value. For example:

TPS resistance = 5 K-ohms
Adjustment value = 5.0 x 0.15 = 750 ± 50 ohms

12 Next, set the multimeter to the 100 ohms scale. Connect the positive (+ve) meter probe to the yellow wire terminal and the negative (-ve) probe to the black terminal and note the reading with the throttle twistgrip closed. The reading should agree with the result obtained in Step 11 – in the case of the example given, the value should be 750 ± 50 ohms.
13 If the actual adjustment value does not correspond with the calculated value, loosen the sensor mounting screws, then, with the throttle fully closed, turn the sensor clockwise or anti-clockwise until the calculated value is indicated.
14 Once the sensor is correctly positioned, apply a drop of Loctite 243 to the threads of the mounting screws and tighten them securely.
15 Install the remaining components in the reverse order of removal.

Notes

Chapter 6
Frame and suspension

Contents

Degrees of difficulty

Easy, suitable for novice with little experience	**Fairly easy,** suitable for beginner with some experience	**Fairly difficult,** suitable for competent DIY mechanic	**Difficult,** suitable for experienced DIY mechanic	**Very difficult,** suitable for expert DIY or professional

Specifications

Front forks

Static drop – all models	25 to 40 mm
Fork tube runout service limit – all models	0.2 mm
Oil type – all models	Motorex SAE 5W racing fork oil

Adjustment settings – standard

2000 – 400 EXC and SX, and 520 EXC and SX

WP 0518U782

Spring preload	7 mm
Compression adjuster	14
Rebound adjuster	14
Oil capacity	450 cc per leg
Oil level	120 mm*

WP 0518U791

Spring preload	6.5 mm
Compression adjuster	14
Rebound adjuster	14
Oil capacity	450 cc per leg
Oil level	140 mm*

2001 – 400 EXC and SX, and 520 EXC and SX

WP 0518V705 and WP 0518V706

Spring preload	6 mm
Compression adjuster	14
Rebound adjuster	12
Oil level – WP 0518V705	130 mm*
Oil level – WP 0518V706	150 mm*

2002 – 250 EXC, 400 EXC and SX, and 520 EXC and SX

WP 1418W710

Spring preload	5 mm
Compression adjuster	20
Rebound adjuster	16
Oil level	100 mm*

WP 0518W712

Spring preload	5 mm
Compression adjuster	20
Rebound adjuster	12
Oil level	130 mm*

Front forks (continued)

Adjustment settings – standard (continued)

2003 – 250 EXC, 450 EXC and SX, and 525 EXC and SX

WP 4860 MXMA (1418X727)

Spring preload	5 mm
Compression adjuster.	18
Rebound adjuster	19
Oil level	90 mm*

WP 4860 MXMA (1418X737)

Spring preload	5 mm
Compression adjuster.	21
Rebound adjuster	20
Oil level	110 mm*

2004 – 250 EXC, 450 EXC and SX, and 525 EXC and SX

WP 4860 MXMA (1418Y747)

Spring preload	5 mm
Compression adjuster.	18
Rebound adjuster	19
Oil level	100 mm*

WP 4860 MXMA (1418Y748)

Spring preload	5 mm
Compression adjuster.	20
Rebound adjuster	20
Oil level	120 mm*

2004 – 400 EXC

WP 4860 MA (1418Y748)

Spring preload	5 mm
Compression adjuster.	20
Rebound adjuster	20
Oil level	120 mm*

2004 – 450 SMR and 525 SMR

WP 4860 MXMA (1418Y767)

Spring preload	5 mm
Compression adjuster.	19
Rebound adjuster	12
Oil level	100 mm*

2004 – 450 SXS and 540 SXS

WP 4860 MXMA (1418Y762)

Spring preload	513 mm (total spring length including pretension spacer)
Compression adjuster.	18
Rebound adjuster	20
Oil level	110 mm*

2005 – 250 EXC, 400 EXC, 450 EXC, and 525 EXC

WP 4860 MA (14187A06)

Spring preload	5 mm
Compression adjuster.	20
Rebound adjuster	20
Oil level	110 mm*

2005 – 450 SX and 525 SX

WP 4860 PAMA (14187A05)

Spring preload	5 mm
Compression adjuster.	22
Rebound adjuster	20
Oil level	100 mm*

2005 – 450 SXS and 540 SXS

WP 4860 MXMA PA CC (14187A16)

Spring preload	5.5 mm
Compression adjuster.	24
Rebound adjuster	25

2005 – 450 SMR and 525 SMR

WP 4860 PAMA (14187A18)

Spring preload	20 mm
Compression adjuster.	19
Rebound adjuster	12
Oil level	100 mm*

Front forks (continued)
Adjustment settings – standard (continued)
  2006 – 250 EXC, 400 EXC, 450 EXC, and 525 EXC
    WP 4860 MXMA (14187B06)
      Spring preload . . . .   5 mm
      Compression adjuster.   20
      Rebound adjuster   21
      Oil level . . . .   110 mm*
  2006 – 450 SX and 525 SX
    WP 4860 MXMA PA (14187B05)
      Spring preload . . . .   5 mm
      Compression adjuster.   20
      Rebound adjuster   20
      Oil level . . . .   100 mm*
  2006 – 450 SMR and 560 SMR
    WP 4860 MXMA PA (14187B18)
      Spring preload . . . .   20 mm
      Compression adjuster.   19
      Rebound adjuster   17
      Oil level . . . .   100 mm*
  2006 – 450 SXS and 540 SXS
    WP 4860 MXMA PA CC (14187B16)
      Spring preload . . . .   5.5 mm
      Compression adjuster.   22
      Rebound adjuster   24
  2007 – 400 EXC, 450 EXC, and 525 EXC
    WP 4860 MXMA (14187C06)
      Spring preload . . . .   –
      Compression adjuster.   20
      Rebound adjuster   15
      Oil level . . . .   110 mm*
  2007 – 450 XC and 525 XC
    WP 4860 MXMA PA (14187C29)
      Spring preload . . . .   2 turns
      Compression adjuster.   18
      Rebound adjuster   20
      Oil level . . . .   110 mm*
*Oil level is measured from the top of the outer tube with the fork spring removed and the leg fully compressed.

Rear shock absorber
Static sag – all models . . . .   35 mm
Riding sag – all models . . . .   95 to 105 mm
Adjustment settings – standard
  2000 – 400 EXC and SX, and 520 EXC and SX
    WP 1218U721
      Spring preload . . . .   6 mm
      Compression adjuster.   5
      Rebound adjuster.   20
    WP 1218U716
      Spring preload . . . .   6 mm
      Compression adjuster.   5
      Rebound adjuster   18
  2001 – 400 EXC and SX, and 520 EXC and SX
    WP 1218V732 and WP 1218V733
      Spring preload . . . .   6 mm
      Compression adjuster.   5
      Rebound adjuster   25
  2002 – 250 EXC, 400 EXC and SX, and 520 EXC and SX
    WP 5018 PDS DCC (1218W738)
      Spring preload . . . .   4 mm
      Compression adjuster (low speed)   15
      Compression adjuster (high speed)   2
      Rebound adjuster   25
    WP 5018 PDS MCC (1218W739)
      Spring preload . . . .   5 mm
      Compression adjuster.   15
      Rebound adjuster   25

Rear shock absorber (continued)

Adjustment settings – standard (continued)

2003 – 250 EXC, 450 EXC and SX, and 525 EXC and SX

WP 5018 PDS DCC (1218X760)

Spring preload	6 mm
Compression adjuster (low speed)	15
Compression adjuster (high speed)	2
Rebound adjuster	26

WP 5018 PDS MCC 1218X761

Spring preload	8 mm
Compression adjuster.	17
Rebound adjuster	26

2004 – 250 EXC, 400 EXC, 450 EXC and SX, and 525 EXC and SX

WP 5018 PDS DCC (1218Y771)

Spring preload	5 mm
Compression adjuster (low speed)	12
Compression adjuster (high speed)	2
Rebound adjuster	22

WP 5018 PDS MCC 1218Y772

Spring preload	6 mm
Compression adjuster.	19
Rebound adjuster	24

2004 – 450 SXS and 540 SXS

WP 5018 PDS DCC (1218Y780)

Spring preload	7 mm
Compression adjuster (low speed)	15
Compression adjuster (high speed)	2
Rebound adjuster	24

2004 – 2006 450 SMR, 525 SMR and 560 SMR

WP 5018 PDS DCC (1218Y787 – 2004, 12187A15 – 2005, 12187B15 – 2006)

Spring preload	8 mm
Compression adjuster (low speed)	13
Compression adjuster (high speed)	2
Rebound adjuster	19

2005 – 250 EXC, 400 EXC, 450 EXC, and 525 EXC

WP 5018 PDS MCC 14187A06

Spring preload	7 mm
Compression adjuster.	15
Rebound adjuster	22

2005 – 450 SX and 525 SX

WP 5018 PDS DCC (12187A05)

Spring preload	7 mm
Compression adjuster (low speed)	15
Compression adjuster (high speed)	2
Rebound adjuster	22

2005 and 2006 450 SXS and 540 SXS

WP 5018 PDS II DCC (12187A12 – 2005, 12187B12 – 2006)

Spring preload	5 mm
Compression adjuster (low speed)	12
Compression adjuster (high speed)	2
Rebound adjuster	25

2006 – 250 EXC, 400 EXC, 450 EXC, and 525 EXC

WP 5018 PDS MCC

Spring preload	6 mm
Compression adjuster.	15
Rebound adjuster	22

2006 – 450 SX and 525 SX

WP 5018 PDS DCC (12187B05)

Spring preload	5 mm
Compression adjuster (low speed)	15
Compression adjuster (high speed)	2.5
Rebound adjuster	22

2007 – 400 EXC, 450 EXC, and 525 EXC

WP 5018 PDS MCC (12187C06)

Spring preload	5 mm
Compression adjuster.	15
Rebound adjuster	25

Rear shock absorber (continued)

Adjustment settings – standard (continued)
  2007 – 450 XC and 525 XC
    WP 5018 PDS DCC (12187C29)
      Spring preload . . . . 5 mm
      Compression adjuster (low speed) 15
      Compression adjuster (high speed) 1
      Rebound adjuster 24

Torque settings

Gear lever pivot bolt . . . . 10 Nm*
Rear brake pedal pivot bolt nut . . . . 45 Nm*
Sidestand bracket nut . . . . 30 Nm*
Sidestand pivot bolt . . . . 15 Nm*
Rear sub-frame mounting bolts . . . . 35 Nm*
Handlebar clamp bolts . . . . 20 Nm*
Handlebar bracket bolts . . . . 40 Nm*
Front brake master cylinder clamp bolts . . . . 15 Nm
Fork compression adjusters . . . . 25 Nm
Fork top bolt locknuts . . . . 25 Nm
Fork clamp bolts
  2000 to 2004
    Top yoke . . . . 20 Nm*
    Bottom yoke . . . . 15 Nm*
  2005 and 2006 – SX
    Top yoke . . . . 15 Nm*
    Bottom yoke . . . . 10 Nm*
  2005 to 2007 – all other models with non-adjustable fork offset
    Top yoke . . . . 20 Nm*
    Bottom yoke . . . . 15 Nm*
  2005 to 2007 – all other models with adjustable fork offset
    Top yoke . . . . 17 Nm*
    Bottom yoke . . . . 12 Nm*
Steering stem clamp bolt . . . . 15 Nm*
Steering stem bottom bolt . . . . 60 Nm*
Rear shock absorber mounting bolts
  2000 to 2004 . . . . 60 Nm*
  2005 to 2007 . . . . 70 Nm*
Rear shock absorber adjuster ring clamp screw . . . . 5 Nm
Swingarm pivot bolt nut . . . . 100 Nm

Use thread locking compound Loctite 243

1 General information

All models use an all-welded, tubular steel cradle frame with a bolt-on aluminium rear sub-frame.

Front suspension is by a pair of oil-damped, White Power USD telescopic forks with internal coil springs. The forks are adjustable for spring pre-load, compression and rebound damping.

On XC and certain EXC models, the front fork offset can be changed to suit different riding conditions by altering the position of the steering stem.

At the rear, an aluminium alloy swingarm acts on a single, White Power shock absorber. The shock is adjustable for spring pre-load, compression and rebound damping. Depending on the type of shock fitted, either mono (MCC) or dual (DCC) compression damping settings are available.

2 Frame

1 The frame should not require attention unless accident damage has occurred. In most cases, frame renewal is the only satisfactory remedy for such damage. A few frame specialists have the jigs and other equipment necessary for straightening the frame to the required standard of accuracy, but even then there is no simple way of assessing to what extent the frame may have been over-stressed.

2 After the machine has covered a high mileage, the frame should be examined closely for signs of cracking or splitting at the welded joints. Loose engine mountings and sub-frame bolts can cause ovaling or fracturing of the mounts themselves. Minor damage can often be repaired by welding, depending on the extent and nature of the damage, but this is a task for an expert.

3 Remember that a frame which is out of alignment will cause handling problems. If misalignment is suspected as the result of an accident, first check the wheel alignment (see Chapter 7). To have the frame checked thoroughly it will be necessary to strip the machine completely.

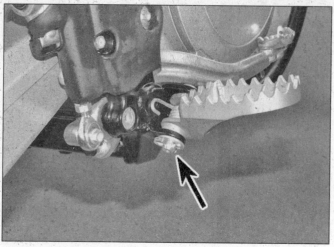

3.1 Remove the split pin and washer (arrowed)

3.2 Note the location of the spring (arrowed)

3 Footrests, brake pedal and gearchange lever

Footrests and brake pedal

Removal

1 To remove the footrest, first remove the split pin and washer on the end of the pivot pin (see illustration).

2 Note how the ends of the footrest spring are located, then withdraw the pivot pin and remove the footrest (see illustration).

3 To remove the brake pedal, first undo the screw(s) securing the right-hand frame cover and, if fitted, the clip, then draw the cover off (see illustrations).

4 Disconnect the brake pedal return spring (see illustration).

5 Undo the bolt securing the joint on the rear brake master cylinder pushrod to the brake pedal and separate the pushrod from the pedal (see illustration).

6 Counter-hold the brake pedal pivot bolt and undo the nut (see illustration). Support the pedal and withdraw the bolt.

Installation

7 There are two sealed bearings fitted inside the brake pedal. Refer to *Tools and Workshop Tips* in the *Reference* section to check the bearings and, if necessary, renew them.

8 Ensure that the pivot bolt is clean and free from corrosion. Install the bolt and the pedal, then apply a drop of specified locking compound to the threads and tighten the nut to the torque setting specified at the beginning of this Chapter.

9 Install the brake pedal return spring (see illustration 3.4).

10 Align the joint on the master cylinder pushrod with the brake pedal and install the bolt, then tighten it securely (see illustration 3.5).

11 Ensure there is between 3 to 5 mm free travel in the pedal before the pushrod contacts the master cylinder piston. If necessary, follow the procedure in Chapter 1, Section 3, and adjust the freeplay.

12 Install the footrest in the reverse order of removal. Locate the ends of the spring so that the footrest is held in the down position. Secure the pivot pin with a new split pin and bend the ends of the split pin around the pivot pin

Gearchange lever

13 Follow the procedure in Chapter 2, Section 21, to remove and install the gearchange lever.

3.3a Undo the screw(s) . . .

3.3b . . . and lift the cover off

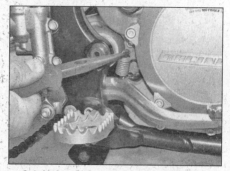

3.4 Unhook the return spring from its bracket

3.5 Undo the bolt (arrowed)

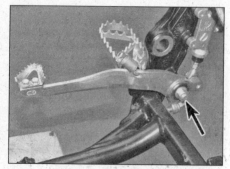

3.6 Undo the nut (arrowed) on the pivot bolt

4.2 Disconnect the sidestand springs

4.3 Sidestand bracket is secured by nut (arrowed)

4.6 Check the arrangement of the springs when the stand is down

bracket and lift the stand assembly off **(see illustration)**.
4 If required, undo the stand pivot bolt and separate the stand from the bracket. Prior to installation, clean the threads of the pivot bolt and apply a drop of specified locking compound, then tighten the bolt to the torque setting specified at the beginning of this Chapter.
5 Installation is the reverse of removal. Tighten the bracket nut to the specified torque setting.
6 Ensure that the springs are fitted the correct way round **(see illustration)**. Check the spring tension – they must hold the stand up when it is not in use. If the springs have sagged, renew them.

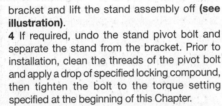

4 Sidestand

1 Support the motorcycle securely in an upright position using an auxiliary stand.
2 Disconnect the stand springs, noting how they fit **(see illustration)**.
3 Undo the nut on the rear of the stand

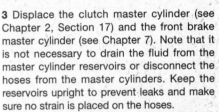

5 Handlebars and levers

Handlebars
Removal

1 Remove the headlight panel or front number plate panel (see Chapter 8).
2 Remove the fuel tank (see Chapter 4).

3 Displace the clutch master cylinder (see Chapter 2, Section 17) and the front brake master cylinder (see Chapter 7). Note that it is not necessary to drain the fluid from the master cylinder reservoirs or disconnect the hoses from the master cylinders. Keep the reservoirs upright to prevent leaks and make sure no strain is placed on the hoses.
4 Loosen the bolts securing the two halves of the throttle twistgrip housing and slide the housing off the end of the handlebar – it is not necessary to detach the throttle cables from the twistgrip (see Chapter 4, Section 3).
5 Release the ties securing the handlebar switch wiring, then displace the handlebar switches (see Chapter 9).
6 The left-hand handlebar grip is glued in position – unless the grip is going to be renewed, leave it in place, otherwise use a craft knife to slit the grip and peel it off the handlebar.
7 Loosen the handlebar clamp bolts evenly, then support the handlebars and lift the clamps off – note the register mark on the inside of each clamp and the two sets of alignment marks on the handlebars **(see illustrations)**. Lift the handlebars off.

5.7a Loosen the clamp bolts (arrowed) evenly

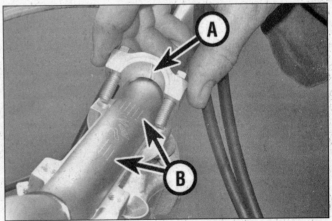

5.7b Note the register mark (A) and the alignment marks (B) on the handlebars

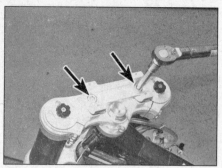

5.8 Undo the bolts (arrowed) securing the handlebar bracket

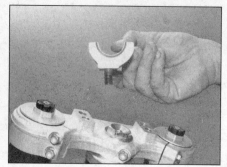

5.9a Bracket bolts are offset

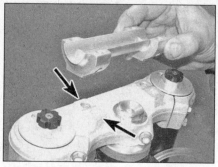

5.9b Front and rear mounting holes for the handlebar bracket

8 Undo the bolts securing the handlebar bracket **(see illustration)**.

9 Lift the bracket off – note that the position of the bracket bolts is offset and that there are front and rear mounting holes for the bracket bolts in the fork top yoke **see illustrations)**.

Installation

10 Installation is the reverse of removal. Note that the handlebar bracket can be located in either the front or rear pair of holes in the top yoke, and that the bracket can be reversed to allow for further adjustment of the handlebar position.

11 Clean the threads of the bracket bolts and apply a drop of specified locking compound, then tighten the bolts to the torque setting specified at the beginning of this Chapter.

12 Align the handlebars and clamps as noted on removal, then tighten the clamps evenly to the specified torque setting. Note that the gap between the bracket and the clamps should be the same front and back.

13 Install the remaining components in the reverse order of removal.

● Adjust throttle cable freeplay (see Chapter 1).

● Check the operation of all switches and the front brake and clutch before riding the machine.

Clutch lever

14 Follow the procedure in Chapter 2, Section 17, to remove and install the clutch lever. **Note:** *Only follow the Steps that apply to removing the lever. It isn't necessary to remove the master cylinder from the handlebar or disassemble the hydraulic system.*

Front brake lever

15 Follow the procedure in Chapter 7, Section 5, to remove and install the front brake lever. **Note:** *Only follow the Steps that apply to removing the lever. It isn't necessary to remove the master cylinder from the handlebar or disassemble the hydraulic system.*

6 Suspension adjustment

Note: *The front and rear suspension on all models is adjustable for spring pre-load, rebound and compression damping. Refer to the advice in the owner's manual supplied with your machine for recommended adjustments to suit different riding conditions.*

Front forks

Spring pre-load

1 First check the pre-load as follows.

2 Support the motorcycle with an auxiliary stand so that the front wheel is off the ground. Measure and record the distance between the top of the axle clamp and the lower edge of the fork outer tube **(see illustration)**.

3 Take the machine off the stand. Standing alongside, apply the front brake and push on the handlebars to compress the forks several times, then measure the distance again. **Note:** *Do not sit on the bike for this test.*

4 The difference between the two measurements represents the static drop.

Compare the difference with the specification shown at the beginning of this Chapter. If the static drop is greater than specified, the spring pre-load must be increased. If it is less than specified, the pre-load must be reduced.

5 There are two methods of adjusting the spring pre-load, depending on the type of top bolt fitted. Top bolts with a series of holes designed for removal with a peg spanner have an integral hex adjuster **(see illustration)**. Turn the centre hex clockwise to increase preload and anti-clockwise to reduce pre-load. One complete turn of the hex equals 1 mm of adjustment. A total of 9 mm of adjustment is available. Ensure that both legs are adjusted by the same amount. If there is insufficient adjustment available to correct the static drop, new fork springs will have to be fitted (see Section 8).

6 Top bolts without a series of holes **(see illustration 6.10)** have pre-load spacers fitted underneath them. To access the spacers, first follow the procedure in Section 7 and remove the fork legs, then unscrew the top bolt from the damper assembly (see Section 8, Steps 3 to 7). If the fork oil is not going to be changed, keep the leg upright to avoid spillage.

7 Work on one fork leg at a time. Note the size (thickness) of the spacers already fitted, then add or subtract spacers to adjust the pre-load **(see illustration)**. **Note:** *Fork legs are pre-loaded individually during manufacture and the amount of pre-load required to balance the fork legs fitted to your bike may not match exactly. Do not alter any original differential between the pre-load spacers.*

6.2 Measure the distance indicated

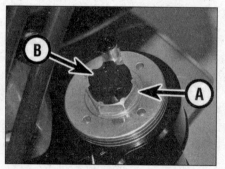

6.5 Pre-load (A) and damping (B) adjusters – top bolt type with removal holes

6.7 Use different thickness spacers to adjust spring pre-load

6.10 Rebound damping adjuster (arrowed)

6.12a Prise off the cap on the underside of the axle clamp

6.12b Compression damping adjuster screw (arrowed)

8 Four sizes of spacer are available – 1.5 mm, 2.5 mm, 5 mm and 10 mm – see a KTM dealer for details. The fork springs should not be pre-tensioned by more than 20 mm. If there is insufficient adjustment available to correct the static drop, new fork springs will have to be fitted (see Section 8).

9 Once the spacers are in place, reassemble the fork leg (see Section 8), then fit the leg onto the bike (see Section 7). **Note:** *If spring pre-load is increased it will probably be necessary to increase the rate of rebound damping.*

Rebound damping

10 Rebound damping is adjusted by turning the knob on the top of the fork top bolt **(see illustration)**. The standard settings are listed in the Specifications at the beginning of this Chapter. To establish the standard setting, turn the knob clockwise all the way, then turn it back anti-clockwise the specified number of clicks.

11 Turn the knob clockwise to increase rebound damping and anti-clockwise to reduce rebound damping. Ensure that both fork legs are adjusted by the same amount.

Compression damping

12 Compression damping is adjusted by turning the screw on the bottom of the fork axle clamp – prise off the cap to access

the screw **(see illustrations)**. The standard settings are listed in the Specifications at the beginning of this Chapter. To establish the standard setting, turn the screw clockwise all the way, then turn it back anti-clockwise the specified number of clicks.

13 Turn the knob clockwise to increase compression damping and anti-clockwise to reduce compression damping. Ensure that both fork legs are adjusted by the same amount.

14 Don't forget to install the caps after adjustment. If the caps are damaged or a loose fit, renew them.

Rear shock absorber

Spring pre-load

15 First check the pre-load as follows.

16 Support the motorcycle with an auxiliary stand so that the rear wheel is off the ground. Measure and record the distance between the centre of the rear axle and a fixed point on the bike **(see illustration)**.

17 Take the machine off the stand. Have an assistant support the bike upright, then measure the distance again. **Note:** *Do not sit on the bike for this test.*

18 The difference between the two measurements represents the static sag. Compare the difference with the specification

shown at the beginning of this Chapter. If the static sag is greater than specified, the spring pre-load must be increased. If it is less than specified, the pre-load must be reduced. **Note:** *KTM advise that a difference of more than 2 mm from specification can have a detrimental effect on the performance of the suspension.*

19 To adjust the spring pre-load, first follow the procedure in Section 11 and remove the shock absorber.

20 Clean the threads at the top of the shock and measure the length of the exposed threads above the adjuster ring **(see illustration)**. This measurement is the spring pre-load – compare this measurement to the standard setting listed in the Specifications at the beginning of this Chapter.

21 To alter the preload, loosen the adjuster ring clamp screw, then, using a suitable C-spanner, turn the adjuster clockwise to increase pre-load and anti-clockwise to reduce pre-load. One complete turn of the adjuster changes the pre-load by approximately 1 mm.

22 Once the pre-load has been adjusted, tighten the clamp screw to the specified torque setting, then install the shock (see Section 11).

23 Next, measure the riding sag as follows. Sit on the bike wearing full riding clothing. Have one assistant hold the bike upright so

6.16 Measure the distance indicated

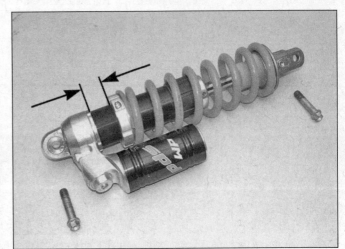

6.20 Measure the length of the exposed threads

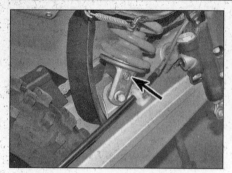

6.26 Rebound damping adjuster screw (arrowed)

6.29 Compression damping adjuster screw (arrowed) – MCC shock

that you can put both feet on the footrests, then bounce the rear suspension up and down so that it finds its level. Stay sitting on the bike with it supported upright, while a second assistant measures the distance between the centre of the rear axle and the same fixed point on the bike as before (see Step 16).

24 The difference between this measurement and the first measurement taken (with the rear wheel off the ground) represents the riding sag. Compare the difference with the specification shown at the beginning of this Chapter. If the riding sag is greater than specified, the shock absorber spring is too soft. If it is less than specified, the shock absorber spring is too hard.

25 A large range of replacement springs is available – see a KTM dealer for details. You will need to supply the dealer with your weight, inclusive of all riding clothing, when ordering a replacement spring. Follow the procedure in Section 11 to remove the shock absorber and fit the new spring. **Note:** *If a harder spring is fitted it will probably be necessary to increase the rebound damping. If a softer spring is fitted it will probably be necessary to reduce the rebound damping.*

Rebound damping

26 Rebound damping is adjusted by turning the screw on the bottom of the shock absorber **(see illustration)**. The standard settings are

listed in the Specifications at the beginning of this Chapter. To establish the standard setting, turn the screw clockwise all the way, then turn it back anti-clockwise the specified number of clicks.

27 Turn the screw clockwise to increase rebound damping and anti-clockwise to reduce rebound damping.

Compression damping

28 The rear shock absorber will have either mono compression control (MCC) or dual compression control (DCC). Dual compression control provides adjustment for both low and high speed shock compression rates – see Specifications at the beginning of this Chapter.

29 On an MCC shock, compression damping is adjusted by turning the screw at the top of the shock **(see illustration)**. The standard settings are listed in the Specifications at the beginning of this Chapter. To establish the standard setting, turn the screw clockwise all the way, then turn it back anti-clockwise the specified number of clicks.

30 Turn the screw clockwise to increase compression damping and anti-clockwise to reduce compression damping.

31 On a DCC shock, low speed compression damping is adjusted by turning the screw at the top of the shock **(see illustration)**. The standard settings are listed in the

Specifications at the beginning of this Chapter. To establish the standard setting, turn the screw clockwise all the way, then turn it back anti-clockwise the specified number of clicks.

32 Turn the screw clockwise to increase low speed compression damping and anti-clockwise to reduce low speed compression damping.

33 On a DCC shock, high speed compression damping is adjusted by turning the hex at the top of the shock **(see illustration 6.31)**. The standard settings are listed in the Specifications at the beginning of this Chapter. To establish the standard setting, turn the hex clockwise all the way, then turn it back anti-clockwise the specified number of turns.

34 Turn the hex clockwise to increase high speed compression damping and anti-clockwise to reduce high speed compression damping.

⚠️ *Warning: Take care not to unscrew the complete damper assembly. The damper unit is filled with nitrogen gas under high pressure and serious injury could result if the assembly is accidentally loosened.*

| 7 | Front fork removal and installation | |

Removal

1 Support the motorcycle securely in an upright position with an auxiliary stand so that the front wheel is off the ground **(see illustration 4.1 in Chapter 2)**.

2 Displace the front brake caliper (see Chapter 7).

3 Remove the front wheel (see Chapter 7).

4 Remove the fork protectors (see Chapter 8).

5 Work on each fork leg individually. Note the routing of the wiring, cables and hoses around the forks.

6 Note the alignment between the top of the fork outer tube and the top yoke, then loosen the fork clamp bolts in the top yoke **(see illustration)**.

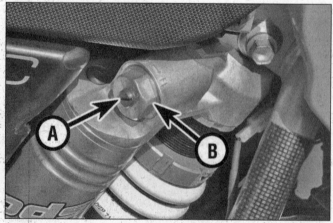

6.31 Low speed compression damping adjuster screw (A), high speed compression damping adjuster hex (B) – DCC shock

7.6 Note the alignment (arrowed)

7.7a Loosen the clamp bolts (arrowed) then loosen the top bolt

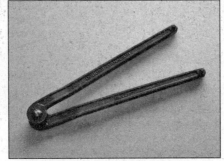

7.7b Special WP tool for removing top bolts with drilled holes

7.8a Loosen the clamp bolts (arrowed) . . .

7.8b . . . then remove the fork leg

7 If the fork legs are to be disassembled, or if the fork oil is being changed, loosen the fork top bolt now **(see illustration)**. Note that top bolts with a series of holes are designed for removal and installation with a peg spanner – White Power Suspension provides a suitable service tool (Part No. T 103) to do this **(see illustration)**. The hex on the top of these bolts is the fork spring pre-load adjuster.

8 Support the fork leg, then loosen but do not remove the fork clamp bolts in the bottom yoke **(see illustration)**. Remove the fork leg by twisting it and pulling it downwards **(see illustration)**. Note which fork leg fits on which side.

HAYNES HiNT *If the fork legs are seized in the yokes, spray the area with penetrating oil and allow time for it to soak in before trying again.*

Installation

9 Remove all traces of corrosion from the fork tubes and the yokes. Slide the fork leg up through the bottom yoke and into the top yoke, making sure the wiring, cables and hoses are the correct side of the leg as noted on removal. Make sure that the leg with the bracket for the disc brake caliper is on the left-hand side. Check that the alignment between the top of the fork tube and the top yoke is as noted on removal, and equal on both sides **(see illustration 7.6)**.

10 Tighten the fork clamp bolts in the bottom yoke to the torque setting specified at the beginning of this Chapter **(see illustration)**.

11 If the fork leg has been dismantled or if the oil has been changed, tighten the top bolt securely – take care not to over-tighten the top bolt and damage the bolt threads **(see illustration 7.7a)**.

12 Tighten the clamp bolts in the top yoke to the specified torque setting **(see illustration)**.

13 Install the remaining components in the reverse order of removal.

14 Check the operation of the front forks and brake before riding the machine.

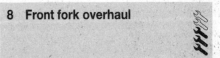
8 Front fork overhaul

Note 1: *This Section describes overhaul of the front forks for the purpose of changing the fork oil, oil seals and bushes. Disassembly and adjustment of the fork damping mechanisms is a specialist task that should only be undertaken by a KTM dealer or White Power Suspension service department.*

Note 2: *The fork leg used to illustrate this procedure was a WP 4860 MXMA unit. Differences between this and other units used on the machines covered in this manual are detailed in the text.*

Disassembly

1 Always dismantle the fork legs separately to avoid interchanging any parts and thus causing an accelerated rate of wear. Store

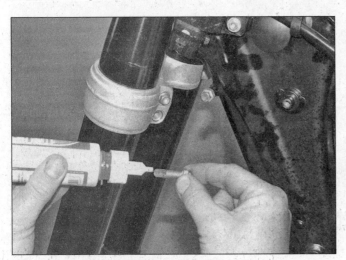

7.10 Thread lock the bottom yoke clamp bolts

7.12 Thread lock the top yoke clamp bolts

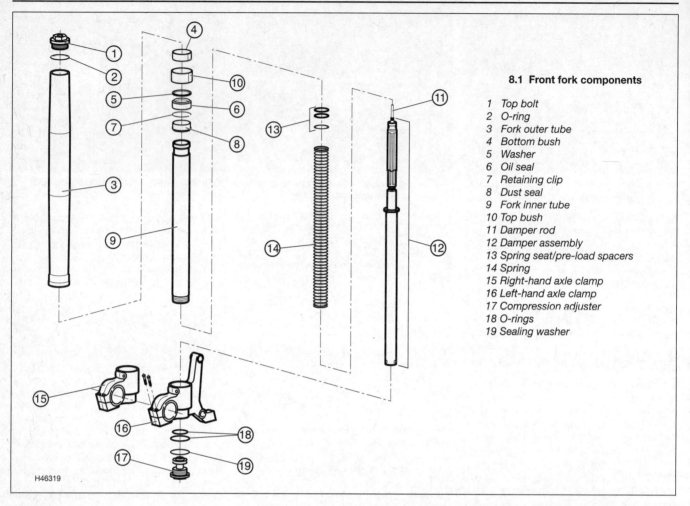

8.1 Front fork components

1 Top bolt
2 O-ring
3 Fork outer tube
4 Bottom bush
5 Washer
6 Oil seal
7 Retaining clip
8 Dust seal
9 Fork inner tube
10 Top bush
11 Damper rod
12 Damper assembly
13 Spring seat/pre-load spacers
14 Spring
15 Right-hand axle clamp
16 Left-hand axle clamp
17 Compression adjuster
18 O-rings
19 Sealing washer

H46319

all components in separate, clearly marked containers **(see illustration)**.

2 Before dismantling the fork leg, note the position of the rebound damping, compression damping and spring pre-load adjusters, then turn the damper settings to their lowest positions (see Section 6).

3 If the fork top bolt was not loosened with the fork on the motorcycle, carefully clamp the fork outer tube in a vice equipped with soft jaws, taking care not to overtighten the vice or score the tube's surface, and loosen the top bolt. Note that top bolts with a series of holes are designed for removal and installation with a peg spanner **(see illustration)**.

4 Support the fork leg in an upright position and unscrew the top bolt – note the location of the O-ring and discard it as a new one must be fitted on reassembly **(see illustration)**.

5 Carefully push the outer tube down over

8.3 Pegs of special tool engage drillings in top bolt

8.4 Note the O-ring (arrowed) on the fork top bolt

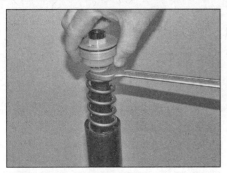

8.5a Hold the lock nut with an open-ended spanner . . .

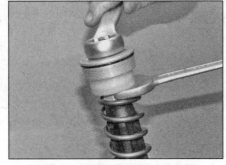

8.5b . . . and loosen the top bolt

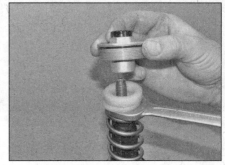

8.6 Unscrew the top bolt

the inner tube. Push the spring down and fit an open-ended spanner onto the top bolt locknut, then counter-hold the nut and loosen the top bolt **(see illustrations)**.

6 Unscrew the top bolt from the damper assembly **(see illustration)**.

7 Lift off the spring seat or pre-load spacers **(see illustration)**. **Note:** *It is important to keep the pre-load spacers for each fork leg separate. Fork legs are pre-loaded individually during manufacture and the amount of pre-load required to balance the fork legs fitted to your bike may not match exactly.*

8 Push the spring down and withdraw the spanner, then lift out the fork spring **(see illustrations)**.

9 Withdraw the damper rod from inside the damper assembly **(see illustration)**.

10 Invert the fork leg over a suitable container and pour out as much fork oil as possible **(see illustration)**.

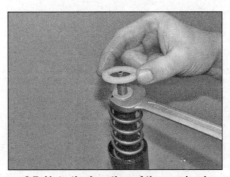

8.7 Note the location of the pre-load spacers

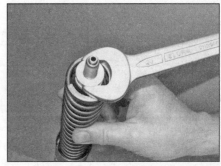

8.8a Remove the spanner . . .

11 Insert the front axle through the axle clamp and loosen the compression adjuster, then unscrew the adjuster from the bottom of the inner tube **(see illustrations)**. Note the

sealing washer and O-rings on the adjuster and discard them as new ones must be fitted.

12 Withdraw the damper assembly from the top of the outer tube **(see illustration)**.

8.8b . . . and lift out the fork spring

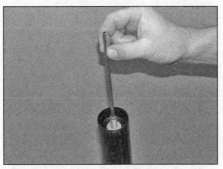

8.9 Withdraw the damper rod

8.10 Pour out the fork oil

8.11a Hold the axle clamp to loosen the compression adjuster . . .

8.11b . . . then unscrew the adjuster

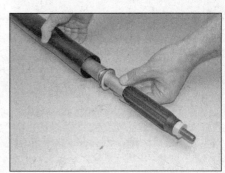

8.12 Withdraw the damper assembly from the fork tube

8.13 Prise off the dust seal

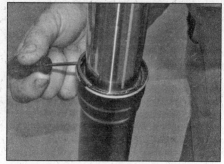

8.14 Prise out the oil seal retaining clip

8.15a Heat the lower end of the fork outer tube . . .

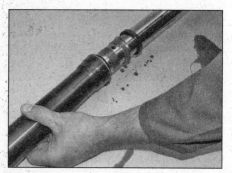

8.15b . . . then pull the tubes apart

8.15c The fork bushes, spacers, washer and oil seal with come out on the inner tube

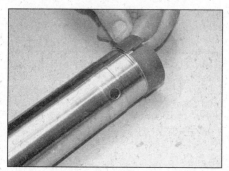

8.16 Ease the top bush off the inner tube

13 Prise the dust seal off the lower end of the outer tube **(see illustration)**.

14 Prise out the oil seal retaining clip from its groove inside the bottom of the outer tube **(see illustration)**. Take care not to scratch the surface of the inner tube.

15 Using a hot air gun, heat the lower end of the outer tube, taking care not to damage the surface of the tube, then pull the inner and outer tubes apart **(see illustrations)**. The fork bushes, any spacers (as fitted), washer and oil seal with come out on the inner tube **(see illustration)**. Note the location of the components on the inner tube as an aid to installation.

16 Note the split in the top fork bush, then ease the bush off the end of the inner tube **(see illustration)**.

17 Where fitted, slide off the bush spacer.

18 Slide off the bottom bush, washer, oil seal, seal retaining clip and dust seal **(see illustration)**. Note which way round the seals are fitted, then discard them as new ones must be fitted.

Inspection

19 Clean all parts in suitable solvent and blow them dry with compressed air, if available.

20 Check the surface of the inner tube for score marks, scratches, flaking or pitted chrome finish and excessive or abnormal wear **(see illustration)**. Renew the inner tubes in both forks if any damage is found.

21 Check the inner tube for runout (bending) using V-blocks and a dial gauge, or have it done by a KTM dealer **(see illustration)**. If the tube is bent, renew it, and renew the damper assembly which is also likely to be damaged

⚠ **Warning: If the inner tube is bent, it should not be straightened – replace it with a new one.**

22 Check the fork spring for cracks and other damage. Check that the springs in both fork legs are the same length. Measure the spring free length and compare the measurement to the length of a new spring. If a spring is defective or has sagged, replace both springs with new ones. Never renew only one spring.

23 Examine the working surface inside the outer tube – if it is worn or scuffed, renew the tube. Examine the working surface of both

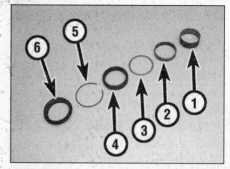

8.18 Fork inner tube components in order of assembly

1	Top bush	4	Oil seal
2	Bottom bush	5	Retaining clip
3	Washer	6	Dust seal

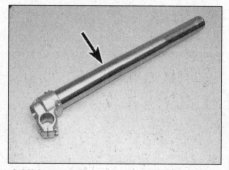

8.20 Inspect the surface of the inner tube

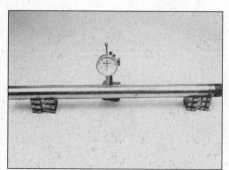

8.21 Check inner tube runout using V-blocks and a dial gauge

8.23 Inspect both bushes for signs of wear

8.24 Examine the axle clamp for cracks and damage

8.26 Tape around the top of the inner tube will protect the inside of the fork seals

bushes – unless they are in as-new condition, renew the bushes **(see illustration)**.

24 Examine the axle clamp for cracks and damage **(see illustration)**. If necessary, the clamp can be unscrewed from the end of the inner tube using the White Power Suspension service tool (Part No. T 1404S). Grip the axle clamp firmly in a vice and assemble the service tool in the top end of the inner tube – a locking pin locates through the holes in the tube and the service tool. Heat the axle clamp, then turn the inner tube anti-clockwise to unscrew it from the clamp. Note the location of the O-ring in the bottom of the clamp and discard it as a new one must be fitted.

Reassembly

25 If the axle clamp has been removed, ensure that the threads inside the clamp and on the bottom of the inner tube are clean. Install a new O-ring inside the clamp. Apply Loctite 2701 to the threads inside the clamp and on the bottom of the tube, then grip the clamp in a vice and screw the inner tube in securely using the service tool.

26 Wrap some tape around the top of the inner tube to protect the inside of the fork seals on assembly **(see illustration)**.

27 Lubricate the inside of the new dust seal with a smear of fork oil, then slide it down over the tube, making sure that it is the correct way round **(see illustration)**.

28 Slide on the oil seal retaining clip **(see illustration)**.

29 Lubricate the inside of the new oil seal

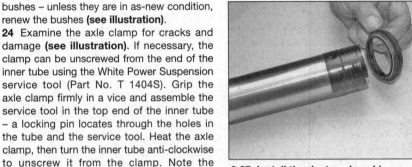

8.27 Install the dust seal, making sure it is the correct way round

8.28 Slide on the oil seal retaining clip

8.29a Install the oil seal . . .

8.29b . . . making sure it is the correct way round

with a smear of fork oil, then slide it down over the tube, making sure that it is the correct way round **(see illustrations)**.

30 Slide on the washer, then remove the tape **(see illustration)**.

31 Lubricate the new fork bushes and, where fitted, the bush spacer, with fork oil. Slide on the bottom bush, the spacer where fitted, then ease the top bush over the end of the inner tube and into its groove **(see illustrations)**.

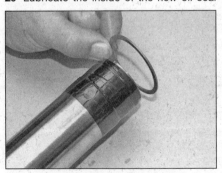

8.30 Slide on the washer

8.31a Slide on the bottom bush . . .

8.31b . . . then install the top bush in its groove

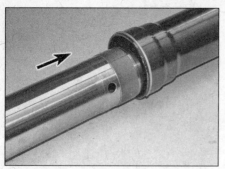

8.32a Insert the inner tube into the bottom of the outer tube (arrowed) . . .

8.32b . . . slide the lower bush and washer into the bottom of the outer tube . . .

8.32c . . . then tap around the washer to ensure the bush is seated

32 Lubricate the inside of the outer tube with fork oil, then insert the inner tube into the bottom of the outer tube. Slide the lower bush and washer into the bottom of the outer tube, then carefully tap around the washer with a small pin punch to ensure

that the bush is located in its seat **(see illustrations)**.
33 Press the oil seal into its seat in the bottom of the outer tube – tap the seal lightly into place until the retaining clip groove is visible above the seal **(see illustration)**.

34 Install the oil seal retaining clip and ensure it is correctly seated in its groove **(see illustration)**.
35 Press the dust seal into its seat in the bottom of the outer tube **(see illustration)**.
36 Lubricate the damper assembly with fork oil, then insert the assembly into the top of the outer tube **(see illustration 8.12)**. Push the assembly all the way down into the inner tube – the lower end of the damper should be visible through the hole in the bottom of the axle clamp **(see illustration)**.
37 Fit a new sealing washer and O-rings onto the compression adjuster and lubricate the O-rings with fork oil **(see illustration)**. Screw the adjuster into the axle clamp, then tighten the adjuster to the torque setting specified at the beginning of this Chapter **(see illustration 8.11a)**.
38 Install the damper rod **(see illustration 8.9)**.
39 Hold the fork leg upright, then compress the outer tube fully over the inner tube and pull the damper up. Slowly pour in the correct quantity of the specified fork oil **(see illustration)**. Pump the damper rod up and down until you feel the cartridge on the lower end of the damper assembly fill with oil. Extend and compress the outer tube several times, then leave the leg upright for ten minutes, with the damper and outer tube fully compressed, to allow any air bubbles to disperse.
40 Measure the fork oil level and compare the result with the specification at the beginning of this Chapter **(see illustration)**. Adjust the level if necessary.

8.33 Install the oil seal . . .

8.34 . . . and secure it with the clip

8.35 Press the dust seal into place

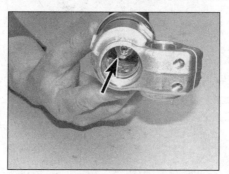

8.36 Note the lower end of the installed damper assembly (arrowed)

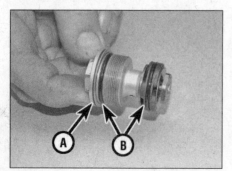

8.37 Sealing washer (A) and O-rings (B) on compression adjuster

8.39 Pour the fork oil in slowly

8.40 Measure the fork oil level

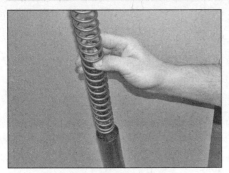

8.42a Install the fork spring . . .

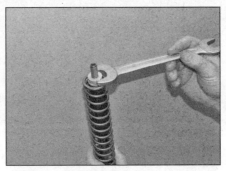

8.42b . . . then fit a spanner onto the top bolt lock nut

8.45 Take care not to cross-thread the top bolt

41 Lubricate a new O-ring with fork oil and fit it onto the fork top bolt.

42 Pull the damper assembly up and install the fork spring, then press the spring down and fit an open-ended spanner onto the top bolt locknut **(see illustrations)**.

43 Install the spring seat or pre-load spacers, referring to the **Note** in Step 7 **(see illustration 8.7)**.

44 Thread the top bolt onto the top of the damper assembly, then counter-hold the top bolt and tighten the locknut **(see illustrations 8.6 and 5b)**. Remove the open-ended spanner.

45 Pull the outer tube up and screw the top bolt into the tube carefully, making sure it is not cross-threaded **(see illustration)**. If required, the top bolt can be tightened once the leg is clamped in the bottom yoke.

46 Follow the procedure in Section 7 and install the fork leg.

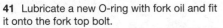

9 Steering stem

Removal

1 Remove the headlight panel or front number plate panel (see Chapter 8).

2 Remove the fuel tank (see Chapter 4).

3 Follow the procedure in Section 5, Step 7, and displace the handlebars. Note that it is not necessary to remove the handlebar components. Secure the handlebars so that no strain is placed on the wiring or the brake and clutch hose. Keep the fluid reservoirs upright to prevent leaks.

4 Remove the instrument cluster and wiring assemblies from the top yoke (see Chapter 9).

5 Remove the front mudguard (see Chapter 8).

6 Remove the front fork legs (see Section 7).

7 Loosen the steering stem clamp bolt in the fork top yoke.

8 Loosen the steering stem bolt, then support the bottom yoke, undo the stem bolt and lift the top yoke off **(see illustrations)**.

9 Lift off the bearing cover, seal and upper bearing inner race **(see illustrations)**.

10 Carefully lower the bottom yoke and steering stem out of the frame – the lower bearing inner race will remain on the steering stem **(see illustration)**.

11 The outer races of both bearings will remain in the steering head (see Section 10).

12 Use a suitable solvent to remove all traces of old grease from the bearings and races and check them for wear or damage as described in Section 10. **Note:** *Do not remove the bearings from the steering head or the steering stem unless they are to be replaced with new ones.*

9.8a Undo the steering stem bolt . . .

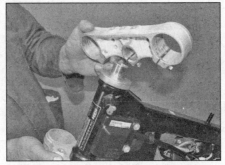

9.8b . . . and lift the top yoke off

9.9a Lift off the bearing cover . . .

9.9b . . . bearing seal . . .

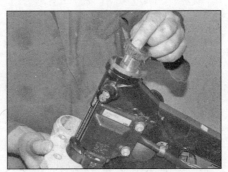

9.9c . . . and upper bearing inner race

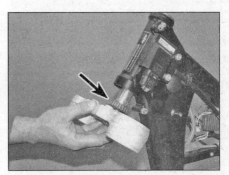

9.10 Lower the steering stem out – note the lower bearing inner race (arrowed)

9.14 Clean and grease the bearings before installation

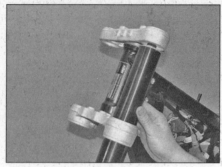

9.17 Check the alignment of the top and bottom yokes

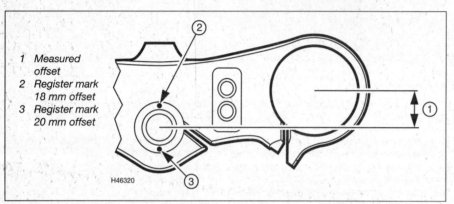

1 Measured offset
2 Register mark 18 mm offset
3 Register mark 20 mm offset

H46320

9.21 Front fork offset - XC and EXC Sixdays models

13 Check the upper bearing seal – if it is damaged or deteriorated, fit a new one.

Installation

14 Apply a liberal quantity of lithium-based grease onto the bearing races in the steering head and work some grease well into both the upper and lower bearings (see illustration).
15 Carefully lift the bottom yoke and steering stem up through the steering head. Install the upper bearing inner race, seal and bearing cover (see illustrations 9.9c, b and a).
16 Install the top yoke, then fit the steering stem bolt and tighten it finger-tight (see illustrations 9.8b and a).
17 Install the fork legs to align the top and bottom yokes, and temporarily tighten the bottom yoke pinch bolts (see illustration).
18 Follow the procedure in Chapter 1, Sec-

tion 21, and adjust the steering head bearings. Note that if new bearings have been fitted, it may be necessary to carry out the procedure several times to allow the bearings to settle.
19 Follow the procedure in Section 7 and install the front forks.
20 Install the remaining components in the reverse order of removal.

Fork offset

21 On XC, EXC Sixdays SX and SMR models, the front fork offset (the distance between the centre of the steering stem and the centre of the fork legs) can be set in either of two positions – unscrew the steering stem bolt and note the position of the register mark on the top edge of the stem (see illustration).
22 If the mark is at the front the offset is

18 mm – this setting provides directional stability on fast race courses.
23 If the mark is at the back the offset is 20 mm – this setting ensures better handling in corners. This is the standard setting.
24 To alter the offset, follow the procedure in Steps 1 to 6 above, then loosen the steering stem bottom bolt on the underside of the bottom yoke.
25 Remove the top yoke (Steps 7 and 8) then lift off the seal and bearing cover and lower the bottom yoke and steering stem out of the frame.
26 Undo the steering stem bottom bolt, then pull the stem out of the bottom yoke. Ensure that the mating surfaces between the stem and the yoke are clean, then turn the stem 180° and install it in the yoke. Clean the threads of the bottom bolt and apply a drop of the specified locking compound, then tighten the bolt finger-tight.
27 Install the steering stem and top yoke in the reverse order of removal – don't forget to check the condition of the upper bearing seal and fit a new one if necessary.
28 Tighten the bottom bolt to the specified torque setting.
29 Follow the procedure in Steps 17 to 20 above.

10 Steering head bearings

Inspection

1 Remove the steering stem (see Section 9) and use a suitable solvent to remove all traces of old grease from the bearings and races.
2 Check the tapered roller bearings for wear or damage. Inspect the rollers for signs of wear and pitting and examine the retainer cage for cracks or splits (see illustration). Inspect the races in the top and bottom of the steering head – they should be polished and free from indentations (see illustrations). If there are signs of wear or damage, renew the bearings.

Renewal

3 The bearing races can be driven out with a suitable drift inserted from the opposite end of

10.2a Inspect the bearing rollers and the retainer cage

10.2b Inspect the bearing races in the top . . .

10.2c . . . and bottom of the steering head

10.3 Drive the races out from the opposite end of the steering head with a suitable drift

the steering head **(see illustration)**. Move the drift around the edge of the bearing so that it is driven out squarely, a little at a time. **Note:** *Driving the bearing out will damage it – do not re-use the bearing.* Note which way round the bearing race is fitted.

4 The new bearing races can be installed in the steering head using a drawbolt arrangement, or by using a large diameter tubular drift **(see illustration)**. Ensure that the drawbolt washer or drift (as applicable) bears only on the outer edge of the bearing and does not contact the bearing surface.

Installation of new bearing outer races is made much easier if the races are left overnight in the freezer. This causes them to contract slightly making them a looser fit. Alternatively, use a freeze spray.

5 To remove the roller bearing race from the steering stem, first drive a chisel between the base of the race and the bottom yoke. Work the chisel around the race to ensure it lifts squarely. Once there is clearance beneath the race, use two levers placed on opposite sides of the race to work it free, using blocks of wood to improve leverage and protect the yoke **(see illustration)**. If the race is firmly in place it will be necessary to use a bearing puller **(see illustration)**.
6 Note the dust cover fitted between the bearing and the bottom yoke – if it is damaged when the bearing is removed, renew it.

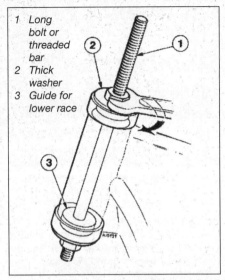

10.4 Drawbolt arrangement for fitting steering head bearings

1 Long bolt or threaded bar
2 Thick washer
3 Guide for lower race

7 Fit the dust cover and new roller bearing race onto the steering stem. A length of tubing with an internal diameter slightly larger than the steering stem will be needed to tap the new race into position **(see illustration)**.
8 Install the steering stem (see Section 9).

11 Rear shock absorber

Removal

1 Support the motorcycle securely in an upright position using an auxiliary stand **(see illustration 4.1 in Chapter 2)**.
2 Remove the rear wheel (see Chapter 7). Unclip the rear brake hose from the swingarm and secure the brake caliper to the rear sub-frame to prevent damage **(see illustration)**.
3 Place a block of wood underneath the swingarm so that it does not drop when the shock absorber bolts are removed **(see illustration)**.
4 Loosen the shock lower mounting bolt **(see illustration)**. Ensure that the swingarm

10.5a Lever the lower bearing race off the steering stem

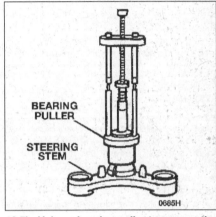

10.5b Using a bearing puller to remove the lower race from the steering stem

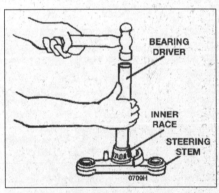

10.7 Drive the new race on with a suitable driver or length of pipe

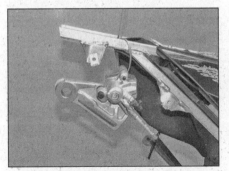

11.2 Secure the brake caliper to the rear sub frame

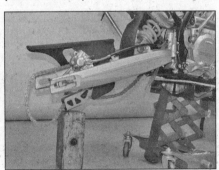

11.3 Support the swingarm with a block of wood

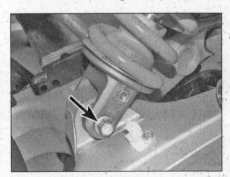

11.4a Loosen the lower mounting bolt (arrowed)

11.4b Support the swingarm and withdraw the bolt

11.5a Loosen the upper mounting bolt (arrowed)

11.5b Support the shock, withdraw the bolt . . .

is supported, then withdraw the bolt **(see illustration)**.

5 Loosen the upper shock mounting bolt **(see illustration)**. Support the shock, then withdraw the bolt and lift the shock out **(see illustrations)**.

Inspection

6 Clean the shock absorber thoroughly. Inspect the body of the shock for obvious damage and the coil spring for looseness, cracks or signs of fatigue **(see illustration)**.

7 Inspect the shock damper rod for signs of bending, pitting and oil leakage **(see illustration)**.

8 If any damage or evidence of oil leakage is found, renew the shock.

 Warning: Do not attempt to disassemble this shock absorber other than to fit a new spring.

Improper disassembly could result in serious injury. Take the shock to a KTM dealer or White Power Suspension specialist for servicing and disposal.

9 Check the spacers, seals and the bearing in the upper shock mount **(see illustration)**. If required, ease out the spacers and seals on both sides of the bearing and check that the bearing turns smoothly.

10 To renew the bearing, first prise out the retaining circlips, then press the bearing out. Press the new bearing in and secure it with new circlips. Fit new seals each side of the bearing, then press the spacers into place.

11 Inspect the spacers, seals and bearing in the lower shock mounting on the swingarm. Drive out the spacers to check the bearing **(see illustration)**. If the bearing is worn or damaged, follow the procedure in Section 13

to renew it. Note that it is not necessary to remove the swingarm to renew this bearing.

12 To remove the spring, first loosen the adjuster ring clamp screw, then, using a suitable C-spanner, turn the adjuster anti-clockwise to reduce pre-load **(see illustration 6.20)**. Turn the adjuster all the way up to the top of the thread.

13 Lift the spring seat and prise out the circlip from the bottom of the shock body, then draw off the spring seat and spring, noting which way round the spring coils fit **(see illustration)**.

14 Install the new spring and the spring seat, and secure them with a new circlip. Ensure that the circlip is located correctly in its groove.

15 Turn the adjuster clockwise to reset the spring pre-load – refer to the standard settings listed in the Specifications at the beginning

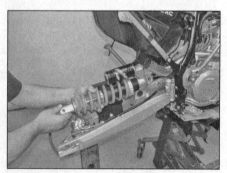

11.5c . . . and lift the shock out

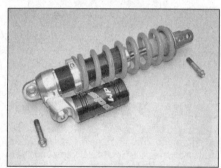

11.6 Clean the shock and inspect it for damage

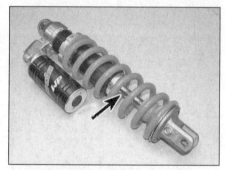

11.7 Check the damper rod for damage and oil leakage (arrowed)

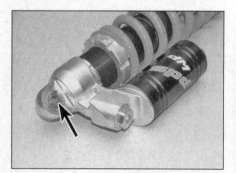

11.9 Check the bearing (arrowed) in the upper shock mount

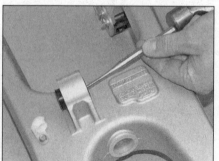

11.11 Drive out the spacers to check the bearing in the lower mount (arrowed)

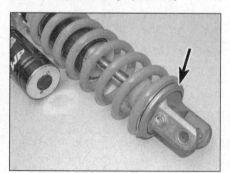

11.13 Lift the spring seat (arrowed) to remove the circlip

12.2a Remove the right-hand frame cover (arrowed) . . .

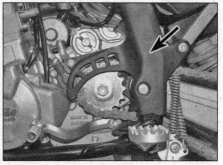

12.2b . . . and the final drive front sprocket cover (arrowed)

12.6a Note the location of the flat on the pivot bolt (arrowed)

of this Chapter. Once the shock has been installed on the bike, check the static sag and adjust the pre-load as necessary (see Section 6). Don't forget to tighten the clamp screw once the pre-load has been adjusted.

Installation

16 Installation is the reverse of removal. Clean the threads of the mounting bolts and apply a drop of the specified locking compound, then tighten the bolts to the torque settings specified at the beginning of this Chapter.
17 If required, follow the procedures in Section 6 to check and adjust the spring pre-load, rebound and compression damping.

12 Swingarm removal and installation

Removal

1 Support the motorcycle securely in an upright position using an auxiliary stand underneath the crankcase (see illustration 4.1 in Chapter 2).
2 Undo the screw(s) and, if fitted, the clips securing the right-hand frame cover, and undo the bolts and, if fitted, the clips securing the final drive front sprocket cover, then draw the covers off (see illustrations).
3 Remove the rear wheel and draw off the

drive chain (see Chapter 7). Displace the rear brake caliper and release the brake hose from the clips on the swingarm, then secure the brake caliper to the rear sub-frame to prevent damage (see illustration 11.2).
Caution: Don't operate the rear brake pedal with the wheel removed.
4 Remove the rear shock absorber (see Section 11).
5 Before removing the swingarm it is advisable to check for play in the bearings (see Chapter 1, Section 4). Any problems which were not evident with the rear wheel and shock in position may now show up.
6 Note how the flat on the right-hand end of the swingarm pivot bolt locates against the swingarm bracket (see illustration). Undo

the pivot bolt nut on the left-hand side, then support the swingarm and withdraw the pivot bolt (see illustrations). Note: *The pivot bolt nut is a self-locking type. A new nut should be fitted on installation, or the old nut secured with suitable non-permanent thread locking compound.*
7 Note how the swingarm pivots locate on each side of the crankcase, then draw the swingarm back and lift it off (see illustrations).
8 Install the frame cover screw insert in the end of the pivot bolt for safekeeping (see illustration).
9 Note the location of the seal covers fitted on each side of the swingarm pivots and remove them if they are loose (see illustration 13.2a).

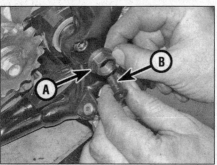

12.6b Undo the pivot bolt nut (A). Note the insert (B) for the sprocket cover bolt

12.6c Support the swingarm and withdraw the pivot bolt

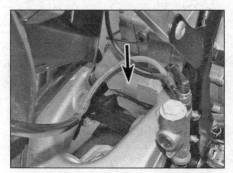

12.7a Swingarm pivots locate either side of the crankcase (arrowed)

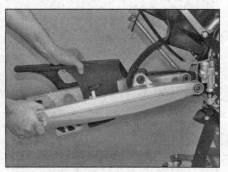

12.7b Draw the swingarm off

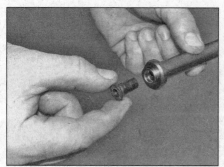

12.8 Install the frame cover screw insert for safekeeping

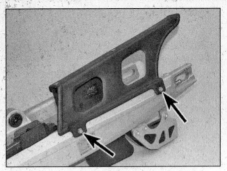

12.10a Undo the screws (arrowed) . . .

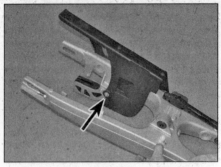

12.10b . . . securing the chainguard (arrowed) . . .

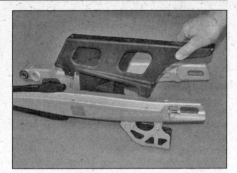

12.10c . . . and lift it off

12.11a Check the chain slider (arrowed) for wear

12.11b Slider protects both sides of the swingarm

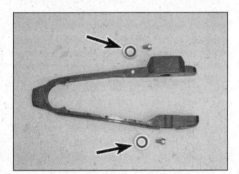

12.11c Note the special cup washers (arrowed) on the fixing screws

10 If required, undo the screws securing the chainguard and lift it off (see illustrations).

11 Inspect both sides of the chain slider – if it is worn or damaged, it should be replaced with a new one (see illustration). Undo the screws securing the slider and lift it off, noting the special cup washers fitted to the chain slider screws (see illustrations).

12 Inspect the plastic liner inside the chain guide – if it is worn or damaged, remove the chain guide and fit a new liner (see illustration).

13 Check the clips for the rear brake hose and renew them if they are sprained or broken (see illustration).

14 Inspect and lubricate the pivot bolt

and swingarm bearings as described in Section 13.

Installation

15 Clean the back of the crankcase and the frame around the swingarm mountings.

16 If removed, install the chain slider, chain guide and chainguard and tighten the mounting screws securely.

17 Ensure the seal covers are fitted on each side of the swingarm pivots. Position the swingarm so that the pivots and frame brackets align, then install the pivot bolt from the right-hand side (see illustration 12.6c). Push the bolt all the way through and align the flat on the right-hand end

against the flat on the swingarm bracket (see illustration 12.6a).

18 Install the pivot bolt nut and tighten it to the torque setting specified at the beginning of this Chapter (see Note Step 6).

19 Move the swingarm up and down through its full travel to ensure that it moves freely, without any binding or rough spots. If it does not move freely, find the cause of the problem before proceeding.

20 Install the remaining components in the reverse order of removal. Check and adjust the drive chain (see Chapter 1, Section 1), and check the operation of the rear suspension and rear brake before riding the machine.

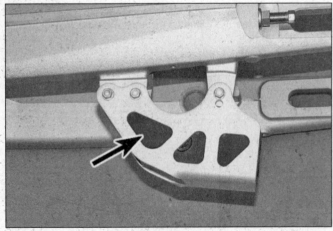

12.12 Renew the chain guide liner (arrowed) if it is worn or damaged

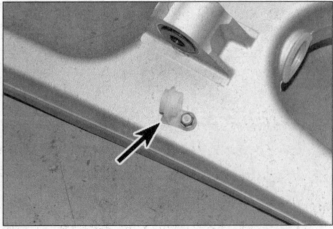

12.13 Check the clips for the rear brake hose (arrowed)

13 Swingarm inspection and bearing renewal

Inspection

1 Clean the swingarm with a suitable solvent, removing all traces of dirt, corrosion and grease. Pay particular attention to the area covered by the chain slider, the slots for the rear axle and the chain adjuster bolts. Unscrew the chain adjusters and check the condition of the threads in the swingarm; if they are damaged consult a specialist engineer or a KTM dealer to have them repaired.

2 Working on one swingarm pivot at a time, remove the seal covers, then draw out the bearing sleeve **(see illustrations)**.

3 Using a flat-bladed screwdriver, carefully prise out the seals from both sides of the bearings **(see illustration)**. Note which way round the seals are fitted. Note the location of any washers fitted behind the seals on the left-hand swingarm pivot.

4 Two needle roller bearings are fitted in each swingarm pivot.

5 Wipe the old grease out of the bearings with a clean rag, then inspect the rollers for signs of wear such as pitting and flat spots **(see illustration)**. Check the bearings for roughness, looseness and any other damage. Clean any corrosion off the sleeve with steel wool, then slip it back into its bearing and check that there is not an excessive amount of freeplay between the two components. Any damaged or worn component must be renewed.

6 Remove any corrosion from the swingarm pivot bolt with steel wool. Check the bolt for straightness by rolling it on a flat surface such as a piece of plate glass, or, if available, check the run-out with V-blocks. Renew the pivot bolt if it is bent. Prior to installation, lubricate the bolt with a smear of lithium-based grease.

7 Check the bearing in the lower shock

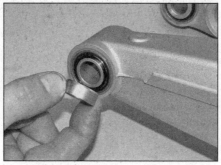

13.2a Remove the seal covers . . .

13.2b . . . and the bearing sleeve

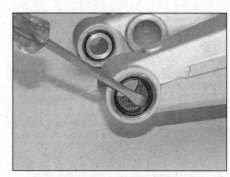

13.3 Prise out the bearing seals

13.5 Clean the bearings and inspect them for wear

mounting. Drive out the spacers and prise out the seals from each side of the bearing **(see illustrations)**. The bearing should turn smoothly without any roughness. If necessary, follow the procedure in Step 15 to renew the bearing.

Bearing renewal

8 The needle roller bearings can be drawn or driven out of their bores, but note that removal will make them unusable; new bearings should be obtained before work commences.

9 Before removal, measure the bearing inset.

It is important to install the new bearings in exactly the right position.

10 Remove the old bearings with a bearing driver or suitably-sized socket, or draw them out with a slide-hammer with knife-edged bearing puller attachment (see *Tools and Workshop Tips* in the *Reference* section).

11 Inspect the bearing seats and remove any scoring or corrosion carefully with steel wool or a suitable scraper.

12 The new bearings should be pressed or drawn into their bores, rather than driven into position. In the absence of a press, a suitable drawbolt arrangement can be made up. Grease

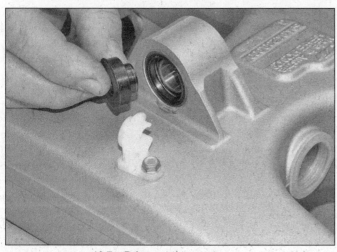

13.7a Drive out the spacers . . .

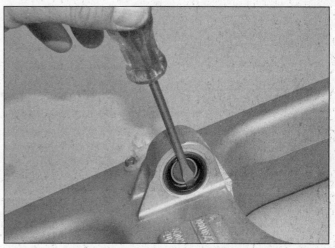

13.7b . . . and lever out the bearing seals in the lower shock mounting

13.14 Install the bearing sleeve and seal covers in both swingarm pivots

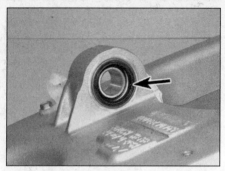

13.15a Measure the lower shock bearing inset (arrowed)

13.15b Use a suitably-sized socket to drive the old bearing out

the bearing locations to ease installation, and ensure the bearings are positioned exactly as noted on removal. Lubricate the new bearings with lithium-based grease.

13 Lubricate the new seals with a smear of grease and press them into place – don't forget to fit the washers between the bearings

and the seals on the left-hand swingarm pivot, if applicable.

14 Install the bearing sleeve and seal covers **(see illustration)**.

15 To renew the lower shock mounting bearing, first measure the bearing inset so that the new bearing is installed in exactly the

right position **(see illustration)**. Drive the old bearing out with a suitably-sized socket **(see illustration)**. Ensure that the bearing seat is clean and apply a smear of grease to ease installation. Drive or press the new bearing in. Lubricate the new seals with a smear of grease and press them into place.

Chapter 7
Brakes, wheels and final drive

Contents

Degrees of difficulty

Easy, suitable for novice with little experience	**Fairly easy,** suitable for beginner with some experience	**Fairly difficult,** suitable for competent DIY mechanic	**Difficult,** suitable for experienced DIY mechanic	**Very difficult,** suitable for expert DIY or professional

Specifications

Brakes

Brake fluid type . . . . DOT 5.1 glycol-based (compatible with DOT 4)
Brake pad and disc minimum thickness . . . . see Chapter 1

Wheels

Rim size
   EXC, MXC, XC models
      Front . . . . 21 in
      Rear . . . . 18 in
   SX and SXS models
      Front . . . . 21 in
      Rear . . . . 19 in
   SMR models
      Front and rear . . . . 17 in
Wheel runout (max)
   Axial (side-to-side) . . . . 2.0 mm
   Radial (out-of-round) . . . . 2.0 mm
Maximum axle runout (front and rear) . . . . 0.25 mm

Tyres

Tyre pressures . . . . see *Pre-ride checks*
Tyre sizes*
   Europe 250, 400, 450, 520 and 525 EXC, MXC Desert
      Front 90/90-21
      Rear 140/80-18
   US 400, 450, 520 and 525 EXC, MXC/XC
      Front 80/100-21
      Rear 110/100-18
   All SX and SXS models
      Front 80/100-21
      Rear 110/90-19
   All SMR models
      Front 120/75-17 KR106
      Rear 165/55-17 KR108

*Refer to the owners handbook, the tyre information label on the swingarm, or your dealer for approved tyre brands.

Final drive

Chain freeplay and stretch limit . . . .   see Chapter 1
Chain type
  2000 to 2002 models . . . .   O-ring 5/8 x 1/4 in
  2003-on models . . . .   X-ring 5/8 x 1/4 in

Torque settings

Front brake caliper mounting bolts . . . .   25 Nm*
Front brake master cylinder clamp bolts . . . .   14 Nm
Brake disc mounting bolts
  2000 to 2005. . . . .   10 Nm*
  2006-on . . . .   15 Nm*
Rear brake master cylinder mounting bolts . . . .   10 Nm*
Rear brake fluid reservoir mounting bolt (early models). . . . .   8 Nm
Rear brake pedal pivot bolt . . . .   50 Nm
Front axle nut . . . .   40 Nm
Front axle clamp bolts
  2000 to 2005. . . . .   10 Nm
  2006-on . . . .   15 Nm
Front sprocket cover bolts . . . .   10 Nm
Front sprocket bolt . . . .   60 Nm*
Rear sprocket nuts . . . .   35 Nm*
Rear axle nut . . . .   80 Nm
Chain guide bolt . . . .   25 Nm
Chain guide roller bolt . . . .   25 Nm*
Use thread locking compound Loctite 243

---

1 General information

All models are fitted with wire-spoked wheels with alloy rims designed for tubed tyres only.

Brakes are of Brembo manufacture. The front brake is a twin piston, sliding caliper, hydraulically-operated disc brake. The rear brake is a single piston, sliding caliper, hydraulically-operated disc brake.

Final drive is by chain and sprockets.

Caution: Disc brake components rarely require disassembly. Do not disassemble components unless absolutely necessary. If a brake hose is loosened, the entire system must be drained and then properly filled and bled upon reassembly. Do not use solvents on internal brake components. Solvents will cause the seals to swell and distort. Use only clean brake fluid or denatured alcohol for cleaning. Use care when working with brake fluid as it can injure your eyes and it will damage painted surfaces and plastic parts.

2 Brake pad renewal

⚠ **Warning: The dust created by the brake system may contain asbestos, which is harmful to your health. Never blow it out with compressed air and don't inhale any of it. An approved filtering mask should be worn when working on the brakes.**

Front brake pads

Removal

1 In operation, the brake caliper slides on its mounting bracket. To make pad removal easier, push the caliper towards the disc to push the pistons back into the caliper – this will relieve pressure between the brake pads and the disc **(see illustration)**.

2 Pull out the two R-clips securing the pad pin in the caliper **(see illustrations)**.

3 Withdraw the pad pin and pull the pads out

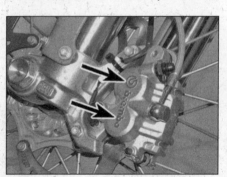

2.1 Push the caliper towards the disc (arrowed)

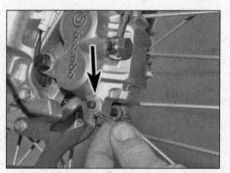

2.2a R-clips fit in the outside end of the pin (arrowed) . . .

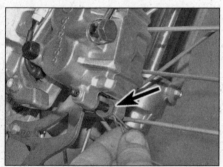

2.2b . . . and between the right-hand pad and the caliper (arrowed)

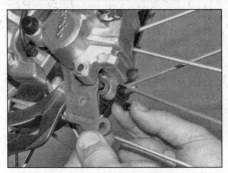

2.3a Pull out the pin, the left-hand pad . . .

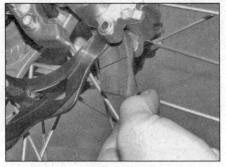

2.3b . . . and the right-hand pad

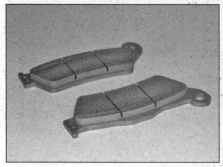

2.5 Check the friction material for wear and contamination

from the bottom of the caliper, noting how they fit **(see illustrations)**.

4 Note the location of the pad spring in the caliper and remove it if it is loose or damaged **(see illustration 3.15a)**. If the pad spring is dislodged when the pads are removed, undo the caliper mounting bolts and slide the caliper off the disc, then assemble the spring in the caliper (see Section 3). **Note:** *Do not operate the brake lever while the pads are out of the caliper.*

Inspection

5 Inspect the surface of both pads for contamination and check that the friction material has not worn down to, or beyond, the minimum thickness specified in Chapter 1 **(see illustration)**. If either pad is worn down to, or beyond, the service limit, is fouled with oil or grease, or is heavily scored or damaged by dirt and debris, both pads must be renewed as a set. **Note:** *It is not possible to degrease the friction material; if the pads are contaminated in any way, new ones must be fitted.*

6 Check that both pads have worn evenly at each end, and that overall they are both worn by the same amount. If uneven wear is noticed, one of the pistons is probably sticking in the caliper, or the caliper bracket slider pins are stuck, in which case the caliper must be overhauled (see Section 3).

7 If the pads are in good condition clean them carefully, using a fine wire brush which is completely free of oil and grease, to remove all traces of dirt and corrosion. Using a pointed instrument, carefully dig out any embedded particles of foreign matter.

8 Spray the caliper with a dedicated brake cleaner to remove any dirt or dust. Remove all traces of corrosion from the pad pin. If the R-clips are corroded, sprained or damaged, renew them. **Note:** *The clips and pin are available as a kit.*

9 Check the condition of the brake disc (see Section 4).

Installation

10 If new pads are being installed, push the pistons as far back into the caliper as

possible using hand pressure or a piece of wood as leverage. This will displace brake fluid back into the brake fluid reservoir, so it may be necessary to remove the reservoir top and siphon out some fluid. **Note:** *Don't lever against the brake disc to push the pistons back into the caliper as damage to the disc will result.*

11 If required, smear the backs of the pads and the pad pin lightly with copper-based grease, making sure that none gets on the front or sides of the pads.

12 Ensure the pad spring is a firm fit in the caliper, then install the pads so that the friction material faces the disc. Fit the right-hand pad first, ensuring that the upper end of the pad is located against the spring on the caliper bracket **(see illustration)**.

13 Push the pad back against the spring inside the caliper and insert the pad pin from

2.12 Push the pad up against the spring (arrowed)

2.14a Install the left-hand pad . . .

the right-hand side to secure the pad **(see illustrations)**.

14 Insert the left-hand pad, then push the pin through to secure the pad **(see illustrations)**.

15 Install the R-clips **(see illustrations 2.2a and b)**.

16 If necessary, top-up the brake fluid reservoir (see *Pre-ride checks*).

17 Operate the brake lever several times to bring the pads into contact with the disc. Check the operation of the front brake before riding the motorcycle.

Rear brake pads

Removal

18 In operation, the brake caliper slides on its mounting bracket. To make pad removal easier, push the caliper towards the disc to push the piston back into the caliper – this will

2.13 Secure the right-hand pad with the pin

2.14b . . . and push the pin all the way through

2.18 Push the caliper towards the disc (arrowed)

2.19a Pull out the right-hand . . .

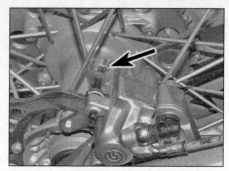

2.19b . . . and left-hand (arrowed) R-clips

relieve pressure between the brake pads and the disc (see illustration).
19 Pull out the two R-clips securing the pad pin in the caliper (see illustrations).
20 Withdraw the pad pin and pull the pads

out from the back of the caliper, noting how they fit (see illustrations). Note: *Do not operate the brake pedal while the pads are out of the caliper.*
21 Note the location of the pad spring in the

caliper and remove it if it is loose or damaged (see illustration).

Inspection

22 Note the location of the shim on the back of the right-hand pad (see illustration). The shim should be a tight fit – don't remove it unnecessarily.
23 Follow the procedure in Steps 5 to 9 to inspect and clean the pads.

Installation

24 If new pads are being installed, push the piston as far back into the caliper as possible using hand pressure or a piece of wood as leverage. This will displace brake fluid back into the brake fluid reservoir, so it may be necessary to remove the reservoir top and siphon out some fluid. Note: *Don't lever against the brake disc to push the piston back into the caliper as damage to the disc will result.*
25 If required, smear the backs of the pads and the pad pin lightly with copper-based grease, making sure that none gets on the front or sides of the pads.
26 Ensure the pad spring is a firm fit in the caliper (see illustration). If the pad spring was dislodged when the pads were removed, ensure it is fitted the right way round (see illustration 2.21).
27 Install the pads so that the friction material faces the disc. Fit the left-hand pad first, ensuring that the inner end is correctly located inside the caliper, then insert the pad pin from the left-hand side to secure the pad (see illustration).

2.20a Pull out the pad pin . . .

2.20b . . . then remove the right . . .

2.20c . . . and left-hand pads

2.21 Note the location of the pad spring

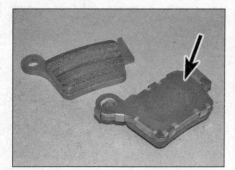

2.22 Note the location of the pad shim (arrowed)

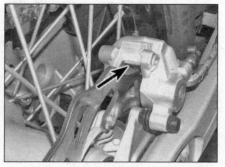

2.26 Check the location of the pad spring (arrowed)

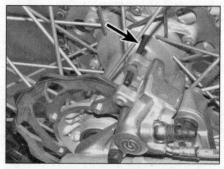

2.27 Insert the pad pin (arrowed) from the left-hand side

2.29 Install the R-clips (arrowed)

28 Insert the right-hand pad with the shim in place, then push the pin through to secure the pad **(see illustrations 2.20b and a).**

29 Install the R-clips **(see illustration).**

30 If necessary, top-up the brake fluid reservoir (see *Pre-ride checks*).

31 Operate the brake pedal several times to bring the pads into contact with the disc. Check the operation of the rear brake before riding the motorcycle.

3 Front brake caliper

⚠ *Warning: If the caliper indicates the need for an overhaul (usually due to leaking fluid or sticky operation), all old brake fluid should be flushed from the system. Also, the dust* created by the brake pads may contain asbestos, which is harmful to your health. Never blow it out with compressed air and do not inhale any of it. An approved filtering mask should be worn when working on the brakes. Do not, under any circumstances, use petroleum-based solvents to clean brake parts. Use clean DOT 5.1 brake fluid, dedicated brake cleaner or denatured alcohol only, as described.

Removal

1 Release the tie securing the speed sensor wiring to the brake caliper bracket, then disconnect the sensor wiring connector **(see illustrations).**

2 If the caliper is just being displaced, undo the caliper mounting bolts and slide the caliper off the disc **(see illustrations 3.4a and b).** Secure the caliper to the bike with a cable-tie to avoid straining the brake hose. **Note:** *Do not operate the brake lever while the caliper is off the disc.*

3 If the caliper is being completely removed or overhauled, first unscrew the brake hose banjo bolt and detach the banjo union, noting its alignment with the caliper **(see illustration).** Discard the sealing washers, as new ones must be used on reassembly. Wrap a clean plastic bag tightly around the end of the hose to prevent dirt entering the system and secure the hose in an upright position to minimise fluid loss. **Note:** *If you are planning to overhaul the caliper and do not have a source of compressed air to blow out the pistons, just loosen the banjo bolt at this stage* and retighten it lightly. The hydraulic system can then be used to force the pistons out of the caliper once the pads have been removed. Disconnect the hose once the pistons have been sufficiently displaced.

4 Undo the caliper mounting bolts and slide the caliper off the disc **(see illustrations).**
Caution: *Overhaul must be done in a spotlessly clean work area to avoid contamination and possible failure of the brake system. To prevent damage to the paint from spilled brake fluid, always cover nearby painted and plastic areas.*

Overhaul

5 Follow the procedure in Section 2 and remove the brake pads.

6 Pull off the caliper bracket, noting how it fits **(see illustration).** Note the location of the speed sensor.

7 Clean the exterior of the caliper with denatured alcohol or brake system cleaner. Note the location of the pad spring **(see illustration 3.15a).**

8 Displace the pistons from their bores using either compressed air or by carefully operating the front brake lever to pump them out. Make sure that both pistons are displaced at the same time. If compressed air is used, direct the air into the fluid inlet on the caliper. Use only low pressure to ease the pistons out – if the air pressure is too high and the pistons are forced out, the caliper may be damaged. If the pistons are being displaced hydraulically, it may be necessary to top-up the fluid reservoir during the procedure. Also, have some clean

3.1a Release the speed sensor wiring . . .

3.1b . . . and disconnect the wiring connector

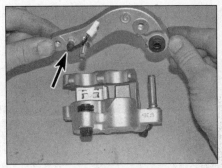

3.3 Detach the banjo union (arrowed) from the caliper

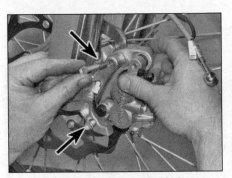

3.4a Undo the mounting bolts (arrowed) . . .

3.4b . . . and slide the caliper off the disc

3.6 Separate the caliper from the bracket. Note the speed sensor (arrowed)

3.9 Displacing a piston with compressed air

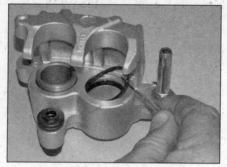

3.10 Removing the caliper seals

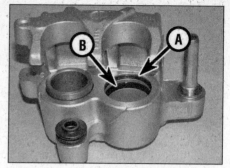

3.13 Install the new dust (A) and piston (B) seals

rag ready to catch the shower of brake fluid when the pistons reach the end of their bores.

⚠️ **Warning: Never place your fingers in front of the pistons in an attempt to catch or protect them when applying compressed air, as serious injury could result.**

9 If one piston sticks in its bore, hold the other piston in place with a block of wood, then try to displace the stuck piston with compressed air **(see illustration)**. If the piston cannot be displaced, the caliper will have to be replaced with a new one – do not try to remove the pistons by levering them out, or by using pliers or any other grips.

10 Remove the dust seals and piston seals from the caliper bores using a soft wooden or plastic tool to avoid scratching the bores **(see illustration)**. Discard the seals as new ones must be fitted on reassembly.

11 Clean the bores with clean brake fluid or brake system cleaner. If compressed air is available, blow it through the fluid galleries in the caliper to ensure they are clear and use it to dry the parts thoroughly (make sure it is filtered and unlubricated).

Caution: Do not, under any circumstances, use a petroleum-based solvent to clean brake parts.

12 Inspect the pistons and caliper bores for signs of corrosion, scratches and pitting. If surface defects are present, the pistons and/or caliper must be renewed. If the caliper is in bad shape, the master cylinder should also be checked.

13 Lubricate the new dust and piston seals with clean brake fluid and install them in their grooves in the caliper bores **(see illustration)**.

14 Lubricate the pistons with clean brake fluid and install them, closed-end first, into

the caliper bores **(see illustration)**. Using your thumbs, push the pistons all the way in, making sure they enter the bores squarely **(see illustration)**.

15 Clean all the old grease and any corrosion off the slider pin on the caliper and the caliper bracket, then lubricate the slider pins with silicone grease **(see illustrations)**. If required, ease the old boots out of the caliper and bracket and fit new ones. Make sure that the pad springs are in place in the caliper and on the caliper bracket, then press the caliper and bracket together **(see illustration)**.

16 Follow the procedure in Section 2 and install the brake pads.

Installation

17 Slide the caliper onto the brake disc, install the mounting bolts and tighten them to the torque setting specified at the beginning of this Chapter **(see illustrations 3.4b and a)**. If necessary, ease the pads apart with a large, flat-bladed screwdriver to obtain the necessary clearance to fit the caliper.

18 Connect the speed sensor wiring connector, then secure the wiring with a cable-tie **(see illustrations 3.1b and a)**.

19 If the caliper was just displaced, operate the brake lever several times to bring the pads into contact with the disc. Now go to Step 22.

20 If the caliper was completely removed, connect the brake hose to the caliper, using new sealing washers on each side of the banjo union. Align the union as noted on

3.14a Install the pistons closed-end first . . .

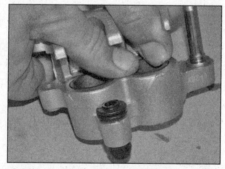

3.14b . . . and press them all the way into the caliper

3.15a Install the pad spring (A). Clean and lubricate the slider pin (B) on the caliper . . .

3.15b . . . and the caliper bracket (arrowed)

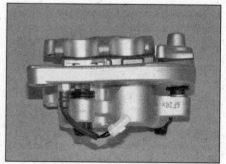

3.15c The assembled caliper

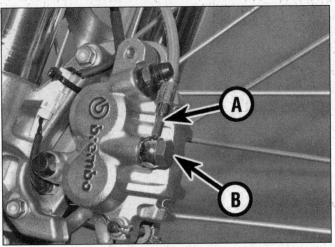

3.20 Align the union (A) and tighten the bolt (B) securely

4.4 Loosen the bolts (arrowed) evenly

removal. Tighten the banjo bolt securely (see illustration).

21 Top-up the fluid reservoir with the specified brake fluid and bleed air out of the system as described in Section 10. Check that there are no fluid leaks

22 Check the operation of the brake before riding the motorcycle. Note that the pads will need careful running-in before full brake performance is restored.

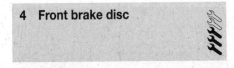

4 Front brake disc

Inspection

1 Follow the procedure in Chapter 1, Section 20, and inspect the brake disc. If the surface of the disc is badly damaged, or if the disc has worn down to the service limit, a new one will have to be fitted (see below).

2 Disc runout can be checked to determine if the disc is warped, and is particularly relevant if the bike has been dropped and the disc or caliper knocked. KTM don't specify a disc runout limit, but a good indication of any warpage can be gained by eye using a wire pointer as described. To check disc runout, position the bike on an auxiliary stand and support it so that the front wheel is raised off the ground. Attach a stiff wire pointer to the fork and position the end close to the surface of the disc about 10 mm (1/2 in) from the outer edge. Rotate the wheel and watch the gap between the disc and the tip of the pointer. If the gap varies as the wheel rotates, first check for play in the wheel bearings (see Chapter 1). If the bearings are worn, install new ones (see Section 16) and repeat this check. If the disc runout is still excessive, a new disc will have to be fitted.

Removal

3 Remove the wheel (see Section 12).

Caution: Don't lay the wheel down and allow it to rest on the disc – the disc could become warped. Set the wheel on wood blocks so the wheel rim supports the weight of the wheel.

4 If you are not replacing the disc with a new one, mark the relationship of the disc to the hub so that it can be installed in the same position. Unscrew the disc retaining bolts, loosening them evenly and a little at a time in a criss-cross pattern to avoid distorting the disc, then remove the disc (see illustration).

5 Note the location of the speed sensor magnet (see illustration). If required, remove the retaining circlip and press the magnet out of the disc. Installation is the reverse of removal – the circlip should be fitted on the inside face of the disc.

Installation

6 Before installing the disc, make sure there is no dirt or corrosion where the disc seats on the hub. If the disc does not sit flat when it is bolted down, it will appear to be warped when checked or when the front brake is used.

7 Install the disc on the hub; align the previously applied register marks if you are reinstalling the original disc.

8 Clean the threads of the disc mounting bolts, then apply a drop of the specified locking compound. Install the bolts and tighten them evenly and a little at a time in a criss-cross pattern to the torque setting specified at the beginning of this Chapter.

9 Clean the brake disc using acetone or brake system cleaner. If a new brake disc has been installed, remove any protective coating from its working surfaces. Always fit new pads if a new disc has been fitted.

10 Install the front wheel (see Section 12).

11 Operate the brake lever several times to bring the pads into contact with the disc. Check the operation of the brake before riding the motorcycle and remember that the new disc and pads will need to bed-in before full braking performance is restored.

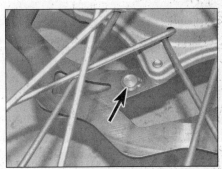

4.5 Location of the speed sensor magnet (arrowed)

5 Front brake master cylinder

1 If the front brake master cylinder is just being displaced, follow the procedure in Step 3. It is not necessary to disconnect the brake hose from the master cylinder.

2 If the master cylinder is leaking fluid, or if the brake lever does not feel firm when the brake is applied and bleeding the brake does not help (see Section 10), and the brake hose is in good condition, then the master cylinder must be overhauled or renewed.

Caution: Overhaul must be done in a spotlessly clean work area to avoid contamination and possible failure of the brake system. To prevent damage to the paint from spilled brake fluid, always cover nearby painted and plastic areas.

Removal

3 If the master cylinder is just being displaced, first cut the cable-tie securing the wiring to the brake hose, then pull back the lever cover and disconnect the brake light switch from the lever bracket (see illustrations). Note the alignment of the master cylinder with the handlebar, then undo the bolts, separate the

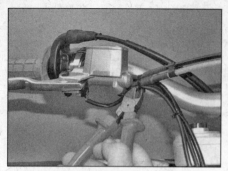

5.3a Separate the wiring from the brake hose

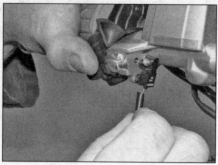

5.3b Disconnect the brake light switch from the lever bracket

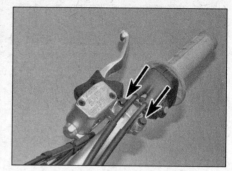

5.3c Undo the bolts (arrowed) . . .

two halves of the clamp and displace the master cylinder **(see illustrations)**. Secure the master cylinder to the bike with a cable-tie to avoid straining the brake hose. Keep the reservoir upright to prevent leakage.

4 If the master cylinder is being completely removed or overhauled, first pull off the lever cover **(see illustration)**. Cut the cable-tie securing the wiring to the brake hose **(see illustration 5.3a)**.

5 Undo the nut on the brake lever pivot bolt, then unscrew the bolt **(see illustration)**. Remove the lever assembly carefully, noting how the pushrod locates inside the boot on the master cylinder **(see illustration)**. On SX and US market MXC models, note the location of the tensioner spring.

6 Disconnect the brake light switch from the lever bracket **(see illustration 5.3b)**.

7 Cover the area around the master cylinder with rag to catch any fluid spills, then loosen the brake hose banjo bolt **(see illustration)**.

8 Note the alignment of the master cylinder with the handlebar, then undo the bolts, separate the two halves of the clamp and lift the master cylinder off **(see illustrations 5.3c and d)**.

9 Undo the brake hose banjo bolt and detach the banjo union from the master cylinder, noting its alignment **(see illustration)**. Discard the sealing washers from each side of the union as new ones must be used on reassembly. Wrap a clean plastic bag tightly around the end of the brake hose to prevent

dirt entering the system and secure it in an upright position.

Overhaul

10 Before disassembling the master cylinder, read through the entire procedure and make sure that you have obtained all the new parts required including some new DOT 5.1 brake fluid.

11 Undo the screws securing the fluid reservoir cover and lift off the cover and diaphragm. Drain the brake fluid into a suitable container. Wipe any remaining fluid out of the reservoir with a clean rag.

12 Inspect the reservoir cover and diaphragm and renew any parts if they are damaged or deteriorated.

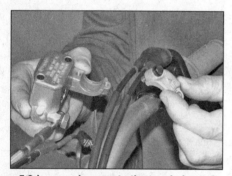

5.3d . . . and separate the two halves of the clamp

5.4 Remove the lever cover

5.5a Unscrew the pivot nut and bolt . . .

5.5b . . . and remove the lever . Note the pushrod (arrowed)

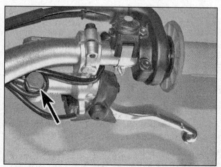

5.7 Loosen the brake hose banjo bolt (arrowed)

5.9 Detach the brake hose from the master cylinder

5.13 Remove the boot and boot spring

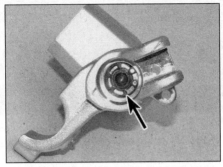

5.14a Note the location of the circlip (arrowed)

5.14b Depress the piston and remove the circlip

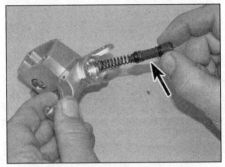

5.15 Withdraw the piston assembly (arrowed) and spring

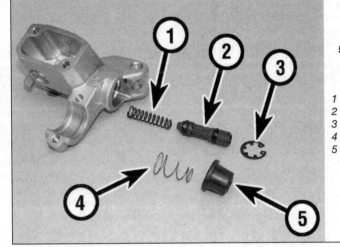

5.16 Components of the front brake master cylinder

1 Piston spring
2 Piston assembly
3 Circlip
4 Boot spring
5 Boot

13 Remove the boot and boot spring from the master cylinder, noting which way the spring is fitted (see illustration).

14 Note the location of the piston circlip, then depress the piston and use circlip pliers to remove the circlip (see illustrations).

15 Withdraw the piston assembly and spring from the master cylinder, noting how they fit (see illustration). If the piston is difficult to remove, apply low pressure compressed air to the brake fluid outlet.

16 Lay the parts out in the proper order to prevent confusion during reassembly (see illustration).

17 Clean the master cylinder with brake system cleaner. If compressed air is available, blow it through the fluid galleries to ensure they are clear and use it to dry the master

cylinder thoroughly (make sure the air is filtered and unlubricated).

Caution: Do not, under any circumstances, use a petroleum-based solvent to clean brake parts.

18 Check the master cylinder bore for corrosion, score marks and pitting. If damage or wear is evident, the master cylinder must be replaced with a new one. If the master cylinder is in poor condition, then the caliper should be checked as well.

19 The boot, circlip, piston assembly and spring are included in the master cylinder rebuild kit. Use all of the new parts, regardless

of the apparent condition of the old ones (see illustration 5.16).

20 Fit the narrow end of the spring onto the inner end of the piston (see illustration). Lubricate the piston assembly with clean brake fluid and fit the assembly into the master cylinder, spring first (see illustration 5.15).

21 Depress the piston and install the new circlip, making sure that it locates properly in its groove (see illustrations 5.14b and a).

22 Install the spring, wide end first, and the boot (see illustration 5.13). Press the boot firmly into its seat in the master cylinder using a suitably-sized socket (see illustration).

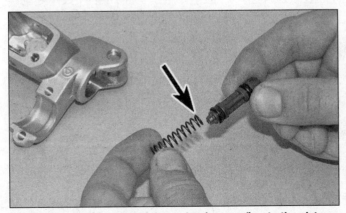

5.20 Fit the narrow end of the spring (arrowed) onto the piston

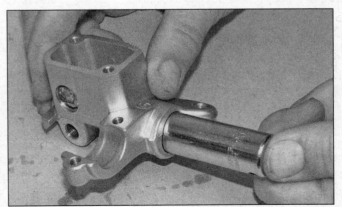

5.22 Installing the boot with a small socket

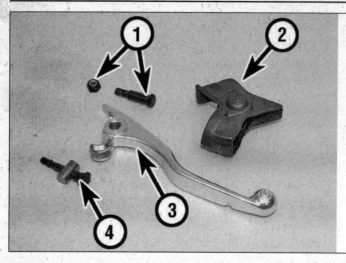

5.23 Components of the front brake lever assembly

1 Pivot nut and bolt
2 Lever cover
3 Brake lever
4 Lever pushrod

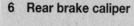

Warning: *If the caliper indicates the need for an overhaul (usually due to leaking fluid or sticky operation), all old brake fluid should be flushed from the system. Also, the dust created by the brake pads may contain asbestos, which is harmful to your health. Never blow it out with compressed air and do not inhale any of it. An approved filtering mask should be worn when working on the brakes. Do not, under any circumstances, use petroleum-based solvents to clean brake parts. Use clean DOT 5.1 brake fluid, dedicated brake cleaner or denatured alcohol only, as described.*

23 Inspect the lever assembly components for wear and renew any parts as necessary **(see illustration)**.

24 Insert the lever pushrod through the boot, then position the lever assembly in the bracket **(see illustrations)**. On SX and US market MXC models, don't forget to install the tensioner spring. Secure the lever with the pivot bolt and tighten the pivot bolt nut securely

25 Connect the brake hose to the master cylinder, using new sealing washers on each side of the banjo union. Align the union as noted on removal **(see illustration)**.

Installation

26 Align the master cylinder with the handlebar as noted on removal, then tighten the clamp bolts to the torque setting specified at the beginning of this Chapter.

27 Install the brake light switch and secure the wiring to the brake hose. Now go to Step 30.

28 If the master cylinder was completely removed, tighten the brake hose banjo bolt securely **(see illustration 5.7)**.

29 Top-up the fluid reservoir with DOT 5.1 brake fluid and bleed air out of the system as described in Section 10. Check that there are no fluid leaks. Don't forget to refit the lever cover **(see illustration 5.4)**.

30 Check the operation of the brake and the brake light before riding the motorcycle.

Removal

1 If the caliper is being completely removed or overhauled, cover the swingarm with rag to catch any fluid spills, then loosen the brake hose banjo bolt **(see illustration)**.

2 Remove the rear wheel (see Section 14).

3 If the caliper is just being displaced, release the brake hose from the clips on the swingarm, then lift the caliper off the swingarm and secure it to the rear sub-frame to prevent damage **(see illustrations)**. **Note:** *Do not operate the brake pedal while the caliper is off the disc.*

4 If the caliper is being completely removed

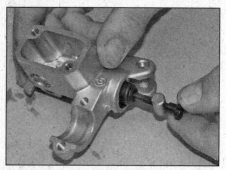

5.24a Insert the lever pushrod through the boot . . .

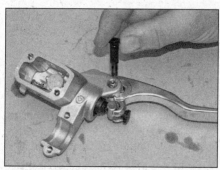

5.24b . . . then position the lever assembly in the bracket

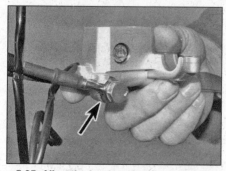

5.25 Align the banjo union (arrowed) as noted on removal

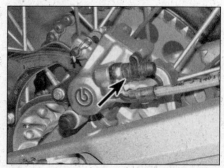

6.1 Loosen the brake hose banjo bolt (arrowed)

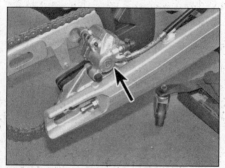

6.3a Displace the caliper (arrowed) from the swingarm . . .

6.3b . . . and secure it to the rear sub frame with a cable-tie

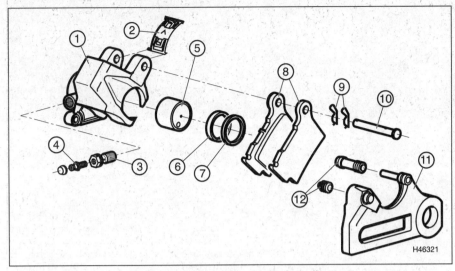

6.6 Components of the rear brake caliper

1 Brake caliper	5 Piston	9 R-clips
2 Pad spring	6 Piston seal	10 Pad pin
3 Banjo bolt	7 Dust seal	11 Caliper bracket
4 Bleed valve	8 Brake pads	12 Slider pin boots

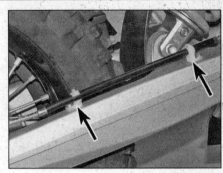

6.18 Secure the brake hose to the swingarm with the clips (arrowed)

or overhauled, unscrew the brake hose banjo bolt and detach the banjo union, noting its alignment with the caliper. Discard the sealing washers, as new ones must be used on reassembly. Wrap a clean plastic bag tightly around the end of the hose to prevent dirt entering the system and secure the hose in an upright position to minimise fluid loss.

Note: *If you are planning to overhaul the caliper and do not have a source of compressed air to blow out the piston, just loosen the banjo bolt at this stage and retighten it lightly. The hydraulic system can then be used to force the piston out of the caliper once the pads have been removed. Disconnect the hose once the piston has been sufficiently displaced.*

Overhaul

5 Follow the procedure in Section 2 and remove the brake pads.

6 Pull off the caliper bracket, noting how it fits **(see illustration)**.

7 Clean the exterior of the caliper with denatured alcohol or brake system cleaner. Note the location of the pad spring.

8 Displace the piston from its bore using either compressed air or by carefully operating the rear brake pedal to pump it out. If compressed air is used, direct the air into the fluid inlet on the caliper. Use only low pressure to ease the piston out – if the air pressure is too high and the piston is forced out, the caliper may be damaged. If the piston is being displaced hydraulically, it may be necessary to top-up the fluid reservoir during the procedure. Also, have some clean rag ready to catch the shower of brake fluid when the piston reaches the end of its bore.

 Warning: Never place your fingers in front of the piston in an attempt to catch or protect it when

applying compressed air, as serious injury could result.

9 If the piston sticks in its bore, try to displace it with compressed air. If the piston cannot be displaced, the caliper will have to be replaced with a new one – do not try to remove the piston by levering it out, or by using pliers or any other grips.

10 Remove the dust and piston seals from the caliper bore using a soft wooden or plastic tool to avoid scratching the bore **(see illustration 3.10)**. Discard the seals as new ones must be fitted on reassembly.

11 Clean the bore with clean DOT 5.1 brake fluid or brake system cleaner. If compressed air is available, blow it through the fluid galleries in the caliper to ensure they are clear and use it to dry the parts thoroughly (make sure it is filtered and unlubricated).

Caution: Do not, under any circumstances, use a petroleum-based solvent to clean brake parts.

12 Inspect the piston and caliper bore for signs of corrosion, scratches and pitting. If surface defects are present, the piston and/ or caliper must be renewed. If the caliper is in bad shape, the master cylinder should also be checked.

13 Lubricate the new dust and piston seals with clean DOT 5.1 brake fluid and install them in their grooves in the caliper bore **(see illustration 3.13)**.

14 Lubricate the piston with clean DOT 5.1 brake fluid and install it, closed-end first, into the caliper bore. Using your thumbs, push the piston all the way in, making sure it enters the bore squarely.

15 Clean all the old grease and any corrosion off the slider pin on the caliper and the caliper bracket, then lubricate the slider pins with silicone grease. If required, ease the old boots

out of the caliper bracket and fit new ones, then press the caliper and bracket together.

16 Make sure that the pad spring is in place in the caliper, then follow the procedure in Section 2 and install the brake pads.

Installation

17 Locate the caliper onto its lug on the swingarm, then install the rear wheel (see Section 14). If necessary, ease the pads apart with a large, flat-bladed screwdriver to obtain the necessary clearance to fit the brake disc between the pads in the caliper.

18 If the caliper was just displaced, secure the brake hose to the swingarm with the clips **(see illustration)**. Operate the brake pedal several times to bring the pads into contact with the disc. Now go to Step 21. Check the operation of the brake before riding the motorcycle.

19 If the caliper was completely removed, connect the brake hose to the caliper, using new sealing washers on each side of the banjo union. Align the union as noted on removal and tighten the banjo bolt securely **(see illustration 6.1)**.

20 Top-up the fluid reservoir with DOT 5.1 brake fluid and bleed air out of the system as described in Section 10. Check that there are no fluid leaks

21 Check the operation of the brake before riding the motorcycle.

---

7 Rear brake disc

Inspection

1 Refer to Section 4 of this Chapter, noting that the pointer or gauge should be attached to the swingarm.

Removal

2 Remove the rear wheel (see Section 14).

Caution: Don't lay the wheel down and allow it to rest on the disc or the sprocket – they could become warped. Set the wheel on wood blocks so the wheel rim supports the weight of the wheel.

7.3 Loosen the bolts (arrowed) evenly

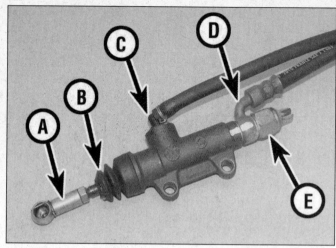

8.9 Rear brake master cylinder assembly – pushrod (A), boot (B), reservoir hose union (C), brake hose banjo union (D) and brake light switch (E)

3 If you are not replacing the disc with a new one, mark the relationship of the disc to the hub so that it can be installed in the same position. Unscrew the disc retaining bolts, loosening them evenly and a little at a time in a criss-cross pattern to avoid distorting the disc, then remove the disc (see illustration).

Installation

4 Before installing the disc, make sure there is no dirt or corrosion where the disc seats on the hub. If the disc does not sit flat when it is bolted down, it will appear to be warped when checked or when the rear brake is used.
5 Install the disc on the hub; align the previously applied register marks if you are reinstalling the original disc.
6 Clean the threads of the disc mounting bolts, then apply a drop of the specified locking compound. Install the bolts and tighten them evenly and a little at a time in a criss-cross pattern to the torque setting specified at the beginning of this Chapter.
7 Clean the brake disc using acetone or brake system cleaner. If a new brake disc has been installed, remove any protective coating from its working surfaces.
8 Install the rear wheel (see Section 14).
9 Operate the brake pedal several times to bring the pads into contact with the disc. Check the operation of the brake before riding the motorcycle.

8 Rear brake master cylinder

1 If the rear brake master cylinder is just being displaced, follow the appropriate procedure below, noting that it is not necessary to disconnect the brake hose from the master cylinder.
2 If the master cylinder is leaking fluid, or if the brake pedal does not feel firm when the

brake is applied and bleeding the brake does not help (see Section 10), and the brake hose is in good condition, then the master cylinder must be overhauled or renewed.
Caution: Overhaul must be done in a spotlessly clean work area to avoid contamination and possible failure of the brake system. To prevent damage to the paint from spilled brake fluid, always cover nearby painted and plastic areas.

2000 to 2003 models

Removal

3 Undo the screws securing the right-hand frame cover and draw the cover off (see illustration 8.37).
4 Displace the boot on the top of the master cylinder and disconnect the rear brake light switch wiring connectors.
5 Undo the bolt securing the joint on the rear brake master cylinder pushrod to the brake pedal and separate the pushrod from the pedal (see illustration 8.38).
6 Unclip the brake hose from the swingarm (see illustration 6.18).
7 If the master cylinder is just being displaced, undo the bolts securing the master cylinder to the frame. Undo the bolt securing the brake fluid reservoir bracket to the crankcase. Displace the master cylinder and reservoir and secure the assembly to the bike with cable-ties to avoid straining the hoses. Keep the reservoir upright to prevent fluid loss.
8 If the master cylinder is being completely removed or overhauled, cover the area around the master cylinder with rag to catch any fluid spills, then loosen the rear brake light switch. Undo the bolts securing the master cylinder to the frame and undo the bolt securing the brake fluid reservoir bracket to the crankcase.
9 Displace the master cylinder and reservoir, then unscrew the brake light switch and detach the brake hose banjo union from the master cylinder (see illustration). Discard the sealing

washers from either side of the banjo union as new ones must be used on reassembly. Wrap a clean plastic bag tightly around the end of the hose to prevent dirt entering the system and secure it in an upright position.

Overhaul

10 Before disassembling the master cylinder, read through the entire procedure and make sure that you have obtained all the new parts required including some new DOT 5.1 brake fluid.
11 Unscrew the fluid reservoir cap and lift off the diaphragm. Drain the brake fluid into a suitable container. Wipe any remaining fluid out of the reservoir with a clean rag.
12 Withdraw the pushrod and pull the boot off the lower end of the master cylinder, noting how it fits (see illustrations).
13 Release the clip securing the reservoir hose to the union on the master cylinder and detach the hose (see illustration). Inspect the hose for cracks or splits and renew it if necessary. Check the hose clips and renew them if they are sprained or corroded. Inspect the reservoir cap and diaphragm and renew any parts if they are damaged or deteriorated.
14 Note the location of the piston circlip in the end of the master cylinder, then use circlip pliers to remove the circlip (see illustrations).
15 Withdraw the piston and spring, noting how they fit (see illustration). If the piston is difficult to remove, apply low pressure compressed air to the brake fluid outlet.
16 Clean the master cylinder with brake system cleaner. If compressed air is available, blow it through the fluid galleries to ensure they are clear and use it to dry the master cylinder thoroughly (make sure the air is filtered and unlubricated).
Caution: Do not, under any circumstances, use a petroleum-based solvent to clean brake parts.
17 Check the master cylinder bore for corrosion, score marks and pitting. If damage

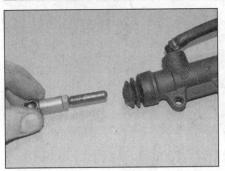

8.12a Draw out the pushrod . . .

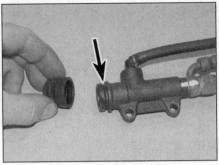

8.12b . . . and pull off the boot noting how it fits in the groove (arrowed)

8.13 Detach the reservoir hose from the union on the master cylinder

8.14a Note the location of the circlip (arrowed) . . .

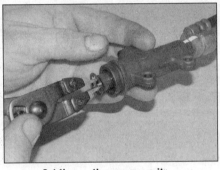

8.14b . . . then remove it . . .

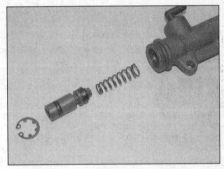

8.15 . . . and withdraw the piston and spring

or wear is evident, the master cylinder must be replaced with a new one. If the master cylinder is in poor condition, then the caliper should be checked as well.

18 The boot, circlip, piston assembly and spring are included in the master cylinder rebuild kit. Use all of the new parts, regardless of the apparent condition of the old ones. Fit them according to the layout of the old piston assembly **(see illustration 8.15).**

19 Fit the narrow end of the spring onto the inner end of the piston. Lubricate the piston assembly with DOT 5.1 brake fluid and fit the assembly into the master cylinder, spring first.

20 Depress the piston and install the new circlip, making sure it is properly located in its groove **(see illustration 8.14a).**

21 Install the boot, making sure the lip is seated properly in the groove **(see illustration 8.12b).**

22 Clean the pushrod and remove any corrosion with steel wool, then lubricate it with a smear of silicone grease. Install the pushrod in the lower end of the master cylinder **(see illustration 8.12a).**

23 Connect the reservoir hose to the master cylinder and secure it with the clip.

Installation

24 If the master cylinder was just displaced, install the master cylinder and fluid reservoir, check the alignment of the hoses, then tighten the mounting bolts to the torque settings specified at the beginning of this Chapter.

Secure the brake hose to the swingarm with the clips.

25 Align the joint on the master cylinder pushrod with the brake pedal and install the bolt, then tighten it securely **(see illustration 8.38).** Ensure there is between 3 to 5 mm free travel in the pedal before the pushrod contacts the master cylinder piston. If necessary, follow the procedure in Chapter 1, Section 3, and adjust the freeplay.

26 Connect the rear brake light switch wiring connectors and install the boot.

27 Install the right-hand frame cover and tighten the screws securely. Check the operation of the brake and the brake light before riding the motorcycle.

28 If the master cylinder was completely removed, connect the brake hose banjo union to the master cylinder, using new sealing washers on each side of the banjo union, and tighten the brake light switch finger-tight.

29 Install the master cylinder and fluid reservoir and tighten the mounting bolts to the torque settings specified at the beginning of this Chapter.

30 Check the alignment of the brake hose, then tighten the rear brake light switch securely. Secure the brake hose to the swingarm with the clips.

31 Connect the pushrod to the brake pedal (see Step 25).

32 Connect the rear brake light switch wiring connectors and install the boot.

33 Fill the fluid reservoir with DOT 5.1

brake fluid and bleed air from the system as described in Section 10. Check that there are no fluid leaks.

34 Install the right-hand frame cover and tighten the screws securely.

35 Check the operation of the brake and the brake light before riding the motorcycle.

2004-on models

Removal

36 Remove the seat (see Chapter 8). Trace the wiring from the brake light switch and disconnect it at the connector. Release the wiring from any clips or ties and feed it back to the master cylinder.

37 Undo the screw and clip securing the right-hand frame cover, then draw the cover off **(see illustration).**

8.37 Remove the right-hand frame cover

8.38 Bolt (arrowed) secures master cylinder pushrod to the brake pedal

8.40 Undo the bolts (arrowed) to displace the master cylinder

38 Undo the bolt securing the joint on the rear brake master cylinder pushrod to the brake pedal and separate the pushrod from the pedal **(see illustration)**.

39 Unclip the brake hose from the swingarm **(see illustration 6.18)**.

40 If the master cylinder is just being displaced, undo the bolts securing the master cylinder to the frame and lift the master cylinder off **(see illustration)**. Secure the master cylinder to the bike with a cable-tie to avoid straining the hose. Keep the master cylinder upright to prevent fluid loss from the reservoir.

41 If the master cylinder is being completely removed or overhauled, cover the area around the master cylinder with rag to catch any fluid spills, then loosen the brake light switch **(see illustration)**.

42 Undo the bolts securing the master cylinder to the frame **(see illustration 8.40)**. Lift

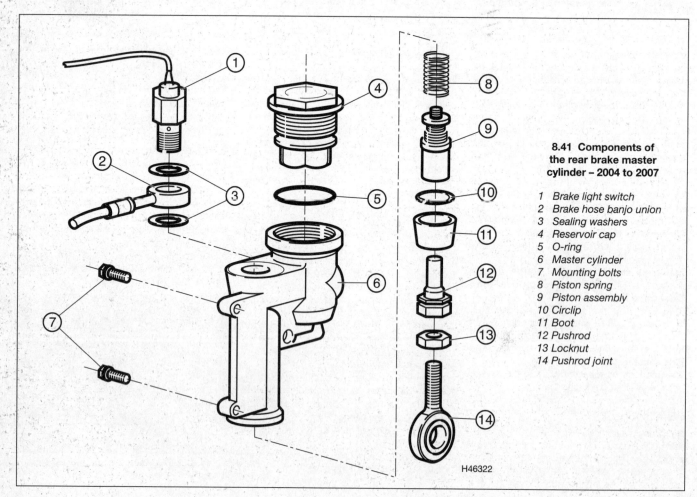

8.41 Components of the rear brake master cylinder – 2004 to 2007

1 Brake light switch
2 Brake hose banjo union
3 Sealing washers
4 Reservoir cap
5 O-ring
6 Master cylinder
7 Mounting bolts
8 Piston spring
9 Piston assembly
10 Circlip
11 Boot
12 Pushrod
13 Locknut
14 Pushrod joint

H46322

the master cylinder off, noting the alignment of the brake hose **(see illustration)**.

43 Unscrew the brake light switch and detach the banjo union from the master cylinder. Discard the sealing washers from each side of the union as new ones must be used on reassembly. Wrap a clean plastic bag tightly around the end of the brake hose to prevent dirt entering the system and secure it in an upright position.

Overhaul

44 Follow the procedure in Steps 10 to 22, noting that on 2004-on models, the brake fluid reservoir is integral with the body of the master cylinder and no diaphragm is fitted below the reservoir cap. Inspect the reservoir cap O-ring and renew it if it is damaged or deteriorated **(see illustration)**.

Installation

45 Follow the procedure in Steps 24 to 35, noting that on 2004-on models, the rear brake light switch wiring should be secured clear of the rear suspension unit after connection.

---

9 Brake hoses and unions

Inspection

1 Brake hose condition should be checked regularly and the hoses renewed at the specified interval (see Chapter 1).

2 Twist and flex the hoses while looking for cracks, bulges and seeping brake fluid. Check extra carefully where the hoses connect with the banjo unions, as this is a common area for hose failure.

3 Check the banjo unions connected to the brake hoses. If the unions are rusted, scratched or cracked, fit new hoses.

Renewal

4 The brake hoses have banjo unions on each end. Cover the surrounding area with plenty of rags and unscrew the banjo bolt at each end

8.42 Note the alignment of the brake hose (arrowed)

of the hose, noting the alignment of the union with the master cylinder or brake caliper **(see illustrations 3.3, 5.9 and 6.1)**. Free the hose from any clips or guides and remove it, noting its routing. Discard the sealing washers.

5 Position the new hose, making sure it is not twisted or otherwise strained, and ensure that it is correctly routed through any clips or guides and is clear of all moving components.

6 Check that the unions align correctly, then install the banjo bolts, using new sealing washers on both sides of the unions. Tighten the banjo bolts securely.

7 Top-up the brake fluid reservoir with DOT 5.1 brake fluid, then flush out the old fluid and bleed air out of the system as described in Section 10.

8 Check the operation of the brakes before riding the motorcycle.

---

10 Brake system bleeding and fluid change

Caution: Support the bike in a upright position and ensure that the fluid reservoirs are level while carrying-out these procedures.

Bleeding the brakes

1 Bleeding the brakes is simply the process

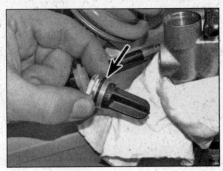

8.44 Check the condition of the reservoir cap O-ring (arrowed)

of removing air from the brake fluid reservoir, master cylinder, hose and brake caliper. Bleeding is necessary whenever a brake system connection is loosened, when a component or hose is renewed, or when the master cylinder or caliper is overhauled. Leaks in the system may also allow air to enter, but leaking brake fluid will reveal their presence and warn you of the need for repair.

2 To bleed the brakes, you will need some new DOT 5.1 brake fluid, a length of clear vinyl or plastic hose, a small container partially filled with clean brake fluid, some rags and a spanner to fit the brake caliper bleed valve. If using a 'one man' type brake bleeding kit, as shown in illustration 10.5b, you'll just need some new DOT 5.1 brake fluid, some rags and a spanner to fit the bleed valve.

3 Cover all painted or plastic components to prevent damage in the event that brake fluid is spilled.

4 Remove the reservoir cover or cap, and the diaphragm where fitted, and slowly pump the brake lever (front brake) or pedal (rear brake) a few times, until no air bubbles can be seen floating up from the holes in the bottom of the reservoir **(see illustration)**. This bleeds the air from the master cylinder end of the line. Temporarily refit the reservoir cap.

5 Pull the dust cap off the bleed valve **(see illustration)**. Attach one end of the clear

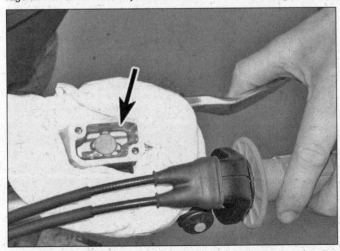

10.4 Bleed air from the top end of the brake system (arrowed)

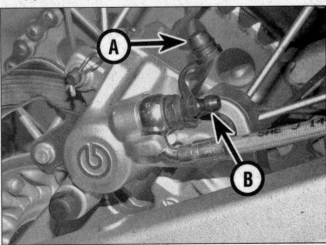

10.5a Pull the cap (A) off the bleed valve (B)

10.5b Set-up for bleeding the brakes

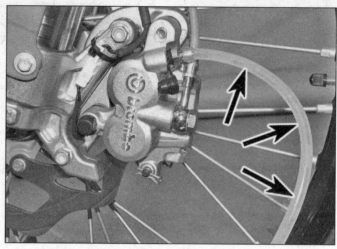

10.7 Check for air bubbles (arrowed) in the brake fluid

vinyl or plastic hose to the bleed valve and submerge the other end in the clean brake fluid in the container **(see illustration)**. **Note:** *To avoid damaging the bleed valve during the procedure, loosen it and then tighten it temporarily with a ring spanner before attaching the hose. With the hose attached, the valve can then be opened and closed with an open-ended spanner.*

6 Remove the reservoir cap and check the fluid level. Do not allow the fluid to drop below the minimum mark or level during the procedure – see *Pre-ride checks* for fluid levels.

7 Carefully pump the brake lever or pedal three or four times and hold it in (front) or down (rear) while opening the caliper bleed valve. When the valve is opened, brake fluid will flow out of the caliper into the clear tubing, and the lever will move toward the handlebar, or the pedal will move down. If there is air in the system there will be air bubbles in the brake fluid coming out of the caliper **(see illustration)**.

8 Retighten the bleed valve, then release the brake lever or pedal gradually. Top-up the reservoir and repeat the process until no air bubbles are visible in the brake fluid leaving the caliper, and the lever or pedal is firm when applied. On completion, disconnect the hose, tighten the bleed valve and install the dust cap.

> **HAYNES HiNT**
> *If it is not possible to produce a firm feel to the lever or pedal, the fluid may be aerated. Let the brake fluid in the system stabilise for a few hours and then repeat the procedure when the tiny bubbles in the system have settled out.*

9 Top-up the reservoir, install the diaphragm (if fitted) and cap, and wipe up any spilled brake fluid. Check the entire system for fluid leaks.

10 Check the operation of the brakes before riding the motorcycle.

Changing the fluid

11 Changing the brake fluid is a similar process to bleeding the brakes and requires the same materials plus a suitable tool for siphoning the fluid out of the reservoir. Also ensure that the container is large enough to take all the old fluid when it is flushed out of the system.

12 Follow Steps 3 and 5, then remove the reservoir cap and siphon the old fluid out of the reservoir. Fill the reservoir with new brake fluid, then follow Step 7.

13 Retighten the bleed valve, then release the brake lever or pedal gradually. Keep the reservoir topped-up with new fluid above the minimum level at all times or air may enter the system and greatly increase the length of the task. Repeat the process until new fluid can be seen emerging from the bleed valve.

> **HAYNES HiNT**
> *Old brake fluid is invariably much darker in colour than new fluid, making it easy to see when all old fluid has been expelled from the system.*

14 Disconnect the hose, then tighten the bleed valve and install the dust cap.

15 Top-up the reservoir, install the diaphragm (if fitted) and cap, and wipe up any spilled brake fluid. Check the entire system for fluid leaks.

16 Check the operation of the brakes before riding the motorcycle.

11 Wheel runout and alignment

Wheel runout

1 In order to carry out a proper inspection of the wheels, it is necessary to support the bike upright so that the wheel being inspected is raised off the ground. Position the motorcycle on an auxiliary stand.

2 Clean the wheels thoroughly to remove mud and dirt that may interfere with the inspection procedure or mask defects. Make a general check of the wheels and tyres (see Chapter 1 and *Pre-ride checks*).

3 Attach a dial gauge to the fork or the swingarm and position its tip against the side of the wheel rim. Spin the wheel slowly and check the axial (side-to-side) runout at the rim **(see illustration)**.

4 In order to accurately check radial (out of round) runout with the dial gauge, remove the wheel from the machine, and the tyre from the wheel. With the axle clamped in a vice and the dial gauge positioned on the top of the rim, the wheel can be rotated to check the runout.

5 An easier, though slightly less accurate, method is to attach a stiff wire pointer to the fork or the swingarm and position the end a fraction of an inch from the edge of the wheel rim where the wheel and tyre join. If the wheel is true, the distance from the pointer to the rim

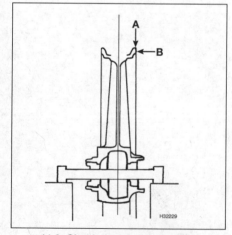

11.3 Check the wheel for radial (out-of-round) runout (A) and axial (side-to-side) runout (B)

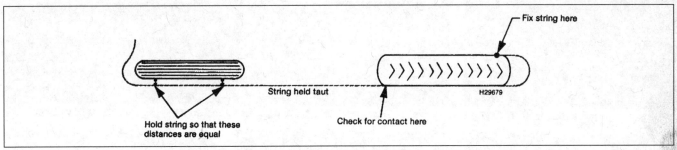

11.10 Wheel alignment check using the string method

will be constant as the wheel is rotated. **Note:** *If wheel runout is excessive, check the wheel bearings very carefully before renewing the wheel.*

Wheel alignment

6 Misalignment of the wheels due to a bent frame or forks can cause strange and possibly serious handling problems. If the frame or

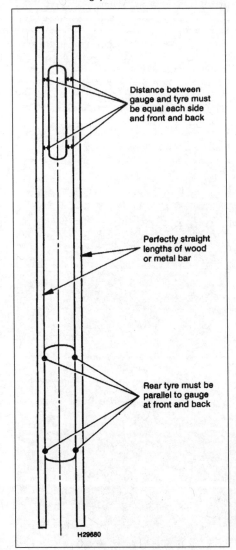

Distance between gauge and tyre must be equal each side and front and back

Perfectly straight lengths of wood or metal bar

Rear tyre must be parallel to gauge at front and back

H29680

11.13 Wheel alignment check using a straight-edge

forks are at fault, repair by a frame specialist or replacement with new parts are the only options.

7 To check wheel alignment you will need an assistant, a length of string or a perfectly straight piece of wood and a ruler. A plumb bob or spirit level for checking that the wheels are vertical will also be required.

8 Support the bike in an upright position, using an auxiliary stand **(see illustration 4.1 in Chapter 2)**. First ensure that the chain adjuster markings coincide on each side of the swingarm (see Chapter 1, Section 1). Next, measure the width of both tyres at their widest points. Subtract the smaller measurement from the larger measurement, then divide the difference by two. The result is the amount of offset that should exist between the front and rear tyres on both sides of the machine.

9 If a string is used, have your assistant hold one end of it about halfway between the floor and the rear axle, with the string touching the back edge of the rear tyre sidewall.

10 Run the other end of the string forward and pull it tight so that it is roughly parallel to the floor **(see illustration)**. Slowly bring the string into contact with the front edge of the rear tyre sidewall, then turn the front wheel until it is parallel with the string. Measure the distance from the front tyre sidewall to the string.

11 Repeat the procedure on the other side of the motorcycle.

12 The distance from the front tyre sidewall to the string should be the same on both sides of the bike and equal to the tyre width offset. If the measurement differs, the wheels are out of alignment by this amount.

13 As previously mentioned, a perfectly

12.2 Loosen both left-hand axle clamp bolts (arrowed)

straight length of wood or metal bar may be substituted for the string **(see illustration)**. The procedure is the same.

14 If the wheels are out of alignment and the fault cannot be traced to obvious damage to the frame or forks, have your machine checked by a KTM dealer.

15 If the front-to-back alignment is correct, the wheels still may be out of alignment vertically.

16 Using a plumb bob or spirit level, check the rear wheel to make sure it is vertical. To do this, hold the string or the plumb bob against the tyre upper sidewall and allow the weight to settle just off the floor. If the string touches both the upper and lower tyre sidewalls and is perfectly straight, the wheel is vertical. If it is not, adjust the stand until it is. Using a spirit level, the level should be held against the upper and lower tyre sidewalls.

17 Once the rear wheel is vertical, check the front wheel in the same manner. If both wheels are not perfectly vertical, the frame and/or major suspension components are bent.

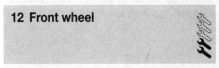

12 Front wheel

Removal

1 Support the motorcycle with an auxiliary stand so that the front wheel is off the ground **(see illustration 4.1 in Chapter 2)**.

2 Loosen the left-hand axle clamp bolts **(see illustration)**.

3 Unscrew the axle nut on the left-hand side **(see illustration)**.

12.3 Undo the axle nut

12.4 Loosen both right-hand axle clamp bolts (arrowed)

12.5a Support the wheel and withdraw the axle

12.5b Disengage the disc from the caliper (arrowed) . . .

4 Loosen the right-hand axle clamp bolts **(see illustration)**.

5 Support the wheel, then withdraw the axle from the right-hand side **(see illustration)**. Draw the wheel forwards carefully to disengage the brake disc from the caliper, and remove the wheel **(see illustrations)**.

Caution: Don't lay the wheel down and allow it to rest on the brake disc – the disc could become warped. Set the wheel on wood blocks so the wheel rim supports the weight of the wheel, or keep the wheel upright. Don't operate the brake lever with the wheel removed.

6 Clean the axle and remove any corrosion using steel wool. Check the axle for straightness by rolling it on a flat surface such as a piece of plate glass. If available, place the axle in V-blocks and check for runout using a

dial gauge. If the axle is bent, replace it with a new one.

7 Remove the spacers from both sides of the hub, noting that they are likely to be a tight fit **(see illustration)**. Clean the spacers and the seals and check the condition of the seals and bearings (see Section 15).

8 Clean the area around the brake caliper and caliper bracket. Note the location of the speed sensor and check that the wiring and wiring connector are secure **(see illustration)**.

Installation

9 Apply a thin coat of lithium-based grease to the axle and to the spacers where they fit inside the seals. Install the spacers and drive them all the way in using a block of wood and a mallet **(see illustrations)**.

10 Ensure that there is sufficient space

between the brake pads to insert the disc – if necessary, ease the pads apart with a large, flat-bladed screwdriver to obtain the necessary clearance **(see illustration)**.

11 Lift the wheel into position between the forks, ensuring the brake disc is located between the pads in the caliper, and insert the axle from the right-hand side **(see illustration 12.5b and a)**.

12 Ensure that the axle is pushed all the way through and install the axle nut finger-tight **(see illustration 12.3)**.

13 Tighten the right-hand axle clamp bolts to the torque setting specified at the beginning of this Chapter, then tighten the axle nut to the specified torque.

14 Loosen the right-hand axle clamp bolts, then take the bike off its auxiliary stand and compress the forks by pressing down on the

12.5c . . . and draw the wheel forwards and out

12.7 Spacers are fitted in both sides of the hub

12.8 Check the brake caliper and speed sensor wiring (arrowed)

12.9a Tap the spacers down . . .

12.9b . . . until they are fitted fully into the seals

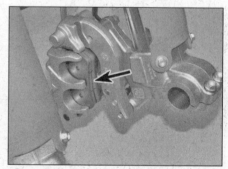

12.10 Ease the brake pads apart at this point before fitting the wheel

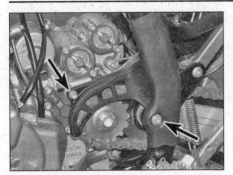

13.1a Undo the sprocket cover bolts (arrowed)

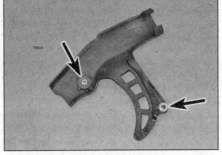

13.1b Note the location of the spacers (arrowed)

13.2 Loosen the sprocket bolt if required

handlebars vigorously to align the wheel and the suspension.

15 Tighten the right and left-hand axle clamp bolts to the specified torque setting.

16 Check the operation of the front brake before riding the motorcycle.

13 Drive chain and sprockets - removal and installation

Drive chain

Note: *As standard, all models are fitted with a drive chain which has a clip-type joining link. If a chain with a riveted 'soft link' has subsequently been fitted, refer to general procedure for breaking and joining the chain in Section 8 of 'Tools and Workshop*

Tips' in the Reference section at the end of this manual.

Removal

1 Undo the bolt(s) securing the front sprocket cover and, if fitted, the clips, then draw the cover off **(see illustration)**. Note the location of the spacers fitted in the cover **(see illustration)**.

2 If the front sprocket is going to be removed, place the transmission in gear and have an assistant apply the rear brake, then loosen the sprocket bolt **(see illustration)**.

3 Position the joining link where it can be worked on easily, such as on the rear sprocket, by rotating the rear wheel. Note how the joining link clip is fitted with its closed end facing the direction of normal chain rotation **(see illustration)**.

4 Use pliers to ease the open end of the

clip over the adjacent pin of the joining link, then slide the clip off the other pin **(see illustrations)**. Don't try to lever the clip off – this will sprain the clip and a new one will have to be fitted.

5 Lift off the link sideplate and the sealing rings **(see illustrations)**.

6 Pull out the joining link, noting the sealing rings on the link **(see illustration)**.

7 Lift the two ends of the chain off the sprocket then draw the chain off the bike.

> **HAYNES HINT** *If you are fitting a new chain, it is good practice to renew the chain and sprockets as a set.*

Installation

8 Route the drive chain around the swingarm

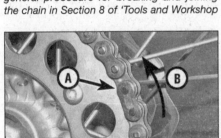

13.3 Closed end of clip (A) should face in direction of chain rotation (B)

13.4a Ease the open end of the clip over the rearmost pin (arrowed) . . .

13.4b . . . then slide the clip over the front pin (arrowed)

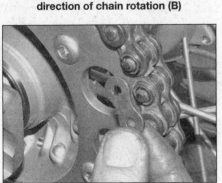

13.5a Lift off the link sideplate . . .

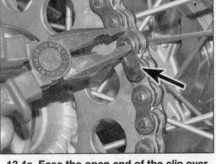

13.5b . . . and the sealing rings (arrowed) . . .

13.6 . . . then pull out the joining link

13.9 Locate the chain around the rear sprocket

13.12 Ease the open end of the clip over the rearmost pin

13.15 Front sprocket bolt should be tightened to the specified torque

13.16 Rotate the rear wheel to check all the sprocket bolts

and front sprocket as noted on removal **(see illustration 13.2)**.

9 Locate the chain around the rear sprocket with the two ends in a convenient position to work on **(see illustration)**.

10 Ensure that the sealing rings are in place on the joining link, then insert the link from the back of the sprocket **(see illustration 13.6)**.

11 Install the sealing rings and sideplate **(see illustrations 13.5b and a)**.

12 Position the clip over the front pin of the joining link with its closed end facing the direction of chain rotation **(see illustration 13.4b)**. Position the open end of the clip

against the rear pin and use pliers to ease the clip into place **(see illustration)**.

13 Rotate the rear wheel in the normal direction of rotation to ensure that the chain is correctly routed and that the closed end of the joining clip is facing the direction of rotation. Install the front sprocket cover and tighten the screws securely.

14 Adjust and, if required, lubricate the chain (see Chapter 1).

Sprockets

Check

15 Check that the front sprocket bolt is

tightened to the specified torque setting **(see illustration)**.

16 Rotate the rear wheel and check that all the rear sprocket bolts are tightened to the specified torque setting **(see illustration)**. Note that self-locking nuts are fitted to the rear sprocket bolts.

17 Check the wear pattern on the front and rear wheel sprockets (see Chapter 1, Section 1). **Note:** *Whenever the sprockets are inspected, follow the procedure in Chapter 1 and check the drive chain as well. If the sprocket teeth are worn excessively, or you are fitting a new chain, renew the chain and sprockets as a set.*

Renewal – front sprocket

18 Remove the front sprocket cover (see Step 1).

19 Place the transmission in gear and have an assistant apply the rear brake, then loosen the sprocket bolt **(see Illustration 13.2)**.

20 Remove the joining link from the drive chain and slip the chain off the front sprocket (see Steps 2 to 6).

21 Unscrew the sprocket bolt and remove the spring washer, noting which way round it fits **(see illustration)**.

22 Slide the sprocket off the transmission output shaft **(see illustration)**. **Note:** *If the sprocket is not being replaced with a new one, mark the outside with a scratch, or dab of paint, so that it can be installed the same way round.*

23 Slide the new sprocket onto the shaft.

24 Install the drive chain (see Steps 8 to 12).

25 Clean the threads of the sprocket bolt and apply a drop of the specified locking compound. Install the spring washer, dished face inwards, and the sprocket bolt and tighten the bolt to the torque setting specified at the beginning of this Chapter.

26 Install the front sprocket cover and tighten the cover bolts to the specified torque setting.

Renewal – rear sprocket

27 Remove the rear wheel (see Section 14).

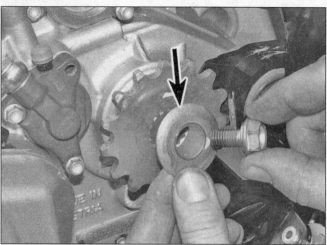

13.21 Note which way round the spring washer (arrowed) is fitted

13.22 Slide the sprocket off the transmission shaft

13.28 Counter-hold the bolts . . .

13.28b . . . and undo the nuts on the back of the sprocket

14.2a Undo the axle nut . . .

Caution: Don't lay the wheel down and allow it to rest on the brake disc or sprocket – they could become warped. Set the wheel on wood blocks so the wheel rim supports the weight of the wheel. Don't operate the rear brake pedal with the wheel removed.

28 Counter-hold the bolts and undo the nuts securing the sprocket to the hub assembly **(see illustrations)**. **Note:** *If the sprocket is not being replaced with a new one, mark the outside with a scratch, or dab of paint, so that it can be installed the same way round.*

29 Before installing the sprocket, make sure there is no dirt or corrosion where the sprocket seats on the hub.

30 Installation is the reverse of removal. Note that the nuts are of the self-locking type and new ones should be use on installation. Alternatively, clean the threads of the bolts and apply a drop of suitable non-permanent locking compound prior to installation.

31 Tighten the sprocket bolts evenly and in a criss-cross sequence to the torque setting specified at the beginning of this Chapter.

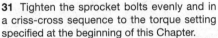
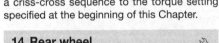
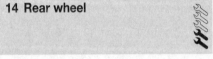

14 Rear wheel

Removal

Note: *On 2000 to 2003 models, the axle nut is located on the left-hand side of the bike. On 2004-on models, the axle nut is located on the right-hand side of the bike, as illustrated in this procedure.*

1 Support the motorcycle with an auxiliary stand so that the rear wheel is off the ground **(see illustration 4.1 in Chapter 2)**.

2 Undo the axle nut, then remove the nut and right-hand chain adjuster plate **(see**

illustrations)**. Note which way round the adjuster plate is fitted.

3 Push the axle out towards the left-hand side so that the left-hand adjuster plate is clear of the swingarm, then push the wheel forwards in the swingarm and lift the chain off the rear sprocket **(see illustrations)**.

4 Support the wheel and withdraw the axle, then remove the rear wheel carefully **(see illustration)**. The rear brake caliper should remain in place, supported by its lug on the inside of the swingarm **(see illustration)**. If required, secure the caliper temporarily with a cable-tie.

Caution: Don't lay the wheel down and allow it to rest on the disc or the sprocket – they could become warped. Set the wheel on wood blocks so the wheel rim supports the weight of the wheel, or keep the wheel upright. Don't operate the brake pedal with the wheel removed.

14.2b . . . and remove the chain adjuster plate

14.3a With the adjuster plate (arrowed) clear of the swingarm . . .

14.3b . . . push the wheel forwards and lift off the chain

14.4a Withdraw the axle . . .

14.4b . . . and remove the wheel

14.4c Note how the brake caliper is located on the swingarm

14.6 Spacers are fitted in both sides of the hub

14.7 Tap the spacers into place with a hammer and block of wood

10 Lift the chain onto the sprocket **(see illustrations 14.3b).**

11 Pull the wheel back so that the axle can be pushed all the way through – ensure that the left-hand adjuster plate is positioned correctly, then install the right-hand adjuster plate and tighten the axle nut finger-tight. Push the wheel forwards to ensure that the adjuster plates are firmly against the adjusters **(see illustrations).**

12 Adjust the chain tension as described in Chapter 1, then tighten the axle nut to the torque setting specified at the beginning of this Chapter.

13 Apply the rear brake to bring the pads into contact with the disc. Check the operation of the rear brake before riding the motorcycle.

14.11a Ensure that the adjuster plates (arrowed) . . .

14.11b . . . are pushed firmly against the head of the adjusters (arrowed)

15 Wheel bearings

Note: *Always renew the wheel bearings in sets, never individually. Avoid using a high pressure cleaner on the wheel bearing area.*

1 The procedure for inspecting, removing and installing the bearings is the same for the front and rear wheels.

2 Remove the wheel (see Section 12 or 14 as applicable).

3 Remove the spacers from both sides of the hub, noting that they may be a tight fit, and wipe any dirt off the seals.

4 Lay the wheel on wood blocks so the rim supports the weight of the wheel.

5 Inspect the seals for damage and deterioration. If there is evidence that the seals have failed, such as grease from inside the bearings leaking past the seal, or dirt and corrosion inside the hub, lever them out with a large, flat-bladed screwdriver **(see illustration).** Use a block of wood to protect the edge of the hub and note which way round the seals are fitted.

6 Check the condition of the bearings by turning the inner race. The race should turn smoothly and freely without any rough spots or notchiness, and the inner race should not be a loose fit in the ball race **(see illustration).**

5 Clean the axle and remove any corrosion using steel wool. Check the axle for straightness by rolling it on a flat surface such as a piece of plate glass. If available, place the axle in V-blocks and check for runout using a dial gauge. If the axle is bent, replace it with a new one.

6 Remove the spacers from both sides of the hub, noting that they may be a tight fit **(see illustration).** Clean the spacers and the seals and check the condition of the seals and bearings (see Section 15).

Installation

7 Apply a thin coat of lithium-based grease to the axle and to the spacers where they fit

inside the seals. Install the spacers and drive them all the way in using a block of wood and a mallet **(see illustration).**

8 If displaced, locate the rear brake caliper bracket over the lug on the inside of the swingarm. Ensure that there is sufficient space between the brake pads to insert the disc – if necessary, ease the pads apart with a large, flat-bladed screwdriver to obtain the necessary clearance.

9 Ensure that the chain is in place over the swingarm. Lift the wheel into position, ensuring the brake disc is located between the pads in the caliper, and insert the axle from the left-hand side **(see illustrations 14.4b and a).** Ensure that the axle passes through the brake caliper bracket.

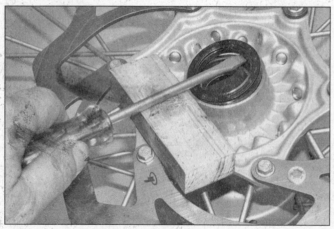

15.5 Remove the seals with a flat-bladed screwdriver

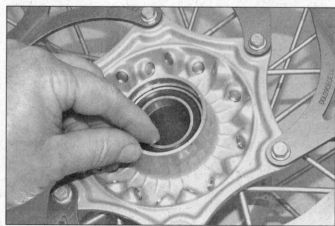

15.6 Check that the bearings turn freely

15.8a Drive out the bearing from the opposite side of the wheel

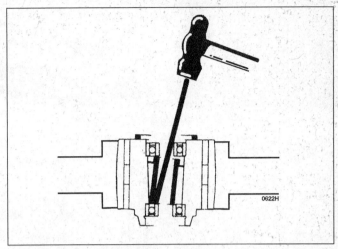

15.8b Locate the drift as shown when driving out the bearings

7 Only remove the bearings from the wheel if they are unserviceable and new ones are going to be fitted.

8 To renew the bearings, insert a metal rod (preferably a brass punch) through the centre of the bearing on one side of the hub, and tap evenly around the inner race of the bearing on

15.11 Driving in a new bearing with a large socket

the other side to drive it out **(see illustrations)**. The bearing spacer will come out with the bearing.

9 Turn the wheel over and drive out the remaining bearing using the same procedure.

10 Thoroughly clean the hub area of the wheel with a suitable solvent and inspect the bearing seats for scoring and wear. If the seats are damaged, consult a KTM dealer before reassembling the wheel.

11 Install a new bearing into its seat in one side of the hub, with the marked or sealed side facing outwards. Using an old bearing, a bearing driver or a socket large enough to contact the outer race of the bearing, drive it in until it's completely seated **(see illustration)**.

12 Turn the wheel over, install the bearing spacer and drive the other bearing into place.

13 Lubricate the new seals with a smear of grease and press them squarely into place in the hub **(see illustration)**. If required, level the seals with the hub using a hammer and block of wood **(see illustration)**.

14 Clean the brake disc using acetone or brake system cleaner, then install the wheel (see Section 12 or 14 as applicable).

16 Tyres – general information and fitting

General information

1 The wheels are designed to take tubed tyres only. Tyre sizes are given in the Specifications at the beginning of this Chapter.

2 Refer to *Pre-ride checks* at the beginning of this manual for tyre maintenance.

3 When selecting new tyres, refer to the tyre information in the Owner's Handbook, assuming that the wheels have not been changed from standard – cross-check with the original fitment tyres if you are not sure. Ensure that front and rear tyre types are compatible, and of the correct size and speed rating; if

15.13a Press in the new seals . . .

15.13b . . . and level them with a block of wood

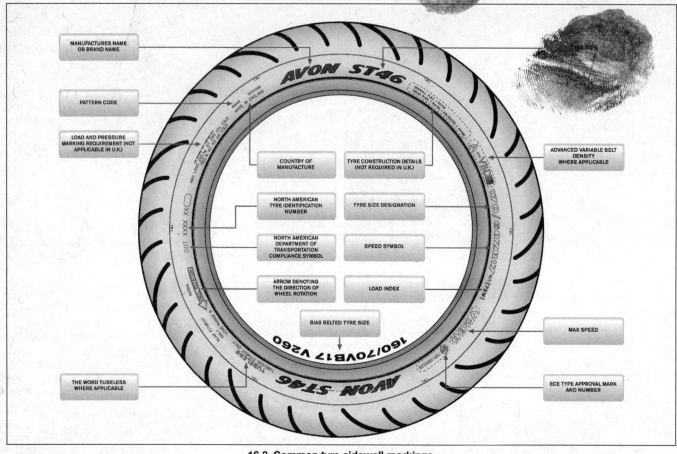

MANUFACTURES NAME
OR BRAND NAME

PATTERN CODE

LOAD AND PRESSURE
MARKING REQUIREMENT (NOT
APPLICABLE IN U.K.)

COUNTRY OF
MANUFACTURE

TYRE CONSTRUCTION DETAILS
(NOT REQUIRED IN U.K.)

ADVANCED VARIABLE BELT
DENSITY
WHERE APPLICABLE

NORTH AMERICAN
TYRE IDENTIFICATION
NUMBER

TYRE SIZE DESIGNATION

NORTH AMERICAN
DEPARTMENT OF
TRANSPORTATION
COMPLIANCE SYMBOL

SPEED SYMBOL

ARROW DENOTING
THE DIRECTION OF
WHEEL ROTATION

LOAD INDEX

BIAS BELTED TYRE SIZE

MAX SPEED

THE WORD TUBELESS
WHERE APPLICABLE

ECE TYPE APPROVAL MARK
AND NUMBER

TYRE TYPE

16.3 Common tyre sidewall markings

necessary, seek advice from a KTM dealer or motorcycle tyre specialist **(see illustration)**. If the machine is for road use, ensure you fit appropriate tyres.

Removal and installation

4 To remove and install the tyres you will need at least two, preferably three, motorcycle tyre levers, some tyre fitting lubricant, powdered chalk, a pump and pressure gauge. A pair of rim protectors is also useful.
5 Remove the wheel (see Section 12 or 14 as applicable), then lay it on wood blocks so the rim supports the weight. Alternatively, lay the wheel on a thick pad or blanket, brake disc side uppermost.
6 Unscrew the valve core to deflate the tyre, then fully loosen the rim locknut **(see illustration)**.
7 Using the tyre levers, push the bead of the tyre away from the rim all the way round on both sides of the wheel.
8 Once the bead is completely free of the rim, lubricate the bead to help ease it over the wheel rim.
9 Push the tyre bead into the well of the rim at the point directly opposite to the valve, then remove the valve retaining nut and push the valve through the rim into the tyre.
10 Insert one tyre lever under the bead at the valve and lift the bead over the rim **(see illustration)**. If available, use a rim protector between the tyre and the wheel rim. If lifting the bead at the valve is difficult, make sure that the bead opposite is pushed fully down into the well of the rim.
11 Hold the bead over the rim with the first tyre lever, then insert the second lever 2 or 3 inches to one side and repeat the procedure **(see illustration)**.

16.6 Fully loosen the rim locknut

16.10 Starting at the valve, lift the tyre bead over the rim

16.11 Repeat the procedure with a second tyre lever

16.13 Pull out the inner tube

16.15 Lift the remaining bead over the edge of the rim

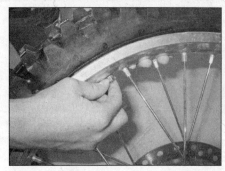

16.19 Partially screw on the retaining nut to hold the valve in place

12 With a small section of the bead up over the rim, remove one of the levers and insert it a further 2 or 3 inches in the other direction, and repeat the procedure again. Don't forget to make sure that the bead opposite is pushed fully down into the well of the rim.

13 Once the first bead is over the rim, lift up the free side of the tyre and pull out the inner tube **(see illustration)**.

14 It is not necessary to completely remove the tyre from the wheel rim in order to fit a new inner tube. However, if the tube has been punctured and a foreign object may be imbedded in the tyre, it is easier to check once the tyre is off.

15 Stand the wheel upright and push the rim down hard so that the lower edge of the remaining bead is pressed fully into the well of the rim, then pull the upper edge of the bead over the rim at the top. If the tyre is tight, lubricate the bead and use the tyre levers to lift the bead over the rim **(see illustration)**.

16 Before installing the tyre, check the condition of the rim tape fitted in the well of the rim to protect the inner tube from the ends of the spokes. If the tape is not a tight fit, or is damaged, fit a new one.

17 Before installing the tyre, lay it on the wheel and check for a directional arrow on the sidewall to ensure that the tyre is fitted the right way round **(see illustration 16.3)**.

18 Lubricate the first bead and push it over the rim. Inflate the inner tube just enough to prevent it getting trapped between the tyre bead and the rim, and sprinkle the tube with

powdered chalk to prevent it sticking to the inside of the tyre.

19 Lift up the free side of the tyre and install the tube with the valve stem next to the hole in the rim. Once the tube is in place, push the valve stem through the hole in the rim and start the retaining nut on the stem **(see illustration)**.

20 Lubricate the second bead. Start working directly opposite the valve stem, pushing the bead over the edge of the rim and into the well. Work in both directions around the rim towards the valve.

21 Keep checking to ensure that the inner tube is not trapped and use the tyre levers if necessary **(see illustration)**.

22 When fitting the tyre in the area adjacent to the rim lock, push the rim lock inwards so that the bead locates between the lock and the rim **(see illustration)**.

23 When fitting the last section of bead over

the rim, loosen the retaining nut and push the valve stem inwards to ensure that the inner tube is not trapped.

24 Once the second bead is in place, check that the valve stem and rim lock are pointing to the centre of the hub. If they're angled in either direction, rotate the tyre round the rim to straighten them out. Run the retaining nut further onto the valve stem but do not tighten it fully.

25 Inflate the tyre to approximately 1 1/2 times the recommended pressure (see *Pre-ride checks*) to check that the guidelines on both sidewalls are the same distance from the edge of the rim around the circumference of the tyre.

26 Once the tyre bead is correctly seated on the rim, deflate the tyre to the correct pressure and fit the valve cap. Tighten the valve stem retaining nut finger-tight. Tighten the rim locknut securely.

16.21 Take care not to trap the inner tube

16.22 Rim lock (arrowed) should secure the tyre bead against the wheel rim

Chapter 8
Bodywork

Contents

Degrees of difficulty

Easy, suitable for novice with little experience	**Fairly easy,** suitable for beginner with some experience	**Fairly difficult,** suitable for competent DIY mechanic	**Difficult,** suitable for experienced DIY mechanic	**Very difficult,** suitable for expert DIY or professional

Specifications

Torque settings

Fork protector bolts . . . . 10 Nm
Front mudguard mounting bolts. . . . . 10 Nm
Seat retaining nut . . . . 20 Nm

1 General information

1 This Chapter covers the procedures necessary to remove and install the body parts.

2 In the case of damage to the body parts, it is usually necessary to remove the broken component and replace it with a new (or used) one. The material from which the body panels are made does not lend itself to conventional repair techniques. There are, however, some shops that specialise in 'plastic welding', so it may be worthwhile seeking the advice of one of these specialists before consigning an expensive component to the bin.

3 When installing a body panel, first study it closely, noting any fasteners and associated fittings removed with it, to be sure of returning everything to its correct place. Check that all fasteners are in good condition – any that are faulty must be replaced with new ones before the panel is reassembled. Check also that all mounting brackets are straight, and repair or renew them if necessary before attempting to install the panel.

4 Tighten the fasteners securely, but be careful not to overtighten any of them or the panel may break (not always immediately) due to the uneven stress.

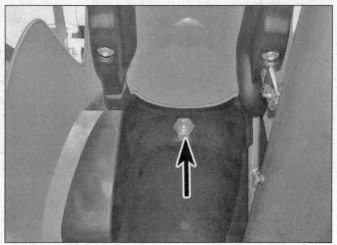

2.1 Location of the seat retaining nut (arrowed)

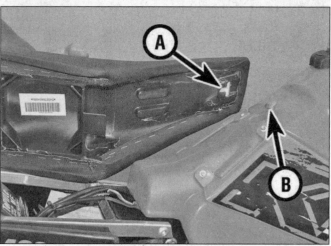

2.2 Release clip (A) from stud (B)

2 Seat

1 The seat is secured by a nut on the underside of the mudguard (see illustration).
2 Undo the nut, then ease the seat rearwards to release the clip at the front from the stud on the top of the fuel tank (see illustration).
3 Installation is the reverse of removal. Ensure that the seat is pushed fully forwards and lies flat against the fuel tank before installing the

fixing nut (see illustration). Tighten the nut to the torque setting specified at the beginning of this Chapter.

3 Radiator/fuel tank side panels

1 Remove the seat (see Section 2).
2 The left and right-hand side panels are retained by five screws each (see illustration).
3 Undo the screws carefully, noting the

location of any washers, then lift the panels off.
4 On installation, ensure all the mounting holes in the panels align with the screw holes in the fuel tank and radiator. Note that the front mounting screw locates in a bracket on the radiator (see illustrations).
5 Take care not to overtighten the side panel screws.

4 Number plate panels

1 On 2000 to 2003 models, number plate panels are fitted on both sides of the rear mudguard unit.
2 To remove the panels, turn the two quick-release fasteners anti-clockwise, then pull them outwards (see illustration). Draw the panel forwards and off.
3 Installation is the reverse of removal.

5 Headlight panel

1 Where fitted, undo the screw securing the

2.3 Seat should lay flat against the fuel tank

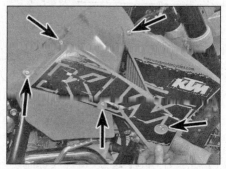

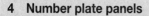

3.2 Side panels are retained by screws (arrowed)

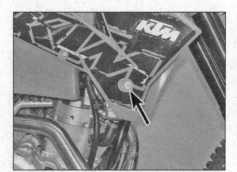

3.4a Front mounting screw (arrowed) . . .

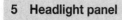

3.4b . . . locates in radiator bracket (arrowed)

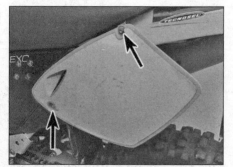

4.2 Panel is secured by two quick-release fasteners (arrowed)

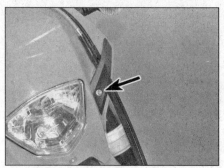

5.1a Undo the screw (arrowed) . . .

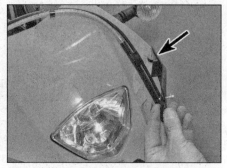

5.1b . . . and remove the guide. Note the tab (arrowed)

5.2 Release the straps (arrowed)

brake hose guide and lift it off, noting how it fits **(see illustrations)**.

2 Release the straps securing the panel to the top of the fork legs **(see illustration)**.

3 Lift the panel off the pegs on the front mudguard **(see illustration)**.

4 Disconnect the headlight wiring connector **(see illustration)**.

5 Installation is the reverse of removal. Ensure that the headlight is securely connected.

6 Check the operation of the headlight and adjust the headlight aim (see Chapter 1, Section 8) before riding the bike.

6 Fork protectors

1 The fork protectors are secured by bolts at the bottom of the fork legs **(see illustration)**.

2 Undo the bolts and lift the fork protector off carefully **(see illustration)**.

3 Inspect the fork protectors for damage and splits and renew them if necessary.

4 Installation is the reverse of removal. Tighten the mounting bolts to the torque setting specified at the beginning of this Chapter.

7 Front mudguard

1 Remove the headlight panel (see Section 5).

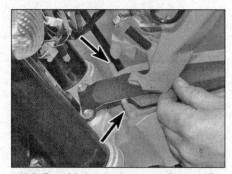

5.3 Panel is located on pegs (arrowed)

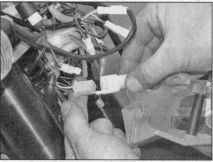

5.4 Disconnect the headlight wiring connector

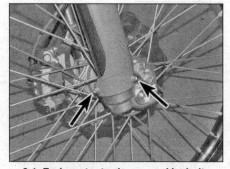

6.1 Fork protector is secured by bolts (arrowed)

6.2 Lift the protector off carefully

2 Clean the underside of the mudguard, then undo the bolts securing the mudguard to the underside of the fork bottom yoke **(see illustration)**.

3 Undo the bolts securing the mudguard bracket to the bottom yoke, then draw the mudguard forward and off **(see illustrations)**.

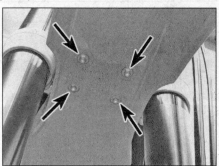

7.2 Undo the bolts (arrowed) on the underside of the mudguard

7.3a Undo the bolts on the bottom fork yoke

7.3b Draw the mudguard forwards

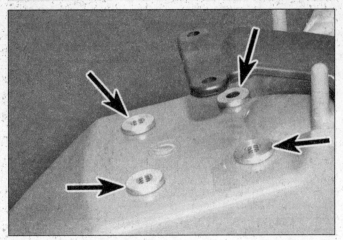

7.4 Note the location of the spacers (arrowed)

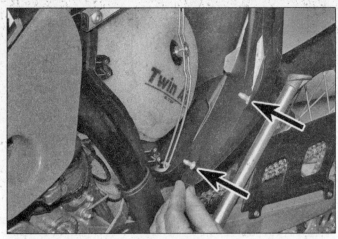

8.4 Pull the front edge of the panel away to release the clips (arrowed) on the inside

4 Note the location of the spacers in the mudguard (see illustration).
5 Installation is the reverse of removal – don't forget to install the spacers in the mudguard. Tighten the mounting bolts to the torque setting specified at the beginning of this Chapter.
6 Follow the procedure in Section 5 to install the headlight panel.

8 Rear mudguard unit

1 Remove the seat (see Section 2).
2 Disconnect the tail light and turn signal wiring connectors (see Chapter 9).
3 On 2000 to 2003 models, remove the number plate panels (see Section 4).
4 On 2004-on models, pull the front edge of the left-hand side panel away carefully to release the pegs on the inside of the panel

from the clips on the frame, then lift the panel off (see illustration).
5 Undo the nut and shouldered bolt securing the mudguard unit to the frame (see illustration).
6 Undo the bolts securing the underside of the mudguard unit to the left and right-hand sides of the rear sub-frame (see illustration).
7 Undo the bolts securing the left and right-hand sides of the mudguard unit to the

rear sub-frame (see illustration). Note the shouldered washers (see illustration).
8 Draw the mudguard unit rearwards and off the bike (see illustration).
9 Installation is the reverse of removal. Ensure that the wiring is not trapped between the unit and the rear sub-frame. Don't forget to check the operation of the brake/tail light and the rear turn signals before installing the seat.

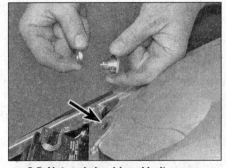

8.5 Nut and shouldered bolt secure mudguard to frame lug (arrowed)

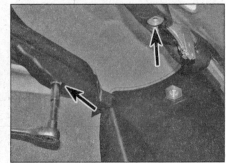

8.6 Undo the bolts on the underside of the rear subframe

8.7a Undo the bolts on the left and right-hand sides

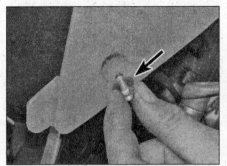

8.7b Note the location of the shouldered washers (arrowed)

8.8 Draw the mudguard unit off rearwards

Chapter 9
Electrical system

Contents

Degrees of difficulty

Easy, suitable for novice with little experience	**Fairly easy,** suitable for beginner with some experience	**Fairly difficult,** suitable for competent DIY mechanic	**Difficult,** suitable for experienced DIY mechanic	**Very difficult,** suitable for expert DIY or professional

Specifications

Battery
Capacity .... 12 V, 4 Ah or 5 Ah
Charging rate
  Normal .... 0.5 A for 5 to 10 hrs
  Quick charge .... 5 A for 30 minutes

Alternator
Regulated voltage output
  No load.. 14 V at 1500 rpm
  With load. .... 12 V approx at 1500 rpm
  With load. .... 13 V approx at 5000 rpm
Charge current
  No load.. 1.3 ± 0.1 A at 1500 rpm
  With load. .... - 0.6 ± 0.1 A at 1500 rpm
  With load. .... 0.0 ± 0.1 A at 5000 approx rpm
Stator coil resistance
  4K-3A stator* .... 0.74 ± 0.15 ohms
  4K-3B stator
    Between yellow and earth (ground) .... 0.65 ± 0.15 ohms
    Between yellow and white .... 0.16 ± 0.03 ohms
  fitted to 2000 to 2003 SX models only

Fuses
Main fuse .... 10 A
Cooling fan fuse (where fitted) .... 5 A

Bulbs
Headlight
  Main/dipped .... 35/35 W
  Sidelight .... 5 W
Brake/tail light .... 21/5 W
Turn signals .... 10 W
Instrument light....................................... 1.2 W
Warning lights.. 5 W

Speedometer
Sensor gap . . . .   2 to 4 mm
Battery CR2430

Torque settings
Alternator cover screws . . . .   10 Nm
Alternator stator mounting bolts
  4K-3A stator . . . .   6 Nm*
  4K-3B stator . . . .   10 Nm*
Starter motor mounting bolts
  2000 to 2005 models . . . .   8 Nm*
  2006-on models . . . .   10 Nm*
Use thread locking compound Loctite 243

1 General information

All models covered in this manual have a 12-volt electrical system charged by a single-phase alternator which is mounted on the end of the crankshaft.

EXC models are equipped with a comprehensive electrical system including lights, horn and turn signals. The system incorporates a regulator/rectifier which maintains the alternator output within the specified range to prevent overcharging, and converts the ac (alternating current) output of the alternator to dc (direct current) to power the lights and other components and to charge the battery.

EXC models are fitted with an electric starter motor. The starting system includes the motor, the battery, the relay and the starter switch.

On SX models, the alternator provides power for the ignition system (see Chapter 5). On 2004-on SX models, there are no charging coils in the alternator.

Note: *Keep in mind that electrical parts, once purchased, cannot be returned. To avoid unnecessary expense, make very sure the faulty component has been positively identified before buying a replacement part.*

2 Fault finding

Warning: To prevent the risk of short circuits, the battery negative (-ve) terminal should be disconnected before any of the bike's other electrical components are disturbed. Don't forget to reconnect the terminal securely once work is finished or if battery power is needed for circuit testing.

1 A typical electrical circuit consists of an electrical component, the switches, relays, etc, related to that component and the wiring and connectors that link the component to the power source and the frame.

2 Before tackling any troublesome electrical circuit, first study the wiring diagram thoroughly to get a complete picture of what makes up that individual circuit. Trouble spots, for instance, can often be narrowed down by noting if other components related to that circuit are operating properly or not. If several components or circuits fail at one time, chances are the fault lies either in the fuse or in the common earth (ground) connection, as several circuits are often routed through the same fuse and earth (ground) connections.

3 Electrical problems often stem from simple causes, such as loose or corroded connections or a blown fuse. Prior to any electrical fault finding, always visually check the condition of the fuse, wires and connections in the problem circuit. Intermittent failures can be especially frustrating, since you can't always duplicate the failure when it's convenient to test. In such situations, a good practice is to clean all connections in the affected circuit, whether or not they appear to be good. All of the connections and wires should also be wiggled to check for looseness which can cause intermittent failure.

4 If you don't have a multimeter it is highly advisable to obtain one – they are not expensive and will enable a full range of electrical tests to be made. Go for a modern digital one with LCD display as they are easier to use. A continuity tester and/or test light are useful for certain electrical checks as an alternative, though are limited in their usefulness compared to a multimeter **(see illustrations)**.

Continuity checks

5 The term continuity describes the uninterrupted flow of electricity through an electrical circuit. Continuity can be checked with a multimeter set either to its continuity function (a beep is emitted when continuity is found), or to the resistance (ohms / Ω) function, or with a dedicated continuity tester. Both instruments are powered by an internal battery, therefore the checks are made with the ignition OFF. As a safety precaution, always disconnect the battery negative (-) lead before making continuity checks, particularly if ignition system checks are being made.

6 If using a multimeter, select the continuity function if it has one, or the resistance (ohms) function. Touch the meter probes together and check that a beep is emitted or the meter reads zero, which indicates continuity. If there is no continuity there will be no beep or the meter will show infinite resistance. After using the meter, always switch it OFF to conserve its battery.

7 A continuity tester can be used in the same way – its light should come on or it should beep to indicate continuity in the switch ON position, but should be off or silent in the OFF position.

8 Note that the polarity of the test probes doesn't matter for continuity checks, although care should be taken to follow specific test procedures if a diode or solid-state component is being checked.

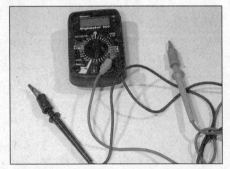

2.4a A digital multimeter can be used for all electrical tests

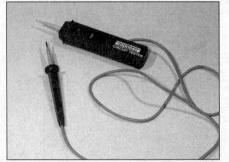

2.4b A battery powered continuity tester

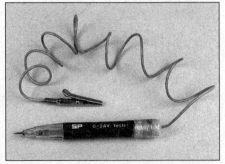

2.4c A simple test light can be used for voltage checks

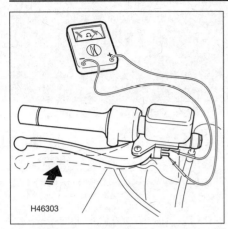

2.10 Testing a brake light switch for continuity

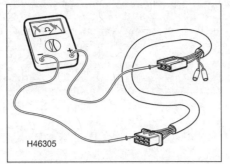

2.12 Testing for continuity in a wiring loom

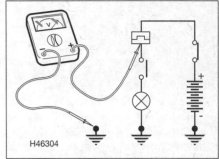

2.15 Connect the multimeter in parallel, or across the load, as shown

Switch continuity checks

9 If a switch is at fault, trace its wiring to the wiring connectors. Separate the connectors and inspect them for security and condition. A build-up of dirt or corrosion here will most likely be the cause of the problem – clean up and apply a water dispersant such as WD40, or alternatively use a dedicated contact cleaner and protection spray.

10 If using a multimeter, select the continuity function if it has one, or the resistance (ohms) function, and connect its probes to the terminals in the connector **(see illustration)**. Simple ON/OFF type switches, such as brake light switches, only have two wires whereas combination switches, like the handlebar switches, have many wires. Study the wiring diagram to ensure that you are connecting to the correct pair of wires. Continuity should be indicated with the switch ON and no continuity with it OFF.

Wiring continuity checks

11 Many electrical faults are caused by damaged wiring, often due to incorrect routing or chaffing on frame components. Loose, wet or corroded wire connectors can also be the cause of electrical problems.

12 A continuity check can be made on a single length of wire by disconnecting it at each end and connecting the meter or continuity tester probes to each end of the wire **(see illustration)**. Continuity should be indicated if the wire is good. If no continuity is shown, suspect a broken wire.

13 To check for continuity to earth in any earth wire connect one probe of your meter or tester to the earth wire terminal in the connector and the other to the frame, engine, or battery earth (-) terminal. Continuity should be indicated if the wire is good. If no continuity is shown, suspect a broken wire or corroded or loose earth point (see below).

Voltage checks

14 A voltage check can determine whether power is reaching a component. Use a

multimeter set to the dc (direct current) voltage scale to check for power from the battery or regulator/rectifier, or set to the ac (alternating current) voltage scale to check for power from the alternator. A test light can be used to check for dc voltage. The test light is the cheaper component, but the meter has the advantage of being able to give a voltage reading.

15 Connect the meter or test light in parallel, i.e. across the load **(see illustration)**.

16 First identify the relevant wiring circuit by referring to the wiring diagram at the end of this manual.

17 If using a meter, check first that the meter leads are plugged into the correct terminals on the meter (red to positive (+), black to negative (-). Set the meter to the appropriate volts function (dc or ac), where necessary at a range suitable for the battery voltage – 0 to 20 vdc. Connect the meter red probe (+) to the power supply wire and the black probe to a good metal earth (ground) on the motorcycle's frame or directly to the battery negative terminal. Battery voltage, or the specified voltage, should be shown on the meter with any relevant switch set to the ON position.

18 If using a test light **(see illustration 2.4c)**, connect its positive (+) probe to the power supply terminal and its negative (-) probe to a good earth (ground) on the motorcycle's frame. With the switch, and if necessary any other relevant switch, ON, the test light should illuminate.

19 If no voltage is indicated, work back towards the power source continuing to check

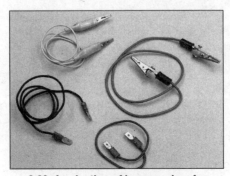

2.23 A selection of jumper wires for making earth (ground) checks

for voltage. When you reach a point where there is voltage, you know the problem lies between that point and your last check point.

Earth (ground) checks

20 Earth connections are made either directly to the engine or frame (such as the starter motor or ignition coil which only have a positive feed) or by a separate wire into the earth circuit of the wiring harness. Alternatively a short earth wire is sometimes run from the component directly to the motorcycle's frame.

21 Corrosion is a common cause of a poor earth connection, as is a loose earth terminal fastener.

22 If total or multiple component failure is experienced, check the security of the main earth lead from the negative (-) terminal of the battery, the earth lead bolted to the engine, and the main earth point(s) on the frame. If corroded, dismantle the connection and clean all surfaces back to bare metal. Remake the connection and prevent further corrosion from forming by smearing battery terminal grease over the connection.

23 To check the earthing of a component, use an insulated jumper wire to temporarily bypass its earth connection **(see illustration)** – connect one end of the jumper wire to the earth terminal or metal body of the component and the other end to the motorcycle's frame. If the circuit works with the jumper wire installed, the earth circuit is faulty.

24 To check an earth wire first check for corroded or loose connections, then check the wiring for continuity (Step 13) between each connector in the circuit in turn, and then to its earth point, to locate the break.

> **HAYNES HiNT** *Remember that all electrical circuits are designed to conduct electricity from the power source, through the wires, switches, relays, etc. to the electrical component (light bulb, starter motor, etc). From there it is directed to the frame (earth), where in the case of battery systems, it is passed back to the battery. Electrical problems are basically an interruption in the flow of electricity.*

3.3a Disconnect the battery negative (-) terminal first

3.3b Displace the cover to access the battery negative (+) terminal

3.4 Battery is secured by two elasticated straps

3 Battery

Caution: Be extremely careful when handling or working around the battery. The electrolyte is very caustic and an explosive gas (hydrogen) is given off when the battery is charging.

1 The battery is of the maintenance free (sealed) type, requiring no regular maintenance other than the checks detailed in Chapter 1, Section 22). Either a 4 Ah or 5 Ah battery will be fitted - it's electrical capacity and charge rate being marked on the battery casing. Note that it's possible to uprate from the 4 to 5 Ah type, but a deeper battery carrier will be required due to the increased height of the 5 Ah battery.

Removal and installation

2 Remove the seat (see Chapter 8).
3 Unscrew the negative (-ve) terminal bolt first and disconnect the lead from the battery **(see illustration)**. Lift up the insulating cover to access the positive (+ve) terminal, then unscrew the bolt and disconnect the lead **(see illustration)**.
4 Unhook the securing straps and lift the battery from the bike **(see illustration)**.

5 Before installation, clean the battery terminals and lead ends to ensure a good electrical connection. Reconnect the leads, connecting the positive (+ve) lead first, and install the insulating cover.
6 Don't forget to secure the battery with the straps, then install the seat (see Chapter 8).

HAYNES HINT *Battery corrosion can be kept to a minimum by applying a layer of petroleum jelly to the terminals after the leads have been connected.*

Charging

7 Ensure the charger is suitable for charging a 12 volt battery.
8 Remove the battery (see above).
9 Before switching the charger ON, connect the charger to the battery, making sure that the positive (+ve) lead on the charger is connected to the positive (+ve) terminal on the battery, and the negative (-ve) lead is connected to the negative (-ve) terminal.
10 KTM recommend that the battery is charged at a rate of 0.5 amp for a maximum of 10 hours. Exceeding this figure can cause the battery to overheat, buckling the plates and rendering it useless. Few owners will have

access to an expensive current controlled charger, so if a normal domestic charger is used, check that after a possible initial peak, the charge rate falls to a safe level **(see illustration)**.
11 If the battery becomes hot during charging **STOP**. Further charging will cause damage.
Note: *In emergencies the battery can be charged at a maximum rate of 5 amps for a period of 30 minutes. However, this is not recommended and the low amp charge is by far the safer method of charging the battery.*
12 When charging is complete, turn the charger OFF and disconnect the leads from the battery terminals. Allow the battery to stand for 30 minutes, then measure the voltage as follows.
13 Using a multimeter set to the volts dc scale, connect the positive (+ve) probe to the battery positive (+ve) terminal and the negative (-ve) probe to the battery negative (-ve) terminal **(see illustration)**. When fully charged there should be more than 12.5 volts present. If the voltage is below 12.0 volts, charge the battery again and repeat the measuring process. If the voltage is still low, the battery is failing and should be replaced with a new one.
14 Install the battery (see above).
15 If the battery voltage falls while the machine is not in use, an electrical system fault may be causing voltage leakage. Refer to

3.10 Ensure that charging rate is safe

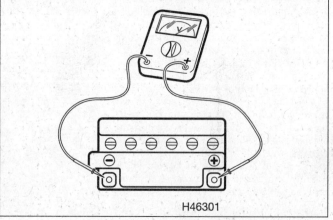

3.13 Checking the battery voltage

4.2 Location of the starter relay unit (arrowed)

4.3 Cooling fan fuse (arrowed)

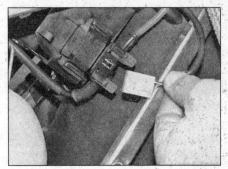

4.4 Disconnect the wiring connector

Chapter 1, Section 22, and perform a leakage test.

16 If the recharged battery discharges rapidly when left disconnected, it is likely that an internal short caused by physical damage or sulphation has occurred. A new battery will be required. A good battery will tend to lose its charge at about 1% per day.

17 If the motorcycle is unused for long periods of time, charge the battery once every month to six weeks and leave it disconnected.

4 Fuse

1 The electrical system is protected by a 10A main fuse.

2 The main fuse is located in the starter relay unit behind the left-hand side panel **(see illustration)** – remove the panel for access (see Chapter 8). The main fuse protects the starter system, the horn and the turn signals.

3 On machines fitted with a radiator cooling fan, a fuse is fitted in the fan motor circuit **(see illustration)**. Remove the fuel tank to access the fuse holder in the fan sub-loom (see Chapter 4).

4 The fuses can be removed and checked visually. To remove the main fuse, first disconnect the relay wiring connector **(see illustration)**.

5 Displace the relay unit from its bracket. Remove the fuse cover, then pull out the fuse **(see illustrations)**. Note the location of the spare fuse. If you can't pull a fuse out with your fingers, use long-nose pliers.

6 A blown fuse is easily identified by a break in the element **(see illustration)**.

7 The fuse is clearly marked with its rating and must only be replaced by a fuse of the same rating. If a spare fuse is used, always replace it with a new one so that a spare is carried on the bike at all times.

 Warning: Never put in a fuse of a higher rating or bridge the terminals with any other substitute, however temporary it may be. Serious damage may be done to the circuit, or a fire may start.

8 If a fuse blows, be sure to check the appropriate wiring circuit very carefully for evidence of a short-circuit – refer to *Wiring Diagrams* at the end of this Chapter. Look especially for trapped or bare wires and chafed, melted or burned insulation. If a new fuse is fitted before the fault is located, it will blow immediately.

9 Occasionally a fuse will blow or cause an open-circuit for no obvious reason. Corrosion of the fuse ends and fuseholder terminals may occur and cause poor electrical contact. If this happens, remove the corrosion with a wire brush or emery paper, then spray the fuse ends and fuseholder terminals with electrical contact cleaner.

5 Lighting system

Note: *The lighting system only works with the engine running. Check that the battery is in good condition before checking the lighting system (see Section 3).*

Headlight

1 If the headlight fails to work, first check the bulb and the bulb terminals (see Section 6).

2 If the bulb is good, disconnect the connector from the bulb terminals and check for voltage at the supply terminal in the connector. Note that on some market models, the headlight switch on the left-hand handlebar has three positions – OFF, low beam and high beam. On American market models, the headlight is operated by the pull switch on the right-hand side of the instrument cluster.

3 Use the left-hand handlebar switch to select the high or low beam as appropriate. If voltage is present, check the earth circuit for an open or poor connection.

4.5a Displace the relay unit . . .

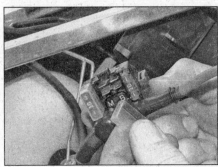

4.5b . . . remove the fuse cover . . .

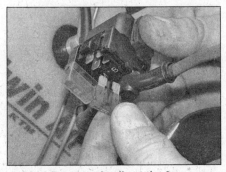

4.5c . . . and pull out the fuse

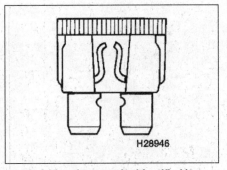

H28946

4.6 A blow fuse can be identified by a break in the element

6.2a Disconnect the wiring connectors . . .

6.2b . . . and remove the bulb cover

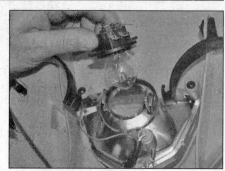

6.3 Remove the bulb and bulbholder

4 If there is no voltage at the supply terminal, the problem lies in the wiring or one of the switches in the circuit. Ensure that the headlight unit wiring connector is secure. Refer to Section 2 for the switch testing procedures, and to the *Wiring Diagrams* at the end of this Chapter.

Sidelight

5 If the sidelight fails to work, first check the bulb and the terminal in the bulbholder (see Section 6).
6 If the bulb is good, ensure that the lighting switch is ON (see Step 2) and check for voltage at the terminal in the bulbholder. If voltage is present, check the earth circuit for an open or poor connection.
7 If no voltage is present, the problem lies in the wiring or one of the switches in the circuit (see Step 4).

Tail light

8 If the tail light fails to work, first check the bulb and the bulb terminals (see Section 8).
9 If the bulb is good, ensure that the lighting switch is ON (see Step 2) and check for voltage at the terminal in the bulbholder. If voltage is present, check the earth circuit for an open or poor connection.
10 If no voltage is present, the problem lies in the wiring or one of the switches in the circuit. Ensure that the tail light unit wiring connector is secure (see Section 9). Refer to Section 2 for the switch testing procedures, and to the *Wiring Diagrams* at the end of this Chapter.

Brake light

11 If the brake light fails to work, first check the bulb and the bulb terminals (see Section 8).
12 If the bulb is good, check for voltage at the supply terminal in the bulbholder, first with the brake lever pulled in, then with the brake pedal pressed down. If voltage is present on both tests, check the earth circuit for an open or poor connection.
13 If voltage is only present on one test, check the appropriate brake light switch (see Section 13).
14 If no voltage is present on both tests, the problem lies in the wiring (see *Wiring Diagrams* at the end of this Chapter).

Instrument and warning lights

15 See Section 15 for instrument and warning light bulb renewal.

Turn signals

16 See Section 10 for the turn signal circuit check.

6 Headlight bulb and sidelight bulb

Note: *It is a good idea to use a paper towel or dry cloth when handling a new bulb to prevent*

injury if the bulb should break and to increase bulb life.

Headlight

1 Follow the procedure in Chapter 8 and displace the headlight panel.
2 Disconnect the headlight wiring connectors and remove the bulb cover **(see illustrations)**.
3 Twist the bulbholder anti-clockwise and withdraw the bulb from the headlight unit **(see illustration)**.
4 Twist the bulb anti-clockwise and withdraw it from the bulbholder **(see illustration)**.
5 Fit the new bulb.
6 Make sure the bulb fits correctly into the bulbholder, then secure the bulbholder in the headlight unit.
7 Install the bulb cover, ensuring it is the right way round, and press it on firmly.
8 Install the wiring connectors.
9 Install the headlight panel (see Chapter 8) and check the operation of the headlight.

Sidelight

10 Follow the procedure in Chapter 8 and displace the headlight panel.
11 Pull the bulbholder out of its socket in the headlight unit, then carefully pull the bulb out of the holder **(see illustrations)**.
12 Carefully press the new bulb into the bulbholder, then install the bulbholder by pressing it in.
13 Install the headlight panel (see Chapter 8) and check the operation of the sidelight.

6.4 Remove the bulb from the bulbholder

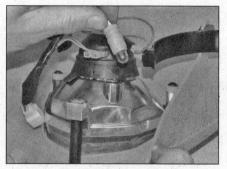

6.11a Pull the bulbholder out of its socket . . .

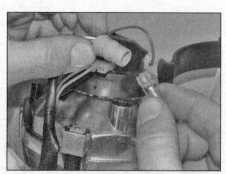

6.11b . . . then pull the bulb out of the holder

7 Headlight unit

1 Remove the headlight panel (see Chapter 8).
2 Unscrew the headlight aim adjuster **(see illustration)**.
3 Undo the screws securing the headlight unit in the panel and lift the unit out **(see illustration)**.
4 Installation is the reverse of removal. Make sure the wiring is correctly connected and secured. Check the operation of the headlight and sidelight. Check the headlight aim (see Chapter 1, Section 8).

8 Brake/tail light bulb

Note: *It is a good idea to use a paper towel or dry cloth when handling a new bulb to prevent injury if the bulb should break and to increase bulb life.*
1 Remove the two screws securing the lens and lift it off **(see illustrations)**.
2 Push the bulb into the holder and twist it anti-clockwise to remove it **(see illustration)**.
3 Check the socket terminals for corrosion and clean them if necessary. Line up the pins of the new bulb with the slots in the socket, then push the bulb in and turn it clockwise

7.2 Unscrew the adjuster (arrowed)

until it locks into place. **Note:** *If the pins on the bulb are offset, the bulb can only be installed one way.*
4 Install the lens in the reverse order of removal.
5 Check the operation of the tail light and the brake light.

9 Tail light unit

1 Remove the seat (see Chapter 8).
2 Trace the wiring from the back of the light unit and the turn signals and disconnect it at the connectors **(see illustration)**.
3 Remove the mudguard unit and separate the number plate bracket from the mudguard (see Chapter 8).

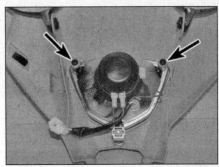

7.3 Headlight unit is secured by screws (arrowed)

4 Undo the nuts securing the tail light unit to the number plate bracket and lift it off **(see illustration)**.
5 Installation is the reverse of removal. Check the operation of the tail light, brake light and the rear turn signals before installing the seat.

10 Turn signal circuit and relay

Circuit

1 Most turn signal problems are the result of a burned-out bulb or corroded bulbholder (see Section 11). This is especially true when the turn signals function properly in one direction, but fail to flash in the other direction. Check the individual turn signal wiring connectors, the switch (see Section 16) and the main fuse (see Section 4).
2 The battery provides power for operation of the turn signals, so if they do not operate, always check the battery voltage (see Section 3).
3 If all the other components of the turn signal circuit are good, check the turn signal relay.

Turn signal relay

4 The turn signal relay is located at the front of the bike, below the instrument cluster **(see**

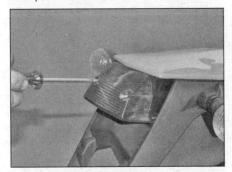

8.1a Undo the two screws . . .

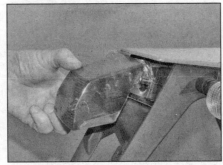

8.1b . . . and lift the light lens off

8.2 Push the bulb in and twist it anti-clockwise

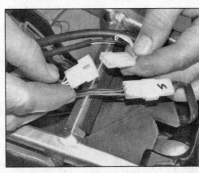

9.2 Disconnect the wiring connectors

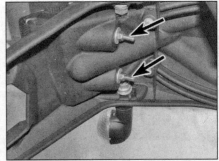

9.4 Tail light unit is secured by nuts (arrowed)

10.4 Location of the turn signal relay

11.1a Remove the screw (arrowed) . . .

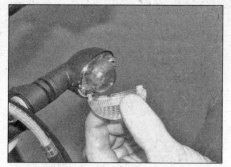

11.1b . . . and lift off the lens

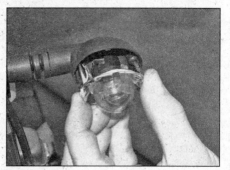

11.2a Draw out the reflector unit . . .

11.2b . . . and unclip the bulb cover

11.3 Push the bulb in and twist it anti-clockwise

illustration). Remove the headlight panel for access (see Chapter 8).

5 Disconnect the relay wiring connectors, then use an insulated jumper wire to bridge the two connector terminals, leaving the relay isolated. Select LEFT and RIGHT with the handlebar signal switch – the appropriate signal lights should come on, but they will not flash. Turn the signal switch OFF.

6 If the signal lights come on, fit a new relay.

7 If the lights do not come on, follow the procedure in Section 2 and use a test light or multimeter set to the 0 to 20 volts DC range to check for voltage in the supply wiring connector at the relay (see Wiring Diagrams at the end of this Chapter). Battery voltage should be shown.

8 If no voltage is present at the relay, check the wiring between the relay and the main fuse for continuity.

9 If voltage is present at the relay, using the appropriate wiring diagram, check the wiring between the relay, turn signal switch and turn signal lights for continuity.

11 Turn signal bulbs

1 Remove the screw securing the lens and lift it off, noting how the tab on the edge of the lens locates (see illustrations).

2 Draw out the reflector unit and unclip the bulb cover from the reflector (see illustrations).

3 Push the bulb into the holder and twist it anti-clockwise to remove it (see illustration).

4 Check the socket terminals for corrosion and clean them if necessary. Line up the pins of the new bulb with the slots in the socket, then push the bulb in and turn it clockwise until it locks into place.

5 Clip the bulb cover in place, install the

reflector unit in its housing and fit the lens.

6 Tighten the fixing screw carefully to avoid damaging the lens.

7 Check the operation of the turn signals.

12 Turn signal assemblies

Front

1 The front turn signals are mounted on the headlight panel or a bracket across the front of the fork top yoke (see illustrations). Remove the headlight panel for access (see Chapter 8).

2 If not already done, disconnect the turn signal wiring connectors (see illustration).

3 Undo the nut securing the signal assembly and lift it off.

4 Installation is the reverse of removal. Check the operation of the turn signals.

12.1a Front turn signals on the headlight panel

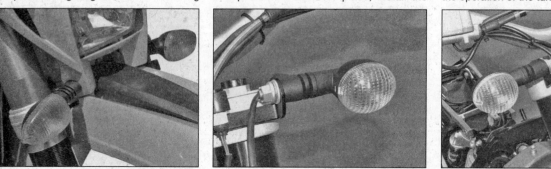

12.1b Front turn signal mounted on bracket

12.2 Location of turn signal wiring connector

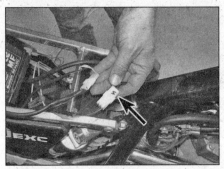

12.6 Rear turn signals wiring connector (arrowed)

Rear

5 Remove the seat (see Chapter 8).
6 Trace the wiring from the back of the tail light unit and the turn signals and disconnect it at the connectors **(see illustration)**.
7 Remove the mudguard unit and separate the number plate bracket from the mudguard (see Chapter 8).
8 Undo the nut securing the signal assembly and lift it off.
9 Installation is the reverse of removal. Check the operation of the turn signals.

13 Brake light switches

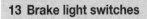

Switch check

1 Before checking the switches, check the brake light circuit (see Section 5, Steps 11 to 14).
2 The front brake light switch is mounted on the handlebar lever bracket. Remove the headlight panel (see Chapter 8), then trace the wiring from the switch and disconnect it at the connector **(see illustration)**.
3 Using a continuity tester, follow the procedure in Section 2 and connect the probes to the wire terminals on the switch side of the connector. With the brake lever at rest, there should be no continuity. With the brake lever applied, there should be continuity. If the switch does not behave as described, replace it with a new one.
4 The rear brake light switch is mounted on the rear brake master cylinder (see Chapter 7, Section 8). On 2000 to 2003 models, pull back the boot and disconnect the wiring connectors from the switch. On later models, remove the seat (see Chapter 8), then trace the wiring from the brake light switch and disconnect it at the connector.
5 Follow the procedure in Step 3 to check the switch.
6 If the switches are good, use a test light or multimeter set to the 0 to 20 ac volts range to check for voltage on the supply side of the switch wiring (see *Wiring Diagrams* at the end of this Chapter). Remember that the lighting system only works with the engine running. Approximately 12 volts ac should be shown.

13.2 Trace the wiring to the connector

7 If no voltage is present, check the wiring between the switch and the alternator for continuity. If voltage is present, check the wiring between the switch and the brake light.

Switch renewal

8 Follow the procedure in Chapter 7, Section 5, to renew the front brake light switch.
9 Follow the procedure in Chapter 7, Section 8, to renew the rear brake light switch.

14 Speedometer

1 All models are fitted with an electronic speedometer, activated by a speed sensor mounted on the front brake caliper bracket and a sensor magnet located in the brake disc.
2 On 2000 to 2004 models, the speedometer

14.5a Location of the speed sensor . . .

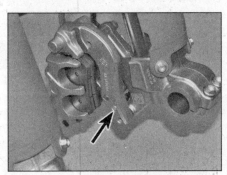

14.6a Speed sensor tip (arrowed) on inside of caliper bracket

14.3 Speedometer function buttons (arrowed) – 2005 to 2007 models

is powered by the alternator when the engine is running.
3 On 2005-on models, the speedometer is activated as soon as one of the function buttons is pressed or the sensor detects that the wheel is turning **(see illustration)**. The speedometer display is illuminated when the engine is running.
4 For full details of speedometer functions refer to the Owner's Manual for your machine. If the clock, speed and lap times cannot be displayed, renew the speedometer battery (see Steps 9 to 14).
5 If the speedometer is thought to be faulty, first check that the disc and caliper bracket are clean, and that the sensor, sensor wiring and magnet are not damaged **(see illustrations)**.
6 Using a feeler gauge, check the clearance between the magnet and the tip of the sensor on the inside of the caliper bracket **(see illustration)**. Compare the result with

14.5b . . . and speed sensor magnet (arrowed)

14.6b Screw the sensor (arrowed) in or out for adjustment

14.10 Disconnect the speedometer wiring connectors

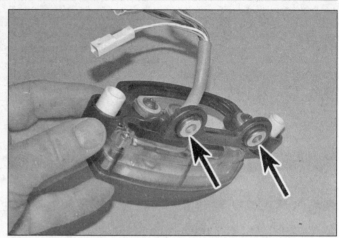

14.11 Note the grommets and spacers on the bracket

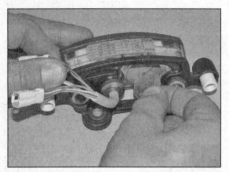

14.12 Use a coin to undo the battery cap

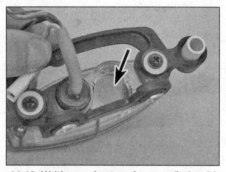

14.13 Writing on battery (arrowed) should face up

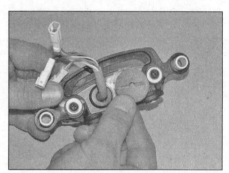

14.14 Tighten the cap securely

the specification at the beginning of this Chapter. If the gap is outside the specification, disconnect the sensor wiring connector and adjust the gap by screwing the sensor in or out of the caliper bracket **(see illustration)**. Don't forget to reconnect the connector and ensure that the wiring is secured to the caliper bracket afterwards.

7 Remove the headlight panel (see Chapter 8) and inspect the wiring and connectors between the sensor and the speedometer.

8 Special instruments are required to check the operation of the speedometer. If it is still believed to be faulty, take it to a KTM dealer for assessment.

Removal

9 Remove the headlight panel (see Chapter 8). Disconnect the battery negative (-ve) terminal.

10 Disconnect the speedometer wiring connectors **(see illustration)**. If applicable, pull the warning light bulbholders out of their sockets (see Section 15).

11 Undo the bolts securing the speedometer bracket to the fork top yoke and lift the speedometer off. Note the grommets and spacers on the bracket **(see illustration)**.

12 To renew the speedometer battery, twist the battery cap anticlockwise using a suitable

coin **(see illustration)**. Note which way up the battery is fitted.

13 Install a new battery of the correct type (see Specifications at the beginning of this Chapter). When installed, the writing on the battery should face up **(see illustration)**.

14 Fit the cap and tighten it securely **(see illustration)**.

Installation

15 Check the condition of the grommets in the mounting holes – if they are damaged or deteriorated, renew them.

16 Installation is the reverse of removal. Make sure that the wiring connectors are secure.

15 Warning light bulbs

Note: *It is a good idea to use a paper towel or dry cloth when handling a new bulb to prevent injury if the bulb should break and to increase bulb life.*

1 Remove the headlight panel (see Chapter 8).

2 Pull the appropriate bulbholder out of the socket in the speedometer bracket, then pull the bulb out of the bulbholder **(see illustrations)**.

15.2a Pull the bulbholder out of the socket . . .

15.2b . . . then pull the bulb out of the bulbholder

3 The bulbs are all of the capless type – check the size and wattage of the old bulb and make sure that you fit a new one that is the same. If the socket contacts are dirty or corroded, scrape them clean and spray with electrical contact cleaner before installing a new bulb. Carefully push the new bulb into the holder, then install the holder securely.

16 Handlebar switches

Check

1 Refer to the procedure in Chapter 1, Section 8, to check the operation of the handlebar switches.

Removal and installation

2 If not already done, disconnect the battery negative (-ve) lead to prevent the possibility of a short circuit, then remove the headlight panel (see Chapter 8).
3 Trace the wiring from the switch to be removed and disconnect it at the connector **(see illustration 13.2)**. Release the wiring from any clips or ties and feed it up to the handlebar.
4 To remove the combination headlight, horn and kill switch, or the turn indicator switch, undo the screws securing the switch housing to the handlebar bracket and lift it off **(see illustrations)**.
5 To remove the starter button, undo the screw securing the button bracket and lift it off **(see illustrations)**.
6 Installation is the reverse of removal. Make sure the wiring connectors are clean and tight and secure the wiring to the handlebars with cable-ties.
7 Test the operation of the switch.

17 Horn

Check

1 If the horn doesn't work, first check the main fuse (see Section 4).
2 The horn is located on the front of the

17.2 Location of the horn (arrowed)

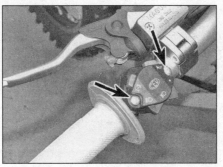

16.4a Screws (arrowed) secure combination switch

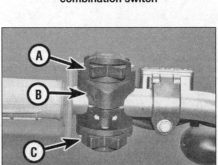

16.4c Combination switch (A), handlebar bracket (B) and turn indicator switch (C)

right-hand radiator **(see illustration)**. To gain access, follow the procedure in Chapter 8 to remove the radiator/fuel tank side panel.
3 Disconnect the wiring connectors from the terminals on the horn **(see illustration)**. Using two jumper wires, apply battery voltage directly to the horn terminals. If the horn sounds, check the switch (see Chapter 1, Section 8) and the wiring between the switch and the horn (see the *Wiring Diagrams* at the end of this Chapter).
4 If the horn doesn't sound, renew it.

Removal and installation

5 If not already done, remove the right-hand radiator/fuel tank side panel.
6 Disconnect the wiring connectors from the horn, then undo the bolt securing the horn bracket and remove it **(see illustration)**.
7 Install the horn and tighten the bolt securely.

17.3 Disconnect the wiring from the terminals (arrowed) . . .

16.4b Screws (arrowed) secure turn indicator switch

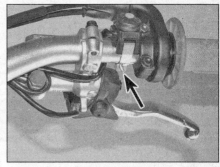

16.5 Screw (arrowed) secures the starter button bracket

Connect the wiring connectors and check the operation of the horn.

18 Starter relay

1 If the starter circuit is faulty, first check that the battery is fully-charged (see Section 3) and that the main fuse is good (see Section 4).
2 The starter relay is located behind the left-hand side panel **(see illustration 4.2)** – remove the panel for access (see Chapter 8).
3 Disconnect the battery negative (-ve) lead (see Section 3).
4 Disconnect the relay wiring connector **(see illustration 4.4)**.
5 Displace the relay from its bracket, then disconnect the battery lead (marked B) and

17.6 . . . then undo the horn bracket bolt

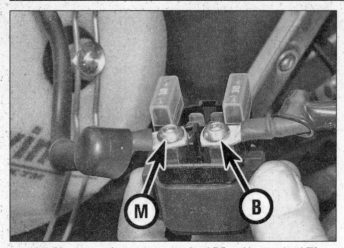

18.5 Disconnect the starter motor lead (M) and battery lead (B)

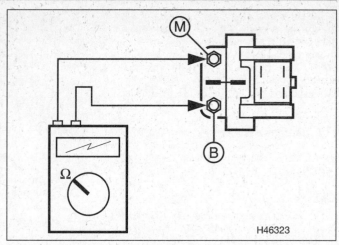

18.6 Connect a multimeter across the battery (B) and starter motor (M) terminals

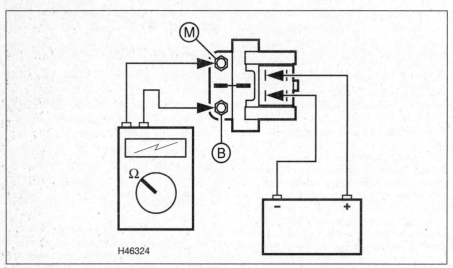

18.7 Connect a 12 volt battery as shown to test the relay operation

across the black and white/red wire terminals in the connector when the starter button is pressed. If there is no battery voltage, refer to the *Wiring Diagrams* at the end of this Chapter and check the starter button (see Chapter 1, Section 8) and the wiring and terminals in the starter circuit.

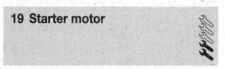

19 Starter motor

Removal

1 If the starter motor fails to turn, first check the battery and the main fuse, then check the operation of the starter relay as described in Section 18.
2 The starter motor is located behind the cylinder (see illustration).
3 Disconnect the battery negative lead.
4 Displace the terminal cover, then undo the nut securing the starter lead to the terminal and detach the lead (see illustration).
5 Undo the bolts securing the starter motor to the crankcase, then draw the starter motor out from the crankcase (see illustrations).

Inspection

6 Check that the starter motor turns freely

starter motor lead (marked M) from the relay terminals (see illustration).
6 Set a multimeter to the ohms x 1 scale and connect it across the relay's battery and starter motor terminals (see illustration). There should be no continuity (infinite resistance).
7 Using two insulated jumper wires, connect a fully-charged 12 volt battery across the black

and white/red wire terminals of the relay (see illustration). At this point the relay should be heard to click and the multimeter read 0 ohms (continuity). If the relay does not click when battery voltage is applied and the multimeter still indicates no continuity, the relay is faulty and must be renewed.
8 If the relay is good, check for battery voltage

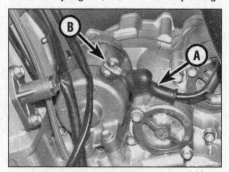

19.2 Location of the starter motor (arrowed)

19.4 Displace the cover (A) then undo the terminal nut (B)

19.5a Undo the bolts (arrowed) . . .

19.5b ...then draw the starter motor out from the crankcase

19.10 Renew the starter motor O-ring (arrowed) before installation

and that the teeth on the pinion are not worn or damaged. If the teeth are damaged, check the condition of the starter reduction gear and starter clutch (see Chapter 2, Section 19).

7 Hold the starter motor securely in a vice. Using heavy-weight jumper leads, connect the negative terminal of a fully charged 12 volt battery to the body of the starter motor, then briefly connect and the positive battery terminal to the starter motor terminal. The motor should spin freely.

8 No individual components are available for the starter motor. If the motor fails to turn, and all other components in the starter circuit are good, have it assessed by a KTM dealer or auto-electrician.

9 If the starter motor is good, follow the procedure in Chapter 2, Section 19, and check the starter reduction gear and starter clutch.

Installation

10 Installation is the reverse of removal. Fit a new O-ring on the end of the starter motor, making sure it is seated in its groove, and lubricate it with a smear of grease **(see illustration)**.

11 Install the starter motor in the crankcase, ensuring the pinion engages with the reduction gear.

12 Align the lugs on the starter motor body with the mounting holes in the crankcase, then install the bolts and tighten them to the torque setting specified at the beginning of this Chapter.

20 Alternator

General information

1 All models are fitted with a single-phase alternator. On EXC and MXC/XC models, the alternator provides power for the lighting system (where fitted) and charges the battery, which in turn provides power for the starter

motor, horn and turn signals. On SX, SXS and SMR models, the alternator provides power for the ignition system (see Chapter 5).

2 If the performance of the alternator is suspect, the charging system as a whole should be checked first, followed by testing of the individual components. **Note:** *Before beginning the checks, make sure the battery is fully charged and that all system connections are clean and tight.*

3 When making the checks, follow the procedures carefully to prevent incorrect connections or short circuits, as irreparable damage to electrical system components may result if short circuits occur.

4 Checking of the charging system output and the performance of the various components within the charging system requires the use of a multimeter (see Section 2).

Alternator output tests

5 To check the regulated voltage output, first remove the seat to access the battery (see Section 3). Start the engine and allow it to idle. Set the multimeter to the volts DC scale and connect it across the battery terminals to measure the voltage output with no load on the system **(see illustration)**. Note the output.

6 Next, switch on the headlight (or select high beam if the headlight is permanently on), apply the brake (brake light on) and sound the horn. Again, note the output.

7 Finally, increase engine speed to approximately 5000 rpm (headlight, brake light and horn still ON) and note the output.

8 Compare the results with the specifications at the beginning of this Chapter.

9 If the results are not as specified, there is a fault in the system.

10 If the voltage output is higher than specified, or if no voltage is recorded, it is likely that the regulator/rectifier is defective. Have the regulator/rectifier checked by a KTM dealer.

11 If the alternator is thought to be faulty,

check the charge current and stator coil resistance as follows.

12 To check the charge current, remove the main fuse (see Section 4). Set the multimeter to the amps x 10 scale and connect it across the fuse terminals in the relay unit. Test with the engine running as in Steps 5, 6 and 7 above and compare the results with the specifications at the beginning of this Chapter.

Alternator stator coils

13 Remove the fuel tank (see Chapter 4). Trace the alternator wiring from the left-hand engine cover and disconnect it at the connector. Set the multimeter to the ohms scale.

14 On 2000 to 2003 SX models (4K-3A stator), measure the resistance between the yellow wire terminal in the engine side of the connector and earth (ground). Compare the result with the specification at the beginning of this Chapter.

15 On all other models (4K-3B stator), measure the resistance between the yellow and white wire terminals in the engine side of the connector, then measure the resistance between the yellow wire terminal and earth (ground). Compare the results with the specifications at the beginning of this Chapter.

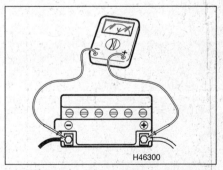

H46300

20.5 Checking the regulated voltage with a multimeter

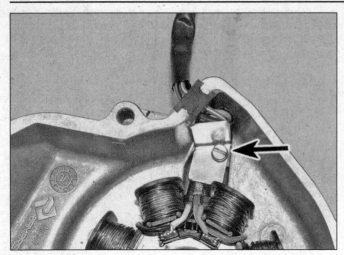

20.18 Undo the screw (arrowed) and remove the clamp

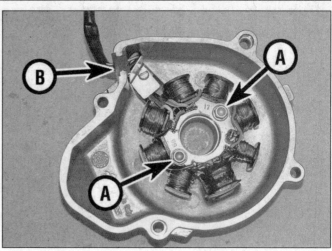

20.19 Stator is secured by bolts (A). Note the wiring grommet (B)

16 If the readings differ greatly from those given in the specifications, particularly if the meter indicates an open circuit (infinite, or very high resistance), it is likely that the alternator stator is faulty. However, first check that the fault is not due to a damaged or broken wire between the alternator and the connector – pinched or broken wires can usually be repaired. **Note:** *KTM stress that 'significant deviations' may be recorded*

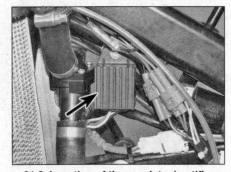

21.2 Location of the regulator/rectifier

due to test conditions. Always have your findings confirmed by a KTM dealer before condemning the component.

Removal and installation

17 The alternator rotor is located on the left-hand end of the crankshaft, the stator is mounted inside the left-hand engine cover. Follow the procedure in Chapter 2, Section 15, to remove the cover and, if required, the rotor. Note that special tools are required to remove the rotor.

18 Undo the screw and remove the wiring clamp **(see illustration)**. On the 4K-3A stator, note the single wire terminal secured by the screw.

19 Undo the bolts securing the stator, then lift out the stator assembly, taking care to ease the wiring grommet out from the cover **(see illustration)**.

20 Prior to installation, apply a small bead of sealant around the wiring grommet, then position the stator in the cover. Clean the threads of the mounting bolts and apply a

drop of the specified locking compound, then install the bolts and tighten them to the torque setting specified at the beginning of this Chapter.

21 Install the wiring clamp and secure it with the screw.

22 Follow the procedure in Chapter 2 to install the alternator cover.

21 Regulator/rectifier

1 The regulator/rectifier is mounted on the frame underneath the fuel tank – remove the fuel tank for access (see Chapter 4).

2 Disconnect the battery negative lead, then trace the wiring from the regulator/rectifier and disconnect it at the connector **(see illustration)**.

3 Undo the bolt securing the regulator/rectifier and lift it off.

4 Installation is the reverse of removal.

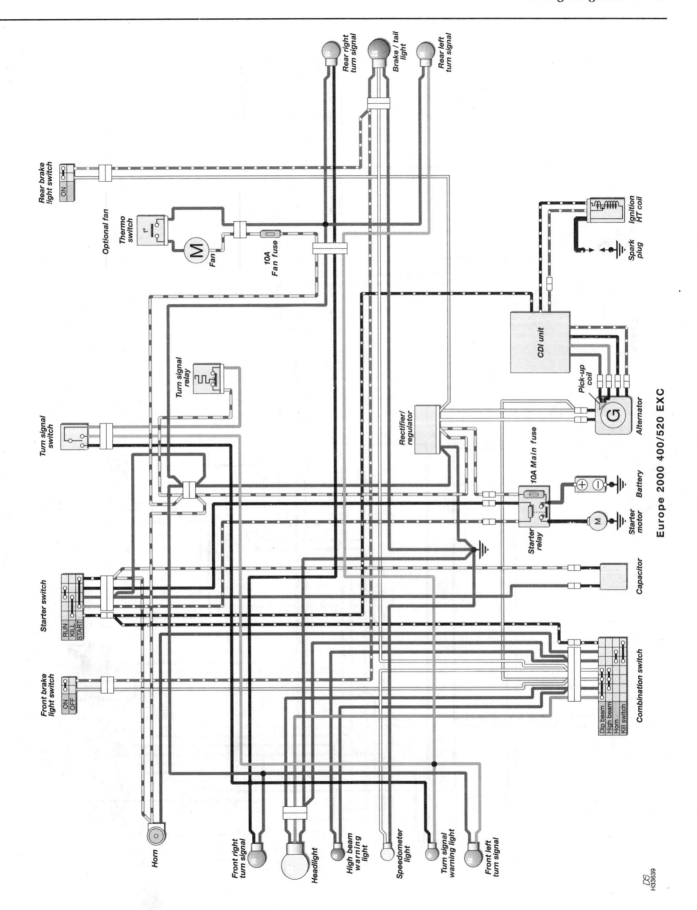

Europe 2000 400/520 EXC

H33639

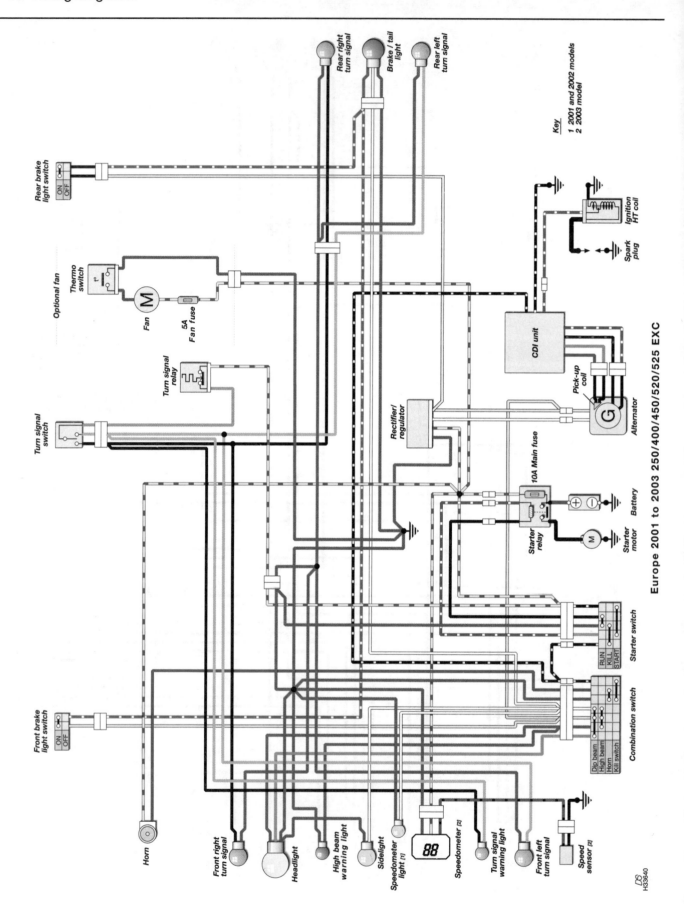

Europe 2001 to 2003 250/400/450/520/525 EXC

Key
1 2001 and 2002 models
2 2003 model

H33640

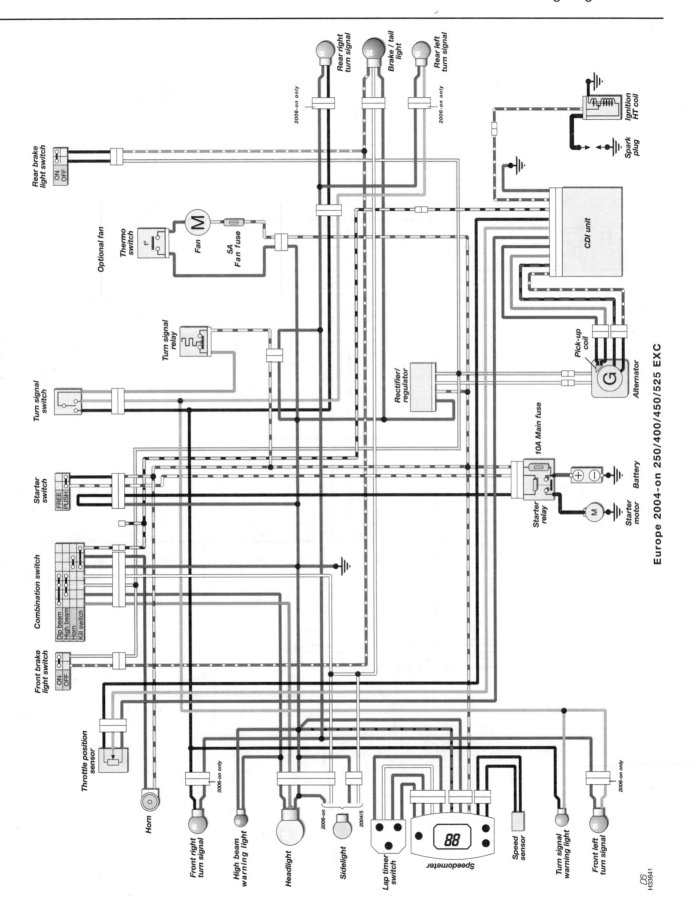

Europe 2004-on 250/400/450/525 EXC

H33641

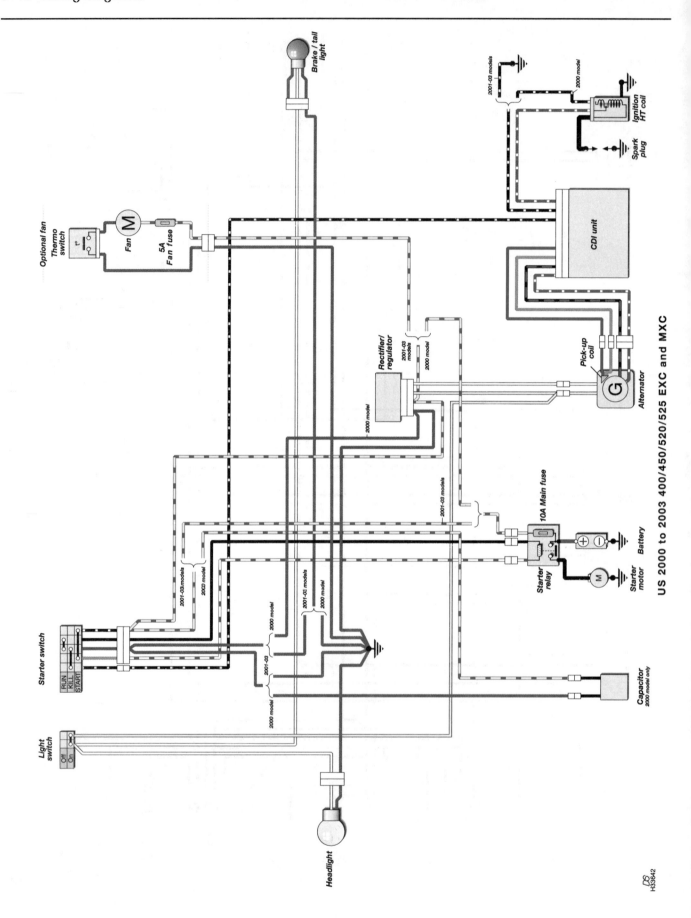

US 2000 to 2003 400/450/520/525 EXC and MXC

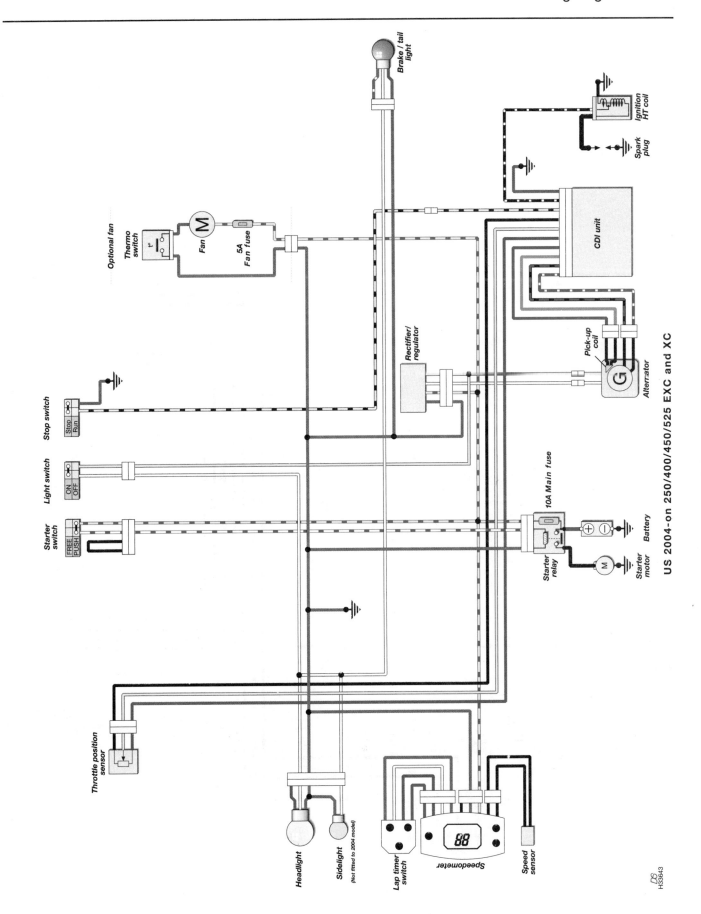

Brake / tail light

Ignition HT coil

Spark plug

CDI unit

Optional fan

Thermo switch

Fan

5A Fan fuse

Rectifier/ regulator

Pick-up coil

Alternator

Stop switch

Stop
Run

Light switch

ON
OFF

Starter switch

FREE
PUSH

10A Main fuse

Battery

Starter relay

Starter motor

Throttle position sensor

Headlight

Sidelight
(Not fitted to 2004 model)

Lap timer switch

Speedometer

Speed sensor

US 2004- on 250/400/450/525 EXC and XC

H33643

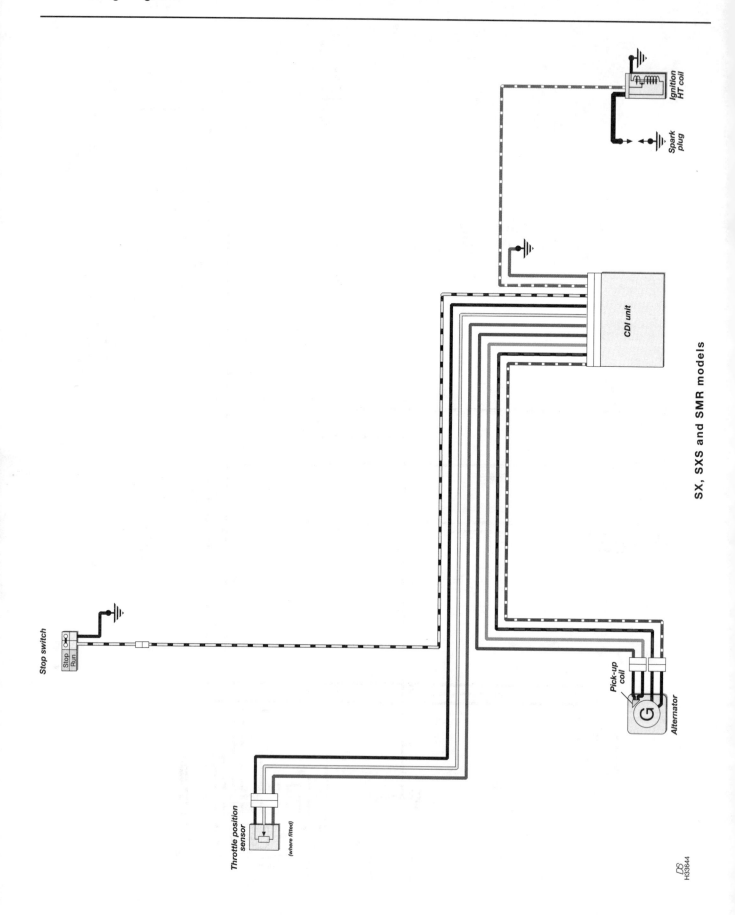

Ignition HT coil

Spark plug

CDI unit

SX, SXS and SMR models

Stop switch

Stop

Run

Pick-up coil

Alternator

G

Throttle position sensor

(where fitted)

H33644

Reference

Tools and Workshop Tips

● Building up a tool kit and equipping your workshop ● Using tools ● Understanding bearing, seal, fastener and chain sizes and markings ● Repair techniques

Conversion Factors

$$34 \text{ Nm} \times 0.738$$
$$= 25 \text{ lbf ft}$$

● Formulae for conversion of the metric (SI) units used throughout the manual into Imperial measures

MOT Test Checks

● A guide to the UK MOT test ● Which items are tested ● How to prepare your motorcycle for the test and perform a pre-test check

Fault Finding

● Common faults and their likely causes ● Links to main Chapters for testing or repair procedures

Technical Terms Explained

Index

Buying tools

A toolkit is a fundamental requirement for servicing and repairing a motorcycle. Although there will be an initial expense in building up enough tools for servicing, this will soon be offset by the savings made by doing the job yourself. As experience and confidence grow, additional tools can be added to enable the repair and overhaul of the motorcycle. Many of the specialist tools are expensive and not often used so it may be preferable to hire them, or for a group of friends or motorcycle club to join in the purchase.

As a rule, it is better to buy more expensive, good quality tools. Cheaper tools are likely to wear out faster and need to be renewed more often, nullifying the original saving.

> ⚠️ **Warning: To avoid the risk of a poor quality tool breaking in use, causing injury or damage to the component being worked on, always aim to purchase tools which meet the relevant national safety standards.**

The following lists of tools do not represent the manufacturer's service tools, but serve as a guide to help the owner decide which tools are needed for this level of work. In addition, items such as an electric drill, hacksaw, files, soldering iron and a workbench equipped with a vice, may be needed. Although not classed as tools, a selection of bolts, screws, nuts, washers and pieces of tubing always come in useful.

For more information about tools, refer to the Haynes *Motorcycle Workshop Practice Techbook* (Bk. No. 3470).

Manufacturer's service tools

Inevitably certain tasks require the use of a service tool. Where possible an alternative tool or method of approach is recommended, but sometimes there is no option if personal injury or damage to the component is to be avoided. Where required, service tools are referred to in the relevant procedure.

Service tools can usually only be purchased from a motorcycle dealer and are identified by a part number. Some of the commonly-used tools, such as rotor pullers, are available in aftermarket form from mail-order motorcycle tool and accessory suppliers.

Maintenance and minor repair tools

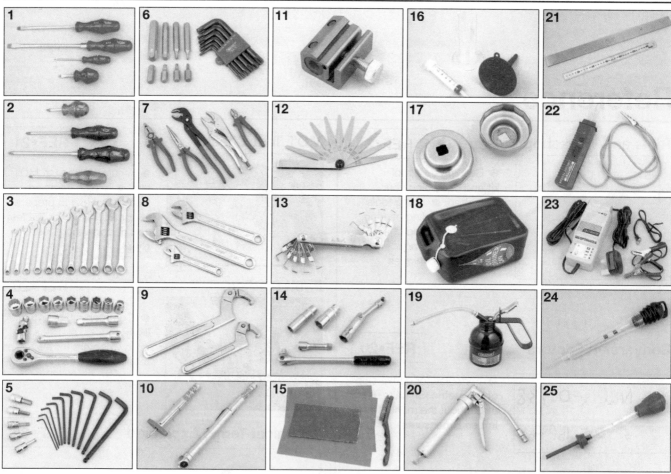

1. Set of flat-bladed screwdrivers
2. Set of Phillips head screwdrivers
3. Combination open-end and ring spanners
4. Socket set (3/8 inch or 1/2 inch drive)
5. Set of Allen keys or bits
6. Set of Torx keys or bits
7. Pliers, cutters and self-locking grips (Mole grips)
8. Adjustable spanners
9. C-spanners
10. Tread depth gauge and tyre pressure gauge
11. Cable oiler clamp
12. Feeler gauges
13. Spark plug gap measuring tool
14. Spark plug spanner or deep plug sockets
15. Wire brush and emery paper
16. Calibrated syringe, measuring vessel and funnel
17. Oil filter adapters
18. Oil drainer can or tray
19. Pump type oil can
20. Grease gun
21. Straight-edge and steel rule
22. Continuity tester
23. Battery charger
24. Hydrometer (for battery specific gravity check)
25. Anti-freeze tester (for liquid-cooled engines)

Repair and overhaul tools

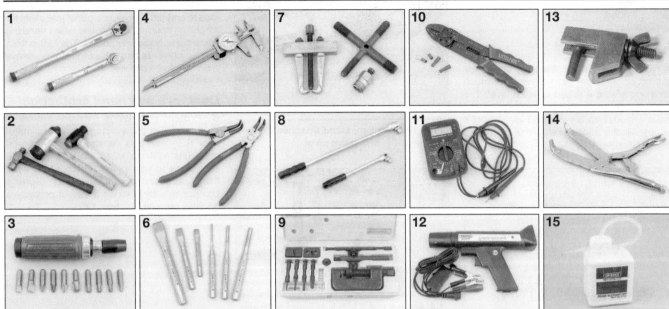

1 Torque wrench
  (small and mid-ranges)
2 Conventional, plastic or
  soft-faced hammers
3 Impact driver set
4 Vernier gauge
5 Circlip pliers (internal and
  external, or combination)
6 Set of cold chisels
  and punches
7 Selection of pullers
8 Breaker bars
9 Chain breaking/
  riveting tool set
10 Wire stripper and
   crimper tool
11 Multimeter (measures
   amps, volts and ohms)
12 Stroboscope (for
   dynamic timing checks)
13 Hose clamp
   (wingnut type shown)
14 Clutch holding tool
15 One-man brake/clutch
   bleeder kit

Specialist tools

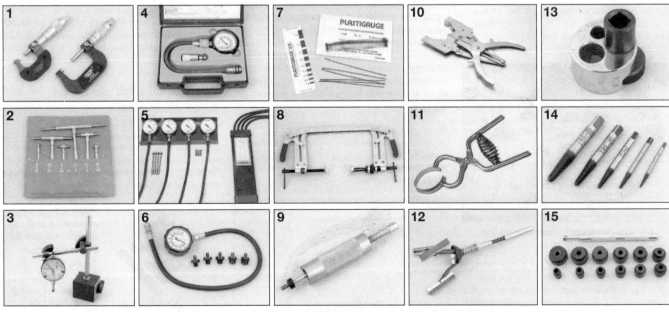

1 Micrometers
  (external type)
2 Telescoping gauges
3 Dial gauge
4 Cylinder
  compression gauge
5 Vacuum gauges (left) or
  manometer (right)
6 Oil pressure gauge
7 Plastigauge kit
8 Valve spring compressor
  (4-stroke engines)
9 Piston pin drawbolt tool
10 Piston ring removal and
   installation tool
11 Piston ring clamp
12 Cylinder bore hone
   (stone type shown)
13 Stud extractor
14 Screw extractor set
15 Bearing driver set

1 Workshop equipment and facilities

The workbench

● Work is made much easier by raising the bike up on a ramp - components are much more accessible if raised to waist level. The hydraulic or pneumatic types seen in the dealer's workshop are a sound investment if you undertake a lot of repairs or overhauls (see illustration 1.1).

1.1 Hydraulic motorcycle ramp

● If raised off ground level, the bike must be supported on the ramp to avoid it falling. Most ramps incorporate a front wheel locating clamp which can be adjusted to suit different diameter wheels. When tightening the clamp, take care not to mark the wheel rim or damage the tyre - use wood blocks on each side to prevent this.
● Secure the bike to the ramp using tie-downs (see illustration 1.2). If the bike has only a sidestand, and hence leans at a dangerous angle when raised, support the bike on an auxiliary stand.

1.2 Tie-downs are used around the passenger footrests to secure the bike

● Auxiliary (paddock) stands are widely available from mail order companies or motorcycle dealers and attach either to the wheel axle or swingarm pivot (see illustration 1.3). If the motorcycle has a centrestand, you can support it under the crankcase to prevent it toppling whilst either wheel is removed (see illustration 1.4).

1.3 This auxiliary stand attaches to the swingarm pivot

1.4 Always use a block of wood between the engine and jack head when supporting the engine in this way

Fumes and fire

● Refer to the Safety first! page at the beginning of the manual for full details. Make sure your workshop is equipped with a fire extinguisher suitable for fuel-related fires (Class B fire - flammable liquids) - it is not sufficient to have a water-filled extinguisher.
● Always ensure adequate ventilation is available. Unless an exhaust gas extraction system is available for use, ensure that the engine is run outside of the workshop.
● If working on the fuel system, make sure the workshop is ventilated to avoid a build-up of fumes. This applies equally to fume build-up when charging a battery. Do not smoke or allow anyone else to smoke in the workshop.

Fluids

● If you need to drain fuel from the tank, store it in an approved container marked as suitable for the storage of petrol (gasoline) (see illustration 1.5). Do not store fuel in glass jars or bottles.

1.5 Use an approved can only for storing petrol (gasoline)

● Use proprietary engine degreasers or solvents which have a high flash-point, such as paraffin (kerosene), for cleaning off oil, grease and dirt - never use petrol (gasoline) for cleaning. Wear rubber gloves when handling solvent and engine degreaser. The fumes from certain solvents can be dangerous - always work in a well-ventilated area.

Dust, eye and hand protection

● Protect your lungs from inhalation of dust particles by wearing a filtering mask over the nose and mouth. Many frictional materials still contain asbestos which is dangerous to your health. Protect your eyes from spouts of liquid and sprung components by wearing a pair of protective goggles (see illustration 1.6).

1.6 A fire extinguisher, goggles, mask and protective gloves should be at hand in the workshop

● Protect your hands from contact with solvents, fuel and oils by wearing rubber gloves. Alternatively apply a barrier cream to your hands before starting work. If handling hot components or fluids, wear suitable gloves to protect your hands from scalding and burns.

What to do with old fluids

● Old cleaning solvent, fuel, coolant and oils should not be poured down domestic drains or onto the ground. Package the fluid up in old oil containers, label it accordingly, and take it to a garage or disposal facility. Contact your local authority for location of such sites or ring the oil care hotline.

OIL CARE
FOLLOW THE CODE

OIL BANK LINE
0800 66 33 66
www.oilbankline.org.uk

Note: It is antisocial and illegal to dump oil down the drain. To find the location of your local oil recycling bank, call this number free.

In the USA, note that any oil supplier must accept used oil for recycling.

2 Fasteners -
screws, bolts and nuts

Fastener types and applications

Bolts and screws

● Fastener head types are either of hexagonal, Torx or splined design, with internal and external versions of each type **(see illustrations 2.1 and 2.2)**; splined head fasteners are not in common use on motorcycles. The conventional slotted or Phillips head design is used for certain screws. Bolt or screw length is always measured from the underside of the head to the end of the item **(see illustration 2.11)**.

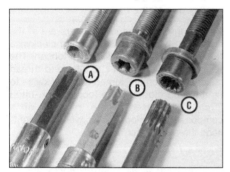

2.1 Internal hexagon/Allen (A), Torx (B) and splined (C) fasteners, with corresponding bits

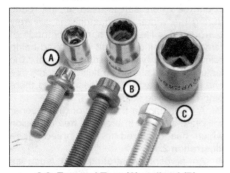

2.2 External Torx (A), splined (B) and hexagon (C) fasteners, with corresponding sockets

● Certain fasteners on the motorcycle have a tensile marking on their heads, the higher the marking the stronger the fastener. High tensile fasteners generally carry a 10 or higher marking. Never replace a high tensile fastener with one of a lower tensile strength.

Washers (see illustration 2.3)

● Plain washers are used between a fastener head and a component to prevent damage to the component or to spread the load when torque is applied. Plain washers can also be used as spacers or shims in certain assemblies. Copper or aluminium plain washers are often used as sealing washers on drain plugs.

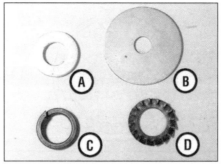

2.3 Plain washer (A), penny washer (B), spring washer (C) and serrated washer (D)

● The split-ring spring washer works by applying axial tension between the fastener head and component. If flattened, it is fatigued and must be renewed. If a plain (flat) washer is used on the fastener, position the spring washer between the fastener and the plain washer.

● Serrated star type washers dig into the fastener and component faces, preventing loosening. They are often used on electrical earth (ground) connections to the frame.

● Cone type washers (sometimes called Belleville) are conical and when tightened apply axial tension between the fastener head and component. They must be installed with the dished side against the component and often carry an OUTSIDE marking on their outer face. If flattened, they are fatigued and must be renewed.

● Tab washers are used to lock plain nuts or bolts on a shaft. A portion of the tab washer is bent up hard against one flat of the nut or bolt to prevent it loosening. Due to the tab washer being deformed in use, a new tab washer should be used every time it is disturbed.

● Wave washers are used to take up endfloat on a shaft. They provide light springing and prevent excessive side-to-side play of a component. Can be found on rocker arm shafts.

Nuts and split pins

● Conventional plain nuts are usually six-sided **(see illustration 2.4)**. They are sized by thread diameter and pitch. High tensile nuts carry a number on one end to denote their tensile strength.

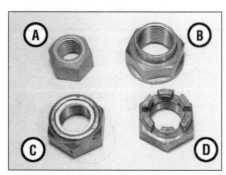

2.4 Plain nut (A), shouldered locknut (B), nylon insert nut (C) and castellated nut (D)

● Self-locking nuts either have a nylon insert, or two spring metal tabs, or a shoulder which is staked into a groove in the shaft - their advantage over conventional plain nuts is a resistance to loosening due to vibration. The nylon insert type can be used a number of times, but must be renewed when the friction of the nylon insert is reduced, ie when the nut spins freely on the shaft. The spring tab type can be reused unless the tabs are damaged. The shouldered type must be renewed every time it is disturbed.

● Split pins (cotter pins) are used to lock a castellated nut to a shaft or to prevent slackening of a plain nut. Common applications are wheel axles and brake torque arms. Because the split pin arms are deformed to lock around the nut a new split pin must always be used on installation - always fit the correct size split pin which will fit snugly in the shaft hole. Make sure the split pin arms are correctly located around the nut **(see illustrations 2.5 and 2.6)**.

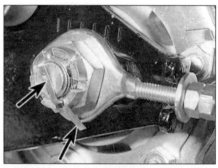

2.5 Bend split pin (cotter pin) arms as shown (arrows) to secure a castellated nut

2.6 Bend split pin (cotter pin) arms as shown to secure a plain nut

Caution: If the castellated nut slots do not align with the shaft hole after tightening to the torque setting, tighten the nut until the next slot aligns with the hole - never slacken the nut to align its slot.

● R-pins (shaped like the letter R), or slip pins as they are sometimes called, are sprung and can be reused if they are otherwise in good condition. Always install R-pins with their closed end facing forwards **(see illustration 2.7)**.

**2.7 Correct fitting of R-pin.
Arrow indicates forward direction**

Circlips (see illustration 2.8)

● Circlips (sometimes called snap-rings) are used to retain components on a shaft or in a housing and have corresponding external or internal ears to permit removal. Parallel-sided (machined) circlips can be installed either way round in their groove, whereas stamped circlips (which have a chamfered edge on one face) must be installed with the chamfer facing away from the direction of thrust load **(see illustration 2.9)**.

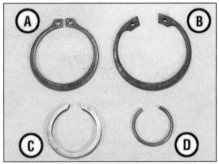

2.8 External stamped circlip (A), internal stamped circlip (B), machined circlip (C) and wire circlip (D)

● Always use circlip pliers to remove and install circlips; expand or compress them just enough to remove them. After installation, rotate the circlip in its groove to ensure it is securely seated. If installing a circlip on a splined shaft, always align its opening with a shaft channel to ensure the circlip ends are well supported and unlikely to catch **(see illustration 2.10)**.

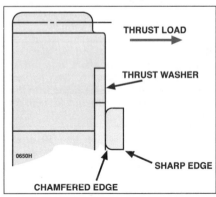

2.9 Correct fitting of a stamped circlip

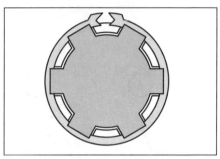

**2.10 Align circlip opening
with shaft channel**

● Circlips can wear due to the thrust of components and become loose in their grooves, with the subsequent danger of becoming dislodged in operation. For this reason, renewal is advised every time a circlip is disturbed.
● Wire circlips are commonly used as piston pin retaining clips. If a removal tang is provided, long-nosed pliers can be used to dislodge them, otherwise careful use of a small flat-bladed screwdriver is necessary. Wire circlips should be renewed every time they are disturbed.

Thread diameter and pitch

● Diameter of a male thread (screw, bolt or stud) is the outside diameter of the threaded portion **(see illustration 2.11)**. Most motorcycle manufacturers use the ISO (International Standards Organisation) metric system expressed in millimetres, eg M6 refers to a 6 mm diameter thread. Sizing is the same for nuts, except that the thread diameter is measured across the valleys of the nut.
● Pitch is the distance between the peaks of the thread **(see illustration 2.11)**. It is expressed in millimetres, thus a common bolt size may be expressed as 6.0 x 1.0 mm (6 mm thread diameter and 1 mm pitch). Generally pitch increases in proportion to thread diameter, although there are always exceptions.
● Thread diameter and pitch are related for conventional fastener applications and the accompanying table can be used as a guide. Additionally, the AF (Across Flats), spanner or socket size dimension of the bolt or nut **(see illustration 2.11)** is linked to thread and pitch specification. Thread pitch can be measured with a thread gauge **(see illustration 2.12)**.

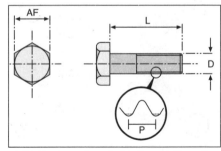

2.11 Fastener length (L), thread diameter (D), thread pitch (P) and head size (AF)

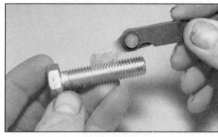

**2.12 Using a thread gauge
to measure pitch**

AF size	Thread diameter x pitch (mm)
8 mm	M5 x 0.8
8 mm	M6 x 1.0
10 mm	M6 x 1.0
12 mm	M8 x 1.25
14 mm	M10 x 1.25
17 mm	M12 x 1.25

● The threads of most fasteners are of the right-hand type, ie they are turned clockwise to tighten and anti-clockwise to loosen. The reverse situation applies to left-hand thread fasteners, which are turned anti-clockwise to tighten and clockwise to loosen. Left-hand threads are used where rotation of a component might loosen a conventional right-hand thread fastener.

Seized fasteners

● Corrosion of external fasteners due to water or reaction between two dissimilar metals can occur over a period of time. It will build up sooner in wet conditions or in countries where salt is used on the roads during the winter. If a fastener is severely corroded it is likely that normal methods of removal will fail and result in its head being ruined. When you attempt removal, the fastener thread should be heard to crack free and unscrew easily - if it doesn't, stop there before damaging something.
● A smart tap on the head of the fastener will often succeed in breaking free corrosion which has occurred in the threads **(see illustration 2.13)**.
● An aerosol penetrating fluid (such as WD-40) applied the night beforehand may work its way down into the thread and ease removal. Depending on the location, you may be able to make up a Plasticine well around the fastener head and fill it with penetrating fluid.

**2.13 A sharp tap on the head of a fastener
will often break free a corroded thread**

● If you are working on an engine internal component, corrosion will most likely not be a problem due to the well lubricated environment. However, components can be very tight and an impact driver is a useful tool in freeing them **(see illustration 2.14)**.

2.14 Using an impact driver to free a fastener

● Where corrosion has occurred between dissimilar metals (eg steel and aluminium alloy), the application of heat to the fastener head will create a disproportionate expansion rate between the two metals and break the seizure caused by the corrosion. Whether heat can be applied depends on the location of the fastener - any surrounding components likely to be damaged must first be removed **(see illustration 2.15)**. Heat can be applied using a paint stripper heat gun or clothes iron, or by immersing the component in boiling water - wear protective gloves to prevent scalding or burns to the hands.

2.15 Using heat to free a seized fastener

● As a last resort, it is possible to use a hammer and cold chisel to work the fastener head unscrewed **(see illustration 2.16)**. This will damage the fastener, but more importantly extreme care must be taken not to damage the surrounding component.

Caution: Remember that the component being secured is generally of more value than the bolt, nut or screw - when the fastener is freed, do not unscrew it with force, instead work the fastener back and forth when resistance is felt to prevent thread damage.

2.16 Using a hammer and chisel to free a seized fastener

Broken fasteners and damaged heads

● If the shank of a broken bolt or screw is accessible you can grip it with self-locking grips. The knurled wheel type stud extractor tool or self-gripping stud puller tool is particularly useful for removing the long studs which screw into the cylinder mouth surface of the crankcase or bolts and screws from which the head has broken off **(see illustration 2.17)**. Studs can also be removed by locking two nuts together on the threaded end of the stud and using a spanner on the lower nut **(see illustration 2.18)**.

2.17 Using a stud extractor tool to remove a broken crankcase stud

2.18 Two nuts can be locked together to unscrew a stud from a component

● A bolt or screw which has broken off below or level with the casing must be extracted using a screw extractor set. Centre punch the fastener to centralise the drill bit, then drill a hole in the fastener **(see illustration 2.19)**. Select a drill bit which is approximately half to three-quarters the

2.19 When using a screw extractor, first drill a hole in the fastener . . .

diameter of the fastener and drill to a depth which will accommodate the extractor. Use the largest size extractor possible, but avoid leaving too small a wall thickness otherwise the extractor will merely force the fastener walls outwards wedging it in the casing thread.

● If a spiral type extractor is used, thread it anti-clockwise into the fastener. As it is screwed in, it will grip the fastener and unscrew it from the casing **(see illustration 2.20)**.

2.20 . . . then thread the extractor anti-clockwise into the fastener

● If a taper type extractor is used, tap it into the fastener so that it is firmly wedged in place. Unscrew the extractor (anti-clockwise) to draw the fastener out.

> ⚠ *Warning: Stud extractors are very hard and may break off in the fastener if care is not taken - ask an engineer about spark erosion if this happens.*

● Alternatively, the broken bolt/screw can be drilled out and the hole retapped for an oversize bolt/screw or a diamond-section thread insert. It is essential that the drilling is carried out squarely and to the correct depth, otherwise the casing may be ruined - if in doubt, entrust the work to an engineer.

● Bolts and nuts with rounded corners cause the correct size spanner or socket to slip when force is applied. Of the types of spanner/socket available always use a six-point type rather than an eight or twelve-point type - better grip

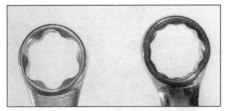

2.21 Comparison of surface drive ring spanner (left) with 12-point type (right)

is obtained. Surface drive spanners grip the middle of the hex flats, rather than the corners, and are thus good in cases of damaged heads **(see illustration 2.21)**.

● Slotted-head or Phillips-head screws are often damaged by the use of the wrong size screwdriver. Allen-head and Torx-head screws are much less likely to sustain damage. If enough of the screw head is exposed you can use a hacksaw to cut a slot in its head and then use a conventional flat-bladed screwdriver to remove it. Alternatively use a hammer and cold chisel to tap the head of the fastener around to slacken it. Always replace damaged fasteners with new ones, preferably Torx or Allen-head type.

HAYNES HiNT

A dab of valve grinding compound between the screw head and screw-driver tip will often give a good grip.

Thread repair

● Threads (particularly those in aluminium alloy components) can be damaged by overtightening, being assembled with dirt in the threads, or from a component working loose and vibrating. Eventually the thread will fail completely, and it will be impossible to tighten the fastener.

● If a thread is damaged or clogged with old locking compound it can be renovated with a thread repair tool (thread chaser) **(see illustrations 2.22 and 2.23)**; special thread

2.22 A thread repair tool being used to correct an internal thread

2.23 A thread repair tool being used to correct an external thread

chasers are available for spark plug hole threads. The tool will not cut a new thread, but clean and true the original thread. Make sure that you use the correct diameter and pitch tool. Similarly, external threads can be cleaned up with a die or a thread restorer file **(see illustration 2.24)**.

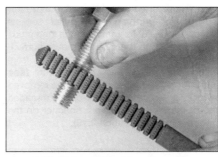

2.24 Using a thread restorer file

● It is possible to drill out the old thread and retap the component to the next thread size. This will work where there is enough surrounding material and a new bolt or screw can be obtained. Sometimes, however, this is not possible - such as where the bolt/screw passes through another component which must also be suitably modified, also in cases where a spark plug or oil drain plug cannot be obtained in a larger diameter thread size.

● The diamond-section thread insert (often known by its popular trade name of Heli-Coil) is a simple and effective method of renewing the thread and retaining the original size. A kit can be purchased which contains the tap, insert and installing tool **(see illustration 2.25)**. Drill out the damaged thread with the size drill specified **(see illustration 2.26)**. Carefully retap the thread **(see illustration 2.27)**. Install the

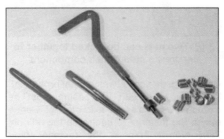

2.25 Obtain a thread insert kit to suit the thread diameter and pitch required

2.26 To install a thread insert, first drill out the original thread . . .

2.27 . . . tap a new thread . . .

2.28 . . . fit insert on the installing tool . . .

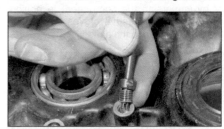

2.29 . . . and thread into the component . . .

2.30 . . . break off the tang when complete

insert on the installing tool and thread it slowly into place using a light downward pressure **(see illustrations 2.28 and 2.29)**. When positioned between a 1/4 and 1/2 turn below the surface withdraw the installing tool and use the break-off tool to press down on the tang, breaking it off **(see illustration 2.30)**.

● There are epoxy thread repair kits on the market which can rebuild stripped internal threads, although this repair should not be used on high load-bearing components.

Thread locking and sealing compounds

● Locking compounds are used in locations where the fastener is prone to loosening due to vibration or on important safety-related items which might cause loss of control of the motorcycle if they fail. It is also used where important fasteners cannot be secured by other means such as lockwashers or split pins.

● Before applying locking compound, make sure that the threads (internal and external) are clean and dry with all old compound removed. Select a compound to suit the component being secured - a non-permanent general locking and sealing type is suitable for most applications, but a high strength type is needed for permanent fixing of studs in castings. Apply a drop or two of the compound to the first few threads of the fastener, then thread it into place and tighten to the specified torque. Do not apply excessive thread locking compound otherwise the thread may be damaged on subsequent removal.

● Certain fasteners are impregnated with a dry film type coating of locking compound on their threads. Always renew this type of fastener if disturbed.

● Anti-seize compounds, such as copper-based greases, can be applied to protect threads from seizure due to extreme heat and corrosion. A common instance is spark plug threads and exhaust system fasteners.

3 Measuring tools and gauges

Feeler gauges

● Feeler gauges (or blades) are used for measuring small gaps and clearances **(see illustration 3.1)**. They can also be used to measure endfloat (sideplay) of a component on a shaft where access is not possible with a dial gauge.

● Feeler gauge sets should be treated with care and not bent or damaged. They are etched with their size on one face. Keep them clean and very lightly oiled to prevent corrosion build-up.

3.1 Feeler gauges are used for measuring small gaps and clearances - thickness is marked on one face of gauge

● When measuring a clearance, select a gauge which is a light sliding fit between the two components. You may need to use two gauges together to measure the clearance accurately.

Micrometers

● A micrometer is a precision tool capable of measuring to 0.01 or 0.001 of a millimetre. It should always be stored in its case and not in the general toolbox. It must be kept clean and never dropped, otherwise its frame or measuring anvils could be distorted resulting in inaccurate readings.

● External micrometers are used for measuring outside diameters of components and have many more applications than internal micrometers. Micrometers are available in different size ranges, eg 0 to 25 mm, 25 to 50 mm, and upwards in 25 mm steps; some large micrometers have interchangeable anvils to allow a range of measurements to be taken. Generally the largest precision measurement you are likely to take on a motorcycle is the piston diameter.

● Internal micrometers (or bore micrometers) are used for measuring inside diameters, such as valve guides and cylinder bores. Telescoping gauges and small hole gauges are used in conjunction with an external micrometer, whereas the more expensive internal micrometers have their own measuring device.

External micrometer

Note: *The conventional analogue type instrument is described. Although much easier to read, digital micrometers are considerably more expensive.*

● Always check the calibration of the micrometer before use. With the anvils closed (0 to 25 mm type) or set over a test gauge (for

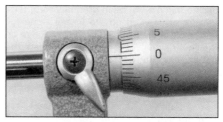

3.2 Check micrometer calibration before use

the larger types) the scale should read zero **(see illustration 3.2)**; make sure that the anvils (and test piece) are clean first. Any discrepancy can be adjusted by referring to the instructions supplied with the tool. Remember that the micrometer is a precision measuring tool - don't force the anvils closed, use the ratchet (4) on the end of the micrometer to close it. In this way, a measured force is always applied.

● To use, first make sure that the item being measured is clean. Place the anvil of the micrometer (1) against the item and use the thimble (2) to bring the spindle (3) lightly into contact with the other side of the item **(see illustration 3.3)**. Don't tighten the thimble down because this will damage the micrometer - instead use the ratchet (4) on the end of the micrometer. The ratchet mechanism applies a measured force preventing damage to the instrument.

● The micrometer is read by referring to the linear scale on the sleeve and the annular scale on the thimble. Read off the sleeve first to obtain the base measurement, then add the fine measurement from the thimble to obtain the overall reading. The linear scale on the sleeve represents the measuring range of the micrometer (eg 0 to 25 mm). The annular scale

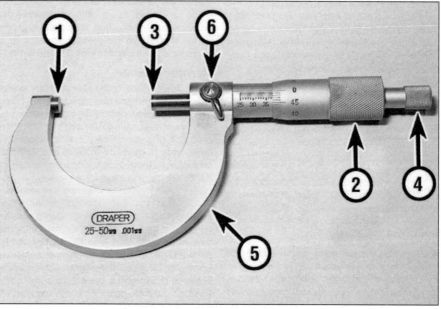

3.3 Micrometer component parts

1 Anvil	3 Spindle	5 Frame
2 Thimble	4 Ratchet	6 Locking lever

on the thimble will be in graduations of 0.01 mm (or as marked on the frame) - one full revolution of the thimble will move 0.5 mm on the linear scale. Take the reading where the datum line on the sleeve intersects the thimble's scale. Always position the eye directly above the scale otherwise an inaccurate reading will result.

In the example shown the item measures 2.95 mm (see illustration 3.4):

Linear scale	2.00 mm
Linear scale	0.50 mm
Annular scale	0.45 mm
Total figure	2.95 mm

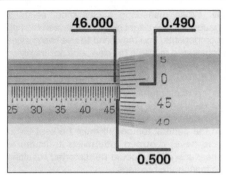

3.5 Micrometer reading of 46.99 mm on linear and annular scales . . .

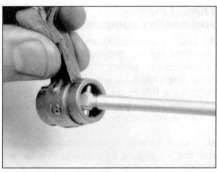

3.7 Expand the telescoping gauge in the bore, lock its position . . .

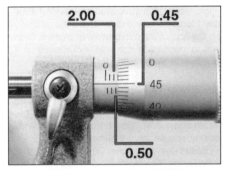

3.4 Micrometer reading of 2.95 mm

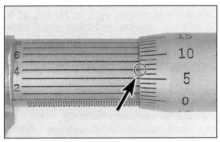

3.6 . . . and 0.004 mm on vernier scale

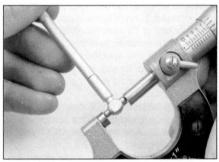

3.8 . . . then measure the gauge with a micrometer

Most micrometers have a locking lever (6) on the frame to hold the setting in place, allowing the item to be removed from the micrometer.
● Some micrometers have a vernier scale on their sleeve, providing an even finer measurement to be taken, in 0.001 increments of a millimetre. Take the sleeve and thimble measurement as described above, then check which graduation on the vernier scale aligns with that of the annular scale on the thimble **Note:** *The eye must be perpendicular to the scale when taking the vernier reading - if necessary rotate the body of the micrometer to ensure this.* Multiply the vernier scale figure by 0.001 and add it to the base and fine measurement figures.

In the example shown the item measures 46.994 mm (see illustrations 3.5 and 3.6):

Linear scale (base)	46.000 mm
Linear scale (base)	00.500 mm
Annular scale (fine)	00.490 mm
Vernier scale	00.004 mm
Total figure	46.994 mm

Internal micrometer

● Internal micrometers are available for measuring bore diameters, but are expensive and unlikely to be available for home use. It is suggested that a set of telescoping gauges and small hole gauges, both of which must be used with an external micrometer, will suffice for taking internal measurements on a motorcycle.
● Telescoping gauges can be used to

measure internal diameters of components. Select a gauge with the correct size range, make sure its ends are clean and insert it into the bore. Expand the gauge, then lock its position and withdraw it from the bore (see illustration 3.7). Measure across the gauge ends with a micrometer (see illustration 3.8).
● Very small diameter bores (such as valve guides) are measured with a small hole gauge. Once adjusted to a slip-fit inside the component, its position is locked and the gauge withdrawn for measurement with a micrometer (see illustrations 3.9 and 3.10).

Vernier caliper

Note: *The conventional linear and dial gauge type instruments are described. Digital types are easier to read, but are far more expensive.*
● The vernier caliper does not provide the precision of a micrometer, but is versatile in being able to measure internal and external diameters. Some types also incorporate a depth gauge. It is ideal for measuring clutch plate friction material and spring free lengths.
● To use the conventional linear scale vernier, slacken off the vernier clamp screws (1) and set its jaws over (2), or inside (3), the item to be measured (see illustration 3.11). Slide the jaw into contact, using the thumbwheel (4) for fine movement of the sliding scale (5) then tighten the clamp screws (1). Read off the main scale (6) where the zero on the sliding scale (5) intersects it, taking the whole number to the left of the zero; this provides the base measurement. View along the sliding scale and select the division which

3.9 Expand the small hole gauge in the bore, lock its position . . .

3.10 . . . then measure the gauge with a micrometer

lines up exactly with any of the divisions on the main scale, noting that the divisions usually represents 0.02 of a millimetre. Add this fine measurement to the base measurement to obtain the total reading.

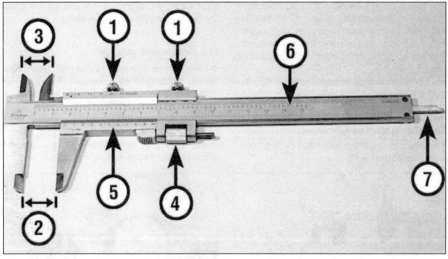

3.11 Vernier component parts (linear gauge)

1 Clamp screws	3 Internal jaws	5 Sliding scale	7 Depth gauge
2 External jaws	4 Thumbwheel	6 Main scale	

In the example shown the item measures 55.92 mm **(see illustration 3.12)**:

Base measurement	55.00 mm
Fine measurement	00.92 mm
Total figure	**55.92 mm**

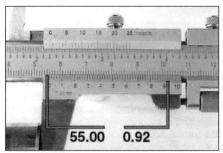

3.12 Vernier gauge reading of 55.92 mm

- Some vernier calipers are equipped with a dial gauge for fine measurement. Before use, check that the jaws are clean, then close them fully and check that the dial gauge reads zero. If necessary adjust the gauge ring accordingly. Slacken the vernier clamp screw (1) and set its jaws over (2), or inside (3), the item to be measured **(see illustration 3.13)**. Slide the jaws into contact, using the thumbwheel (4) for fine movement. Read off the main scale (5) where the edge of the sliding scale (6) intersects it, taking the whole number to the left of the zero; this provides the base measurement. Read off the needle position on the dial gauge (7) scale to provide the fine measurement; each division represents 0.05 of a millimetre. Add this fine measurement to the base measurement to obtain the total reading.

In the example shown the item measures 55.95 mm **(see illustration 3.14)**:

Base measurement	55.00 mm
Fine measurement	00.95 mm
Total figure	**55.95 mm**

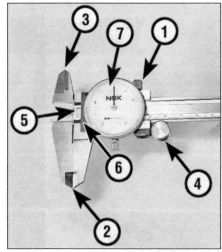

3.13 Vernier component parts (dial gauge)

1 Clamp screw	5 Main scale
2 External jaws	6 Sliding scale
3 Internal jaws	7 Dial gauge
4 Thumbwheel	

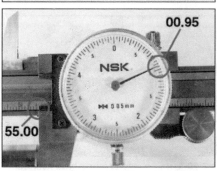

3.14 Vernier gauge reading of 55.95 mm

Plastigauge

- Plastigauge is a plastic material which can be compressed between two surfaces to measure the oil clearance between them. The width of the compressed Plastigauge is measured against a calibrated scale to determine the clearance.
- Common uses of Plastigauge are for measuring the clearance between crankshaft journal and main bearing inserts, between crankshaft journal and big-end bearing inserts, and between camshaft and bearing surfaces. The following example describes big-end oil clearance measurement.
- Handle the Plastigauge material carefully to prevent distortion. Using a sharp knife, cut a length which corresponds with the width of the bearing being measured and place it carefully across the journal so that it is parallel with the shaft **(see illustration 3.15)**. Carefully install both bearing shells and the connecting rod. Without rotating the rod on the journal tighten its bolts or nuts (as applicable) to the specified torque. The connecting rod and bearings are then disassembled and the crushed Plastigauge examined.

3.15 Plastigauge placed across shaft journal

- Using the scale provided in the Plastigauge kit, measure the width of the material to determine the oil clearance **(see illustration 3.16)**. Always remove all traces of Plastigauge after use using your fingernails.

Caution: Arriving at the correct clearance demands that the assembly is torqued correctly, according to the settings and sequence (where applicable) provided by the motorcycle manufacturer.

3.16 Measuring the width of the crushed Plastigauge

Dial gauge or DTI (Dial Test Indicator)

● A dial gauge can be used to accurately measure small amounts of movement. Typical uses are measuring shaft runout or shaft endfloat (sideplay) and setting piston position for ignition timing on two-strokes. A dial gauge set usually comes with a range of different probes and adapters and mounting equipment.

● The gauge needle must point to zero when at rest. Rotate the ring around its periphery to zero the gauge.

● Check that the gauge is capable of reading the extent of movement in the work. Most gauges have a small dial set in the face which records whole millimetres of movement as well as the fine scale around the face periphery which is calibrated in 0.01 mm divisions. Read off the small dial first to obtain the base measurement, then add the measurement from the fine scale to obtain the total reading.

In the example shown the gauge reads 1.48 mm **(see illustration 3.17)**:

Base measurement	1.00 mm
Fine measurement	0.48 mm
Total figure	**1.48 mm**

3.17 Dial gauge reading of 1.48 mm

● If measuring shaft runout, the shaft must be supported in vee-blocks and the gauge mounted on a stand perpendicular to the shaft. Rest the tip of the gauge against the centre of the shaft and rotate the shaft slowly whilst watching the gauge reading **(see illustration 3.18)**. Take several measurements along the length of the shaft and record the

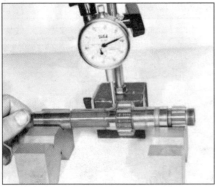

3.18 Using a dial gauge to measure shaft runout

maximum gauge reading as the amount of runout in the shaft. **Note:** *The reading obtained will be total runout at that point - some manufacturers specify that the runout figure is halved to compare with their specified runout limit.*

● Endfloat (sideplay) measurement requires that the gauge is mounted securely to the surrounding component with its probe touching the end of the shaft. Using hand pressure, push and pull on the shaft noting the maximum endfloat recorded on the gauge **(see illustration 3.19)**.

3.19 Using a dial gauge to measure shaft endfloat

● A dial gauge with suitable adapters can be used to determine piston position BTDC on two-stroke engines for the purposes of ignition timing. The gauge, adapter and suitable length probe are installed in the place of the spark plug and the gauge zeroed at TDC. If the piston position is specified as 1.14 mm BTDC, rotate the engine back to 2.00 mm BTDC, then slowly forwards to 1.14 mm BTDC.

Cylinder compression gauges

● A compression gauge is used for measuring cylinder compression. Either the rubber-cone type or the threaded adapter type can be used. The latter is preferred to ensure a perfect seal against the cylinder head. A 0 to 300 psi (0 to 20 Bar) type gauge (for petrol/gasoline engines) will be suitable for motorcycles.

● The spark plug is removed and the gauge either held hard against the cylinder head (cone type) or the gauge adapter screwed into the cylinder head (threaded type) **(see illustration 3.20)**. Cylinder compression is measured with the engine turning over, but not running - carry out the compression test as described in

3.20 Using a rubber-cone type cylinder compression gauge

Fault Finding Equipment. The gauge will hold the reading until manually released.

Oil pressure gauge

● An oil pressure gauge is used for measuring engine oil pressure. Most gauges come with a set of adapters to fit the thread of the take-off point **(see illustration 3.21)**. If the take-off point specified by the motorcycle manufacturer is an external oil pipe union, make sure that the specified replacement union is used to prevent oil starvation.

3.21 Oil pressure gauge and take-off point adapter (arrow)

● Oil pressure is measured with the engine running (at a specific rpm) and often the manufacturer will specify pressure limits for a cold and hot engine.

Straight-edge and surface plate

● If checking the gasket face of a component for warpage, place a steel rule or precision straight-edge across the gasket face and measure any gap between the straight-edge and component with feeler gauges **(see illustration 3.22)**. Check diagonally across the component and between mounting holes **(see illustration 3.23)**.

3.22 Use a straight-edge and feeler gauges to check for warpage

3.23 Check for warpage in these directions

- Checking individual components for warpage, such as clutch plain (metal) plates, requires a perfectly flat plate or piece or plate glass and feeler gauges.

4 Torque and leverage

What is torque?

- Torque describes the twisting force about a shaft. The amount of torque applied is determined by the distance from the centre of the shaft to the end of the lever and the amount of force being applied to the end of the lever; distance multiplied by force equals torque.
- The manufacturer applies a measured torque to a bolt or nut to ensure that it will not slacken in use and to hold two components securely together without movement in the joint. The actual torque setting depends on the thread size, bolt or nut material and the composition of the components being held.
- Too little torque may cause the fastener to loosen due to vibration, whereas too much torque will distort the joint faces of the component or cause the fastener to shear off. Always stick to the specified torque setting.

Using a torque wrench

- Check the calibration of the torque wrench and make sure it has a suitable range for the job. Torque wrenches are available in Nm (Newton-metres), kgf m (kilograms-force metre), lbf ft (pounds-feet), lbf in (inch-pounds). Do not confuse lbf ft with lbf in.
- Adjust the tool to the desired torque on the scale (see illustration 4.1). If your torque wrench is not calibrated in the units specified, carefully convert the figure (see Conversion Factors). A manufacturer sometimes gives a torque setting as a range (8 to 10 Nm) rather than a single figure - in this case set the tool midway between the two settings. The same torque may be expressed as 9 Nm ± 1 Nm. Some torque wrenches have a method of locking the setting so that it isn't inadvertently altered during use.

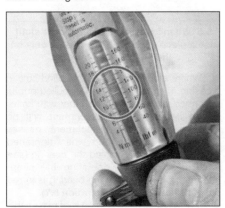

4.1 Set the torque wrench index mark to the setting required, in this case 12 Nm

- Install the bolts/nuts in their correct location and secure them lightly. Their threads must be clean and free of any old locking compound. Unless specified the threads and flange should be dry - oiled threads are necessary in certain circumstances and the manufacturer will take this into account in the specified torque figure. Similarly, the manufacturer may also specify the application of thread-locking compound.
- Tighten the fasteners in the specified sequence until the torque wrench clicks, indicating that the torque setting has been reached. Apply the torque again to double-check the setting. Where different thread diameter fasteners secure the component, as a rule tighten the larger diameter ones first.
- When the torque wrench has been finished with, release the lock (where applicable) and fully back off its setting to zero - do not leave the torque wrench tensioned. Also, do not use a torque wrench for slackening a fastener.

Angle-tightening

- Manufacturers often specify a figure in degrees for final tightening of a fastener. This usually follows tightening to a specific torque setting.
- A degree disc can be set and attached to the socket (see illustration 4.2) or a protractor can be used to mark the angle of movement on the bolt/nut head and the surrounding casting (see illustration 4.3).

4.2 Angle tightening can be accomplished with a torque-angle gauge . . .

4.3 . . . or by marking the angle on the surrounding component

Loosening sequences

- Where more than one bolt/nut secures a component, loosen each fastener evenly a little at a time. In this way, not all the stress of the joint is held by one fastener and the components are not likely to distort.
- If a tightening sequence is provided, work in the REVERSE of this, but if not, work from the outside in, in a criss-cross sequence (see illustration 4.4).

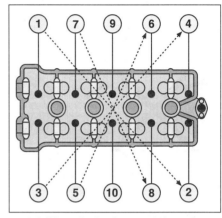

4.4 When slackening, work from the outside inwards

Tightening sequences

- If a component is held by more than one fastener it is important that the retaining bolts/nuts are tightened evenly to prevent uneven stress build-up and distortion of sealing faces. This is especially important on high-compression joints such as the cylinder head.
- A sequence is usually provided by the manufacturer, either in a diagram or actually marked in the casting. If not, always start in the centre and work outwards in a criss-cross pattern (see illustration 4.5). Start off by securing all bolts/nuts finger-tight, then set the torque wrench and tighten each fastener by a small amount in sequence until the final torque is reached. By following this practice,

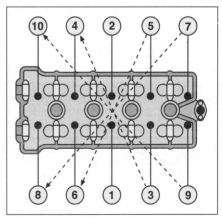

4.5 When tightening, work from the inside outwards

the joint will be held evenly and will not be distorted. Important joints, such as the cylinder head and big-end fasteners often have two- or three-stage torque settings.

Applying leverage

● Use tools at the correct angle. Position a socket wrench or spanner on the bolt/nut so that you pull it towards you when loosening. If this can't be done, push the spanner without curling your fingers around it **(see illustration 4.6)** - the spanner may slip or the fastener loosen suddenly, resulting in your fingers being crushed against a component.

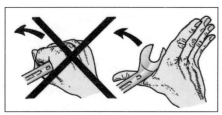

4.6 If you can't pull on the spanner to loosen a fastener, push with your hand open

● Additional leverage is gained by extending the length of the lever. The best way to do this is to use a breaker bar instead of the regular length tool, or to slip a length of tubing over the end of the spanner or socket wrench.
● If additional leverage will not work, the fastener head is either damaged or firmly corroded in place (see *Fasteners*).

5 Bearings

Bearing removal and installation

Drivers and sockets

● Before removing a bearing, always inspect the casing to see which way it must be driven out - some casings will have retaining plates or a cast step. Also check for any identifying markings on the bearing and if installed to a certain depth, measure this at this stage. Some roller bearings are sealed on one side - take note of the original fitted position.
● Bearings can be driven out of a casing using a bearing driver tool (with the correct size head) or a socket of the correct diameter. Select the driver head or socket so that it contacts the outer race of the bearing, not the balls/rollers or inner race. Always support the casing around the bearing housing with wood blocks, otherwise there is a risk of fracture. The bearing is driven out with a few blows on the driver or socket from a heavy mallet. Unless access is severely restricted (as with wheel bearings), a pin-punch is not recommended unless it is moved around the bearing to keep it square in its housing.

● The same equipment can be used to install bearings. Make sure the bearing housing is supported on wood blocks and line up the bearing in its housing. Fit the bearing as noted on removal - generally they are installed with their marked side facing outwards. Tap the bearing squarely into its housing using a driver or socket which bears only on the bearing's outer race - contact with the bearing balls/rollers or inner race will destroy it **(see illustrations 5.1 and 5.2)**.
● Check that the bearing inner race and balls/rollers rotate freely.

5.1 Using a bearing driver against the bearing's outer race

5.2 Using a large socket against the bearing's outer race

Pullers and slide-hammers

● Where a bearing is pressed on a shaft a puller will be required to extract it **(see illustration 5.3)**. Make sure that the puller clamp or legs fit securely behind the bearing and are unlikely to slip out. If pulling a bearing

5.3 This bearing puller clamps behind the bearing and pressure is applied to the shaft end to draw the bearing off

off a gear shaft for example, you may have to locate the puller behind a gear pinion if there is no access to the race and draw the gear pinion off the shaft as well **(see illustration 5.4)**.

> *Caution: Ensure that the puller's centre bolt locates securely against the end of the shaft and will not slip when pressure is applied. Also ensure that puller does not damage the shaft end.*

5.4 Where no access is available to the rear of the bearing, it is sometimes possible to draw off the adjacent component

● Operate the puller so that its centre bolt exerts pressure on the shaft end and draws the bearing off the shaft.
● When installing the bearing on the shaft, tap only on the bearing's inner race - contact with the balls/rollers or outer race with destroy the bearing. Use a socket or length of tubing as a drift which fits over the shaft end **(see illustration 5.5)**.

5.5 When installing a bearing on a shaft use a piece of tubing which bears only on the bearing's inner race

● Where a bearing locates in a blind hole in a casing, it cannot be driven or pulled out as described above. A slide-hammer with knife-edged bearing puller attachment will be required. The puller attachment passes through the bearing and when tightened expands to fit firmly behind the bearing **(see illustration 5.6)**. By operating the slide-hammer part of the tool the bearing is jarred out of its housing **(see illustration 5.7)**.
● It is possible, if the bearing is of reasonable weight, for it to drop out of its housing if the casing is heated as described opposite. If this

5.6 Expand the bearing puller so that it locks behind the bearing . . .

5.7 . . . attach the slide hammer to the bearing puller

method is attempted, first prepare a work surface which will enable the casing to be tapped face down to help dislodge the bearing - a wood surface is ideal since it will not damage the casing's gasket surface. Wearing protective gloves, tap the heated casing several times against the work surface to dislodge the bearing under its own weight **(see illustration 5.8)**.

5.8 Tapping a casing face down on wood blocks can often dislodge a bearing

● Bearings can be installed in blind holes using the driver or socket method described above.

Drawbolts

● Where a bearing or bush is set in the eye of a component, such as a suspension linkage arm or connecting rod small-end, removal by drift may damage the component. Furthermore, a rubber bushing in a shock absorber eye cannot successfully be driven out of position. If access is available to an engineering press, the task is straightforward. If not, a drawbolt can be fabricated to extract the bearing or bush.

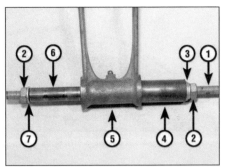

5.9 Drawbolt component parts assembled on a suspension arm

1 Bolt or length of threaded bar
2 Nuts
3 Washer (external diameter greater than tubing internal diameter)
4 Tubing (internal diameter sufficient to accommodate bearing)
5 Suspension arm with bearing
6 Tubing (external diameter slightly smaller than bearing)
7 Washer (external diameter slightly smaller than bearing)

5.10 Drawing the bearing out of the suspension arm

● To extract the bearing/bush you will need a long bolt with nut (or piece of threaded bar with two nuts), a piece of tubing which has an internal diameter larger than the bearing/bush, another piece of tubing which has an external diameter slightly smaller than the bearing/bush, and a selection of washers **(see illustrations 5.9 and 5.10)**. Note that the pieces of tubing must be of the same length, or longer, than the bearing/bush.
● The same kit (without the pieces of tubing) can be used to draw the new bearing/bush back into place **(see illustration 5.11)**.

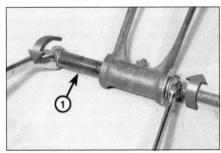

5.11 Installing a new bearing (1) in the suspension arm

Temperature change

● If the bearing's outer race is a tight fit in the casing, the aluminium casing can be heated to release its grip on the bearing. Aluminium will expand at a greater rate than the steel bearing outer race. There are several ways to do this, but avoid any localised extreme heat (such as a blow torch) - aluminium alloy has a low melting point.
● Approved methods of heating a casing are using a domestic oven (heated to 100°C) or immersing the casing in boiling water **(see illustration 5.12)**. Low temperature range localised heat sources such as a paint stripper heat gun or clothes iron can also be used **(see illustration 5.13)**. Alternatively, soak a rag in boiling water, wring it out and wrap it around the bearing housing.

> **Warning: All of these methods require care in use to prevent scalding and burns to the hands. Wear protective gloves when handling hot components.**

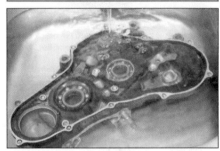

5.12 A casing can be immersed in a sink of boiling water to aid bearing removal

5.13 Using a localised heat source to aid bearing removal

● If heating the whole casing note that plastic components, such as the neutral switch, may suffer - remove them beforehand.
● After heating, remove the bearing as described above. You may find that the expansion is sufficient for the bearing to fall out of the casing under its own weight or with a light tap on the driver or socket.
● If necessary, the casing can be heated to aid bearing installation, and this is sometimes the recommended procedure if the motorcycle manufacturer has designed the housing and bearing fit with this intention.

● Installation of bearings can be eased by placing them in a freezer the night before installation. The steel bearing will contract slightly, allowing easy insertion in its housing. This is often useful when installing steering head outer races in the frame.

Bearing types and markings

● Plain shell bearings, ball bearings, needle roller bearings and tapered roller bearings will all be found on motorcycles **(see illustrations 5.14 and 5.15)**. The ball and roller types are usually caged between an inner and outer race, but uncaged variations may be found.

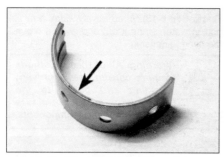

5.14 Shell bearings are either plain or grooved. They are usually identified by colour code (arrow)

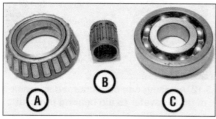

5.15 Tapered roller bearing (A), needle roller bearing (B) and ball journal bearing (C)

● Shell bearings (often called inserts) are usually found at the crankshaft main and connecting rod big-end where they are good at coping with high loads. They are made of a phosphor-bronze material and are impregnated with self-lubricating properties.

● Ball bearings and needle roller bearings consist of a steel inner and outer race with the balls or rollers between the races. They require constant lubrication by oil or grease and are good at coping with axial loads. Taper roller bearings consist of rollers set in a tapered cage set on the inner race; the outer race is separate. They are good at coping with axial loads and prevent movement along the shaft - a typical application is in the steering head.

● Bearing manufacturers produce bearings to ISO size standards and stamp one face of the bearing to indicate its internal and external diameter, load capacity and type **(see illustration 5.16)**.

● Metal bushes are usually of phosphor-bronze material. Rubber bushes are used in suspension mounting eyes. Fibre bushes have also been used in suspension pivots.

5.16 Typical bearing marking

Bearing fault finding

● If a bearing outer race has spun in its housing, the housing material will be damaged. You can use a bearing locking compound to bond the outer race in place if damage is not too severe.

● Shell bearings will fail due to damage of their working surface, as a result of lack of lubrication, corrosion or abrasive particles in the oil **(see illustration 5.17)**. Small particles of dirt in the oil may embed in the bearing material whereas larger particles will score the bearing and shaft journal. If a number of short journeys are made, insufficient heat will be generated to drive off condensation which has built up on the bearings.

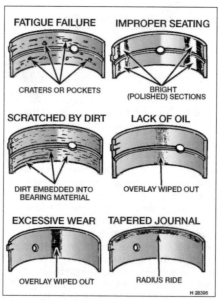

5.17 Typical bearing failures

● Ball and roller bearings will fail due to lack of lubrication or damage to the balls or rollers. Tapered-roller bearings can be damaged by overloading them. Unless the bearing is sealed on both sides, wash it in paraffin (kerosene) to remove all old grease then allow it to dry. Make a visual inspection looking to dented balls or rollers, damaged cages and worn or pitted races **(see illustration 5.18)**.

● A ball bearing can be checked for wear by listening to it when spun. Apply a film of light oil to the bearing and hold it close to the ear - hold the outer race with one hand and spin the inner

5.18 Example of ball journal bearing with damaged balls and cages

5.19 Hold outer race and listen to inner race when spun

race with the other hand **(see illustration 5.19)**. The bearing should be almost silent when spun; if it grates or rattles it is worn.

6 Oil seals

Oil seal removal and installation

● Oil seals should be renewed every time a component is dismantled. This is because the seal lips will become set to the sealing surface and will not necessarily reseal.

● Oil seals can be prised out of position using a large flat-bladed screwdriver **(see illustration 6.1)**. In the case of crankcase seals, check first that the seal is not lipped on the inside, preventing its removal with the crankcases joined.

6.1 Prise out oil seals with a large flat-bladed screwdriver

● New seals are usually installed with their marked face (containing the seal reference code) outwards and the spring side towards the fluid being retained. In certain cases, such as a two-stroke engine crankshaft seal, a double lipped seal may be used due to there being fluid or gas on each side of the joint.

● Use a bearing driver or socket which bears only on the outer hard edge of the seal to install it in the casing - tapping on the inner edge will damage the sealing lip.

Oil seal types and markings

● Oil seals are usually of the single-lipped type. Double-lipped seals are found where a liquid or gas is on both sides of the joint.
● Oil seals can harden and lose their sealing ability if the motorcycle has been in storage for a long period - renewal is the only solution.
● Oil seal manufacturers also conform to the ISO markings for seal size - these are moulded into the outer face of the seal (see illustration 6.2).

6.2 These oil seal markings indicate inside diameter, outside diameter and seal thickness

7 Gaskets and sealants

Types of gasket and sealant

● Gaskets are used to seal the mating surfaces between components and keep lubricants, fluids, vacuum or pressure contained within the assembly. Aluminium gaskets are sometimes found at the cylinder joints, but most gaskets are paper-based. If the mating surfaces of the components being joined are undamaged the gasket can be installed dry, although a dab of sealant or grease will be useful to hold it in place during assembly.
● RTV (Room Temperature Vulcanising) silicone rubber sealants cure when exposed to moisture in the atmosphere. These sealants are good at filling pits or irregular gasket faces, but will tend to be forced out of the joint under very high torque. They can be used to replace a paper gasket, but first make sure that the width of the paper gasket is not essential to the shimming of internal components. RTV sealants should not be used on components containing petrol (gasoline).
● Non-hardening, semi-hardening and hard setting liquid gasket compounds can be used with a gasket or between a metal-to-metal joint. Select the sealant to suit the application: universal non-hardening sealant can be used on virtually all joints; semi-hardening on joint faces which are rough or damaged; hard setting sealant on joints which require a permanent bond and are subjected to high temperature and pressure. **Note:** *Check first if the paper gasket has a bead of sealant*

impregnated in its surface before applying additional sealant.
● When choosing a sealant, make sure it is suitable for the application, particularly if being applied in a high-temperature area or in the vicinity of fuel. Certain manufacturers produce sealants in either clear, silver or black colours to match the finish of the engine. This has a particular application on motorcycles where much of the engine is exposed.
● Do not over-apply sealant. That which is squeezed out on the outside of the joint can be wiped off, whereas an excess of sealant on the inside can break off and clog oilways.

Breaking a sealed joint

● Age, heat, pressure and the use of hard setting sealant can cause two components to stick together so tightly that they are difficult to separate using finger pressure alone. Do not resort to using levers unless there is a pry point provided for this purpose (see illustration 7.1) or else the gasket surfaces will be damaged.
● Use a soft-faced hammer (see illustration 7.2) or a wood block and conventional hammer to strike the component near the mating surface. Avoid hammering against cast extremities since they may break off. If this method fails, try using a wood wedge between the two components.

Caution: If the joint will not separate, double-check that you have removed all the fasteners.

7.1 If a pry point is provided, apply gently pressure with a flat-bladed screwdriver

7.2 Tap around the joint with a soft-faced mallet if necessary - don't strike cooling fins

Removal of old gasket and sealant

● Paper gaskets will most likely come away complete, leaving only a few traces stuck on

Most components have one or two hollow locating dowels between the two gasket faces. If a dowel cannot be removed, do not resort to gripping it with pliers - it will almost certainly be distorted. Install a close-fitting socket or Phillips screwdriver into the dowel and then grip the outer edge of the dowel to free it.

the sealing faces of the components. It is imperative that all traces are removed to ensure correct sealing of the new gasket.
● Very carefully scrape all traces of gasket away making sure that the sealing surfaces are not gouged or scored by the scraper (see illustrations 7.3, 7.4 and 7.5). Stubborn deposits can be removed by spraying with an aerosol gasket remover. Final preparation of

7.3 Paper gaskets can be scraped off with a gasket scraper tool . . .

7.4 . . . a knife blade . . .

7.5 . . . or a household scraper

7.6 Fine abrasive paper is wrapped around a flat file to clean up the gasket face

7.7 A kitchen scourer can be used on stubborn deposits

the gasket surface can be made with very fine abrasive paper or a plastic kitchen scourer **(see illustrations 7.6 and 7.7).**

● Old sealant can be scraped or peeled off components, depending on the type originally used. Note that gasket removal compounds are available to avoid scraping the components clean; make sure the gasket remover suits the type of sealant used.

8 Chains

Breaking and joining final drive chains

● Drive chains for all but small bikes are continuous and do not have a clip-type connecting link. The chain must be broken using a chain breaker tool and the new chain securely riveted together using a new soft rivet-type link. Never use a clip-type connecting link instead of a rivet-type link, except in an emergency. Various chain breaking and riveting tools are available, either as separate tools or combined as illustrated in the accompanying photographs - read the instructions supplied with the tool carefully.

> ⚠ **Warning: The need to rivet the new link pins correctly cannot be overstressed - loss of control of the motorcycle is very likely to result if the chain breaks in use.**

● Rotate the chain and look for the soft link. The soft link pins look like they have been

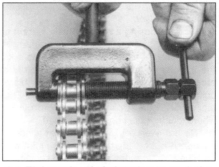

8.1 Tighten the chain breaker to push the pin out of the link . . .

8.2 . . . withdraw the pin, remove the tool . . .

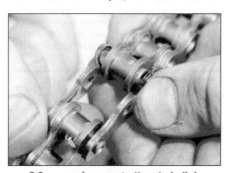

8.3 . . . and separate the chain link

deeply centre-punched instead of peened over like all the other pins **(see illustration 8.9)** and its sideplate may be a different colour. Position the soft link midway between the sprockets and assemble the chain breaker tool over one of the soft link pins **(see illustration 8.1)**. Operate the tool to push the pin out through the chain **(see illustration 8.2)**. On an O-ring chain, remove the O-rings **(see illustration 8.3)**. Carry out the same procedure on the other soft link pin.

> *Caution: Certain soft link pins (particularly on the larger chains) may require their ends to be filed or ground off before they can be pressed out using the tool.*

● Check that you have the correct size and strength (standard or heavy duty) new soft link - do not reuse the old link. Look for the size marking on the chain sideplates **(see illustration 8.10)**.

● Position the chain ends so that they are engaged over the rear sprocket. On an O-ring

8.4 Insert the new soft link, with O-rings, through the chain ends . . .

8.5 . . . install the O-rings over the pin ends . . .

8.6 . . . followed by the sideplate

chain, install a new O-ring over each pin of the link and insert the link through the two chain ends **(see illustration 8.4)**. Install a new O-ring over the end of each pin, followed by the sideplate (with the chain manufacturer's marking facing outwards) **(see illustrations 8.5 and 8.6)**. On an unsealed chain, insert the link through the two chain ends, then install the sideplate with the chain manufacturer's marking facing outwards.

● Note that it may not be possible to install the sideplate using finger pressure alone. If using a joining tool, assemble it so that the plates of the tool clamp the link and press the sideplate over the pins **(see illustration 8.7)**. Otherwise, use two small sockets placed over

8.7 Push the sideplate into position using a clamp

8.8 Assemble the chain riveting tool over one pin at a time and tighten it fully

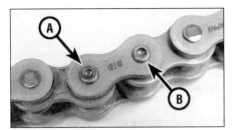

8.9 Pin end correctly riveted (A), pin end unriveted (B)

the rivet ends and two pieces of the wood between a G-clamp. Operate the clamp to press the sideplate over the pins.

● Assemble the joining tool over one pin (following the maker's instructions) and tighten the tool down to spread the pin end securely **(see illustrations 8.8 and 8.9)**. Do the same on the other pin.

 Warning: Check that the pin ends are secure and that there is no danger of the sideplate coming loose. If the pin ends are cracked the soft link must be renewed.

Final drive chain sizing

● Chains are sized using a three digit number, followed by a suffix to denote the chain type **(see illustration 8.10)**. Chain type is either standard or heavy duty (thicker sideplates), and also unsealed or O-ring/X-ring type.

● The first digit of the number relates to the pitch of the chain, ie the distance from the centre of one pin to the centre of the next pin **(see illustration 8.11)**. Pitch is expressed in eighths of an inch, as follows:

8.10 Typical chain size and type marking

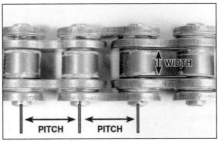

8.11 Chain dimensions

Sizes commencing with a 4 (eg 428) have a pitch of 1/2 inch (12.7 mm)
Sizes commencing with a 5 (eg 520) have a pitch of 5/8 inch (15.9 mm)
Sizes commencing with a 6 (eg 630) have a pitch of 3/4 inch (19.1 mm)

● The second and third digits of the chain size relate to the width of the rollers, again in imperial units, eg the 525 shown has 5/16 inch (7.94 mm) rollers **(see illustration 8.11)**.

9 Hoses

Clamping to prevent flow

● Small-bore flexible hoses can be clamped to prevent fluid flow whilst a component is worked on. Whichever method is used, ensure that the hose material is not permanently distorted or damaged by the clamp.

a) A brake hose clamp available from auto accessory shops **(see illustration 9.1)**.

b) A wingnut type hose clamp **(see illustration 9.2)**.

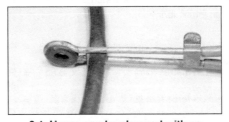

9.1 Hoses can be clamped with an automotive brake hose clamp . . .

9.2 . . . a wingnut type hose clamp . . .

c) Two sockets placed each side of the hose and held with straight-jawed self-locking grips **(see illustration 9.3)**.

d) Thick card each side of the hose held between straight-jawed self-locking grips **(see illustration 9.4)**.

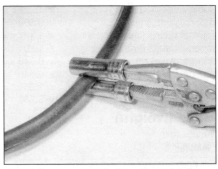

9.3 . . . two sockets and a pair of self-locking grips . . .

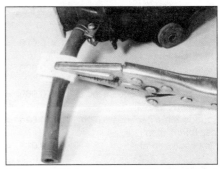

9.4 . . . or thick card and self-locking grips

Freeing and fitting hoses

● Always make sure the hose clamp is moved well clear of the hose end. Grip the hose with your hand and rotate it whilst pulling it off the union. If the hose has hardened due to age and will not move, slit it with a sharp knife and peel its ends off the union **(see illustration 9.5)**.

● Resist the temptation to use grease or soap on the unions to aid installation; although it helps the hose slip over the union it will equally aid the escape of fluid from the joint. It is preferable to soften the hose ends in hot water and wet the inside surface of the hose with water or a fluid which will evaporate.

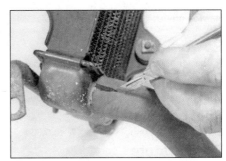

9.5 Cutting a coolant hose free with a sharp knife

Conversion factors

Length (distance)

Inches (in)	x 25.4	= Millimetres (mm)	x 0.0394	= Inches (in)
Feet (ft)	x 0.305	= Metres (m)	x 3.281	= Feet (ft)
Miles	x 1.609	= Kilometres (km)	x 0.621	= Miles

Volume (capacity)

Cubic inches (cu in; in³)	x 16.387	= Cubic centimetres (cc; cm³)	x 0.061	= Cubic inches (cu in; in³)
Imperial pints (Imp pt)	x 0.568	= Litres (l)	x 1.76	= Imperial pints (Imp pt)
Imperial quarts (Imp qt)	x 1.137	= Litres (l)	x 0.88	= Imperial quarts (Imp qt)
Imperial quarts (Imp qt)	x 1.201	= US quarts (US qt)	x 0.833	= Imperial quarts (Imp qt)
US quarts (US qt)	x 0.946	= Litres (l)	x 1.057	= US quarts (US qt)
Imperial gallons (Imp gal)	x 4.546	= Litres (l)	x 0.22	= Imperial gallons (Imp gal)
Imperial gallons (Imp gal)	x 1.201	= US gallons (US gal)	x 0.833	= Imperial gallons (Imp gal)
US gallons (US gal)	x 3.785	= Litres (l)	x 0.264	= US gallons (US gal)

Mass (weight)

Ounces (oz)	x 28.35	= Grams (g)	x 0.035	= Ounces (oz)
Pounds (lb)	x 0.454	= Kilograms (kg)	x 2.205	= Pounds (lb)

Force

Ounces-force (ozf; oz)	x 0.278	= Newtons (N)	x 3.6	= Ounces-force (ozf; oz)
Pounds-force (lbf; lb)	x 4.448	= Newtons (N)	x 0.225	= Pounds-force (lbf; lb)
Newtons (N)	x 0.1	= Kilograms-force (kgf; kg)	x 9.81	= Newtons (N)

Pressure

Pounds-force per square inch (psi; lbf/in²; lb/in²)	x 0.070	= Kilograms-force per square centimetre (kgf/cm²; kg/cm²)	x 14.223	= Pounds-force per square inch (psi; lbf/in²; lb/in²)
Pounds-force per square inch (psi; lbf/in²; lb/in²)	x 0.068	= Atmospheres (atm)	x 14.696	= Pounds-force per square inch (psi; lbf/in²; lb/in²)
Pounds-force per square inch (psi; lbf/in²; lb/in²)	x 0.069	= Bars	x 14.5	= Pounds-force per square inch (psi; lbf/in²; lb/in²)
Pounds-force per square inch (psi; lbf/in²; lb/in²)	x 6.895	= Kilopascals (kPa)	x 0.145	= Pounds-force per square inch (psi; lbf/in²; lb/in²)
Kilopascals (kPa)	x 0.01	= Kilograms-force per square centimetre (kgf/cm²; kg/cm²)	x 98.1	= Kilopascals (kPa)
Millibar (mbar)	x 100	= Pascals (Pa)	x 0.01	= Millibar (mbar)
Millibar (mbar)	x 0.0145	= Pounds-force per square inch (psi; lbf/in²; lb/in²)	x 68.947	= Millibar (mbar)
Millibar (mbar)	x 0.75	= Millimetres of mercury (mmHg)	x 1.333	= Millibar (mbar)
Millibar (mbar)	x 0.401	= Inches of water (inH₂O)	x 2.491	= Millibar (mbar)
Millimetres of mercury (mmHg)	x 0.535	= Inches of water (inH₂O)	x 1.868	= Millimetres of mercury (mmHg)
Inches of water (inH₂O)	x 0.036	= Pounds-force per square inch (psi; lbf/in²; lb/in²)	x 27.68	= Inches of water (inH₂O)

Torque (moment of force)

Pounds-force inches (lbf in; lb in)	x 1.152	= Kilograms-force centimetre (kgf cm; kg cm)	x 0.868	= Pounds-force inches (lbf in; lb in)
Pounds-force inches (lbf in; lb in)	x 0.113	= Newton metres (Nm)	x 8.85	= Pounds-force inches (lbf in; lb in)
Pounds-force inches (lbf in; lb in)	x 0.083	= Pounds-force feet (lbf ft; lb ft)	x 12	= Pounds-force inches (lbf in; lb in)
Pounds-force feet (lbf ft; lb ft)	x 0.138	= Kilograms-force metres (kgf m; kg m)	x 7.233	= Pounds-force feet (lbf ft; lb ft)
Pounds-force feet (lbf ft; lb ft)	x 1.356	= Newton metres (Nm)	x 0.738	= Pounds-force feet (lbf ft; lb ft)
Newton metres (Nm)	x 0.102	= Kilograms-force metres (kgf m; kg m)	x 9.804	= Newton metres (Nm)

Power

Horsepower (hp)	x 745.7	= Watts (W)	x 0.0013	= Horsepower (hp)

Velocity (speed)

Miles per hour (miles/hr; mph)	x 1.609	= Kilometres per hour (km/hr; kph)	x 0.621	= Miles per hour (miles/hr; mph)

Fuel consumption*

Miles per gallon (mpg)	x 0.354	= Kilometres per litre (km/l)	x 2.825	= Miles per gallon (mpg)

Temperature

Degrees Fahrenheit = (°C x 1.8) + 32   Degrees Celsius (Degrees Centigrade; °C) = (°F - 32) x 0.56

It is common practice to convert from miles per gallon (mpg) to litres/100 kilometres (l/100km), where mpg x l/100 km = 282

About the MOT Test

In the UK, all vehicles more than three years old are subject to an annual test to ensure that they meet minimum safety requirements. A current test certificate must be issued before a machine can be used on public roads, and is required before a road fund licence can be issued. Riding without a current test certificate will also invalidate your insurance.

For most owners, the MOT test is an annual cause for anxiety, and this is largely due to owners not being sure what needs to be checked prior to submitting the motorcycle for testing. The simple answer is that a fully roadworthy motorcycle will have no difficulty in passing the test.

This is a guide to getting your motorcycle through the MOT test. Obviously it will not be possible to examine the motorcycle to the same standard as the professional MOT

tester, particularly in view of the equipment required for some of the checks. However, working through the following procedures will enable you to identify any problem areas before submitting the motorcycle for the test.

It has only been possible to summarise the test requirements here, based on the regulations in force at the time of printing. Test standards are becoming increasingly stringent, although there are some exemptions for older vehicles. More information about the MOT test can be obtained from the TSO publications, *How Safe is your Motorcycle* and *The MOT Inspection Manual for Motorcycle Testing.*

Many of the checks require that one of the wheels is raised off the ground. If the motorcycle doesn't have a centre stand, note that an auxiliary stand will be required. Additionally, the help of an assistant may prove useful.

Certain exceptions apply to machines under 50 cc, machines without a lighting system, and Classic bikes - if in doubt about any of the requirements listed below seek confirmation from an MOT tester prior to submitting the motorcycle for the test.

Check that the frame number is clearly visible.

> **HAYNES HiNT** *If a component is in borderline condition, the tester has discretion in deciding whether to pass or fail it. If the motorcycle presented is clean and evidently well cared for, the tester may be more inclined to pass a borderline component than if the motorcycle is scruffy and apparently neglected.*

Electrical System

Lights, turn signals, horn and reflector

✔ With the ignition on, check the operation of the following electrical components. **Note:** *The electrical components on certain small-capacity machines are powered by the generator, requiring that the engine is run for this check.*

   a) *Headlight and tail light. Check that both illuminate in the low and high beam switch positions.*
   b) *Position lights. Check that the front position (or sidelight) and tail light illuminate in this switch position.*
   c) *Turn signals. Check that all flash at the correct rate, and that the warning light(s) function correctly. Check that the turn signal switch works correctly.*
   d) *Hazard warning system (where fitted). Check that all four turn signals flash in this switch position.*
   e) *Brake stop light. Check that the light comes on when the front and rear brakes are independently applied. Models first used on or after 1st April 1986 must have a brake light switch on each brake.*
   f) *Horn. Check that the sound is continuous and of reasonable volume.*

✔ Check that there is a red reflector on the rear of the machine, either mounted separately or as part of the tail light lens.
✔ Check the condition of the headlight, tail light and turn signal lenses.

Headlight beam height

✔ The MOT tester will perform a headlight beam height check using specialised beam setting equipment **(see illustration 1)**. This equipment will not be available to the home mechanic, but if you suspect that the headlight is incorrectly set or may have been maladjusted in the past, you can perform a rough test as follows.
✔ Position the bike in a straight line facing a brick wall. The bike must be off its stand, upright and with a rider seated. Measure the height from the ground to the centre of the headlight and mark a horizontal line on the wall at this height. Position the motorcycle 3.8 metres from the wall and draw a vertical

Headlight beam height checking equipment

line up the wall central to the centreline of the motorcycle. Switch to dipped beam and check that the beam pattern falls slightly lower than the horizontal line and to the left of the vertical line **(see illustration 2)**.

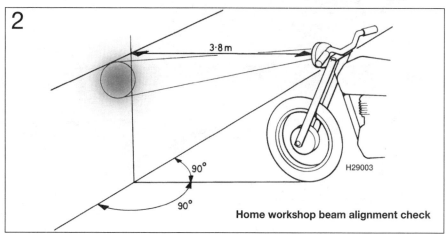

3·8 m

90°

90°

H29003

Home workshop beam alignment check

Exhaust System and Final Drive

Exhaust

✔ Check that the exhaust mountings are secure and that the system does not foul any of the rear suspension components.
✔ Start the motorcycle. When the revs are increased, check that the exhaust is neither holed nor leaking from any of its joints. On a linked system, check that the collector box is not leaking due to corrosion.

✔ Note that the exhaust decibel level ("loudness" of the exhaust) is assessed at the discretion of the tester. If the motorcycle was first used on or after 1st January 1985 the silencer must carry the BSAU 193 stamp, or a marking relating to its make and model, or be of OE (original equipment) manufacture. If the silencer is marked NOT FOR ROAD USE, RACING USE ONLY or similar, it will fail the MOT.

Final drive

✔ On chain or belt drive machines, check that the chain/belt is in good condition and does not have excessive slack. Also check that the sprocket is securely mounted on the rear wheel hub. Check that the chain/belt guard is in place.
✔ On shaft drive bikes, check for oil leaking from the drive unit and fouling the rear tyre.

Steering and Suspension

Steering

✔ With the front wheel raised off the ground, rotate the steering from lock to lock. The handlebar or switches must not contact the fuel tank or be close enough to trap the rider's hand. Problems can be caused by damaged lock stops on the lower yoke and frame, or by the fitting of non-standard handlebars.
✔ When performing the lock to lock check, also ensure that the steering moves freely without drag or notchiness. Steering movement can be impaired by poorly routed cables, or by overtight head bearings or worn bearings. The tester will perform a check of the steering head bearing lower race by mounting the front wheel on a surface plate, then performing a lock to

lock check with the weight of the machine on the lower bearing (see illustration 3).
✔ Grasp the fork sliders (lower legs) and attempt to push and pull on the forks (see

Front wheel mounted on a surface plate for steering head bearing lower race check

illustration 4). Any play in the steering head bearings will be felt. Note that in extreme cases, wear of the front fork bushes can be misinterpreted for head bearing play.
✔ Check that the handlebars are securely mounted.
✔ Check that the handlebar grip rubbers are secure. They should by bonded to the bar left end and to the throttle cable pulley on the right end.

Front suspension

✔ With the motorcycle off the stand, hold the front brake on and pump the front forks up and down (see illustration 5). Check that they are adequately damped.

Checking the steering head bearings for freeplay

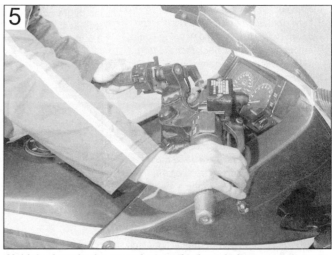

Hold the front brake on and pump the front forks up and down to check operation

Inspect the area around the fork dust seal for oil leakage (arrow)

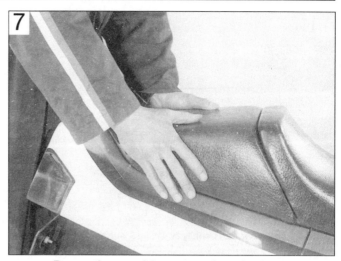

Bounce the rear of the motorcycle to check rear suspension operation

Checking for rear suspension linkage play

✔ Inspect the area above and around the front fork oil seals **(see illustration 6)**. There should be no sign of oil on the fork tube (stanchion) nor leaking down the slider (lower leg). On models so equipped, check that there is no oil leaking from the anti-dive units.

✔ On models with swingarm front suspension, check that there is no freeplay in the linkage when moved from side to side.

Rear suspension

✔ With the motorcycle off the stand and an assistant supporting the motorcycle by its handlebars, bounce the rear suspension **(see illustration 7)**. Check that the suspension components do not foul on any of the cycle parts and check that the shock absorber(s) provide adequate damping.

✔ Visually inspect the shock absorber(s) and check that there is no sign of oil leakage from its damper. This is somewhat restricted on certain single shock models due to the location of the shock absorber.

✔ With the rear wheel raised off the ground, grasp the wheel at the highest point and attempt to pull it up **(see illustration 8)**. Any play in the swingarm pivot or suspension linkage bearings will be felt as movement. **Note:** *Do not confuse play with actual suspension movement.* Failure to lubricate suspension linkage bearings can lead to bearing failure **(see illustration 9)**.

✔ With the rear wheel raised off the ground, grasp the swingarm ends and attempt to move the swingarm from side to side and forwards and backwards - any play indicates wear of the swingarm pivot bearings **(see illustration 10)**.

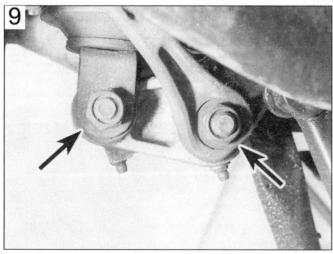

Worn suspension linkage pivots (arrows) are usually the cause of play in the rear suspension

Grasp the swingarm at the ends to check for play in its pivot bearings

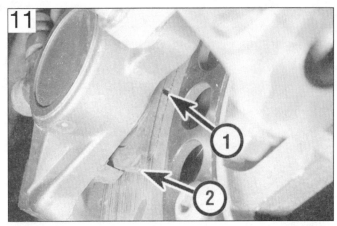

Brake pad wear can usually be viewed without removing the caliper. Most pads have wear indicator grooves (1) and some also have indicator tangs (2)

On drum brakes, check the angle of the operating lever with the brake fully applied. Most drum brakes have a wear indicator pointer and scale.

Brakes, Wheels and Tyres

Brakes

✔ With the wheel raised off the ground, apply the brake then free it off, and check that the wheel is about to revolve freely without brake drag.

✔ On disc brakes, examine the disc itself. Check that it is securely mounted and not cracked.

✔ On disc brakes, view the pad material through the caliper mouth and check that the pads are not worn down beyond the limit (see illustration 11).

✔ On drum brakes, check that when the brake is applied the angle between the operating lever and cable or rod is not too great (see illustration 12). Check also that the operating lever doesn't foul any other components.

✔ On disc brakes, examine the flexible hoses from top to bottom. Have an assistant hold the brake on so that the fluid in the hose is under pressure, and check that there is no sign of fluid leakage, bulges or cracking. If there are any metal brake pipes or unions, check that these are free from corrosion and damage. Where a brake-linked anti-dive system is fitted, check the hoses to the anti-dive in a similar manner.

✔ Check that the rear brake torque arm is secure and that its fasteners are secured by self-locking nuts or castellated nuts with split-pins or R-pins (see illustration 13).

✔ On models with ABS, check that the self-check warning light in the instrument panel works.

✔ The MOT tester will perform a test of the motorcycle's braking efficiency based on a calculation of rider and motorcycle weight. Although this cannot be carried out at home, you can at least ensure that the braking systems are properly maintained. For hydraulic disc brakes, check the fluid level, lever/pedal feel (bleed of air if its spongy) and pad material. For drum brakes, check adjustment, cable or rod operation and shoe lining thickness.

Wheels and tyres

✔ Check the wheel condition. Cast wheels should be free from cracks and if of the built-up design, all fasteners should be secure. Spoked wheels should be checked for broken, corroded, loose or bent spokes.

✔ With the wheel raised off the ground, spin the wheel and visually check that the tyre and wheel run true. Check that the tyre does not foul the suspension or mudguards.

✔ With the wheel raised off the ground, grasp the wheel and attempt to move it about the axle (spindle) (see illustration 14). Any play felt here indicates wheel bearing failure.

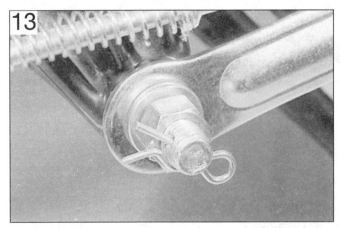

Brake torque arm must be properly secured at both ends

Check for wheel bearing play by trying to move the wheel about the axle (spindle)

Checking the tyre tread depth

Tyre direction of rotation arrow can be found on tyre sidewall

Castellated type wheel axle (spindle) nut must be secured by a split pin or R-pin

Two straightedges are used to check wheel alignment

✔ Check the tyre tread depth, tread condition and sidewall condition **(see illustration 15)**.

✔ Check the tyre type. Front and rear tyre types must be compatible and be suitable for road use. Tyres marked NOT FOR ROAD USE, COMPETITION USE ONLY or similar, will fail the MOT.

✔ If the tyre sidewall carries a direction of rotation arrow, this must be pointing in the direction of normal wheel rotation **(see illustration 16)**.

✔ Check that the wheel axle (spindle) nuts (where applicable) are properly secured. A self-locking nut or castellated nut with a split-pin or R-pin can be used **(see illustration 17)**.

✔ Wheel alignment is checked with the motorcycle off the stand and a rider seated. With the front wheel pointing straight ahead, two perfectly straight lengths of metal or wood and placed against the sidewalls of both tyres **(see illustration 18)**. The gap each side of the front tyre must be equidistant on both sides. Incorrect wheel alignment may be due to a cocked rear wheel (often as the result of poor chain adjustment) or in extreme cases, a bent frame.

General checks and condition

✔ Check the security of all major fasteners, bodypanels, seat, fairings (where fitted) and mudguards.

✔ Check that the rider and pillion footrests, handlebar levers and brake pedal are securely mounted.

✔ Check for corrosion on the frame or any load-bearing components. If severe, this may affect the structure, particularly under stress.

This Section provides an easy reference-guide to the more common faults that are likely to afflict your machine. Obviously, the opportunities are almost limitless for faults to occur as a result of obscure failures, and to try and cover all eventualities would require a book. Indeed, a number have been written on the subject.

Successful troubleshooting is not a mysterious 'black art' but the application of a bit of knowledge combined with a systematic and logical approach to the problem. Approach any troubleshooting by first accurately identifying the symptom and then checking through the list of possible causes, starting with the simplest or most obvious and progressing in stages to the most complex.

Take nothing for granted, but above all apply liberal quantities of common sense.

The main symptom of a fault is given in the text as a major heading below which are listed the various systems or areas which may contain the fault. Details of each possible cause for a fault and the remedial action to be taken are given, in brief, in the paragraphs below each heading. Further information should be sought in the relevant Chapter.

1 Engine doesn't start or is difficult to start

- [ ] Starter motor doesn't rotate
- [ ] Starter motor rotates but engine does not turn over
- [ ] Starter works but engine won't turn over (seized)
- [ ] No fuel flow
- [ ] Engine flooded
- [ ] No spark or weak spark
- [ ] Compression low
- [ ] Stalls after starting
- [ ] Rough idle

2 Poor running at low speed

- [ ] Spark weak
- [ ] Fuel/air mixture incorrect
- [ ] Compression low
- [ ] Poor acceleration

3 Poor running or no power at high speed

- [ ] Firing incorrect
- [ ] Fuel/air mixture incorrect
- [ ] Compression low
- [ ] Knocking or pinking
- [ ] Miscellaneous causes

4 Overheating

- [ ] Engine overheats
- [ ] Firing incorrect
- [ ] Fuel/air mixture incorrect
- [ ] Compression too high
- [ ] Engine load excessive
- [ ] Lubrication inadequate
- [ ] Miscellaneous causes

5 Clutch problems

- [ ] Clutch slipping
- [ ] Clutch not disengaging completely

6 Gearchange problems

- [ ] Doesn't go into gear, or lever doesn't return
- [ ] Jumps out of gear
- [ ] Overselects

7 Abnormal engine noise

- [ ] Knocking or pinking
- [ ] Piston slap or rattling
- [ ] Valve noise
- [ ] Other noise

8 Abnormal driveline noise

- [ ] Clutch noise
- [ ] Transmission noise
- [ ] Final drive noise

9 Abnormal frame and suspension noise

- [ ] Front end noise
- [ ] Shock absorber noise
- [ ] Brake noise

10 Excessive exhaust smoke

- [ ] White smoke
- [ ] Black smoke
- [ ] Brown smoke

11 Poor handling or stability

- [ ] Handlebar hard to turn
- [ ] Handlebar shakes or vibrates excessively
- [ ] Handlebar pulls to one side
- [ ] Poor shock absorbing qualities

12 Braking problems

- [ ] Brakes are spongy, don't hold
- [ ] Brake lever or pedal pulsates
- [ ] Brakes drag

13 Electrical problems

- [ ] Battery dead or weak
- [ ] Battery overcharged

1 Engine doesn't start or is difficult to start

Starter motor doesn't rotate

- [ ] Fuse blown. Check main fuse (Chapter 9).
- [ ] Battery voltage low. Check and recharge battery (Chapter 9).
- [ ] Starter motor defective. Make sure the wiring to the starter is secure. Make sure the starter relay clicks when the start button is pushed. If the relay clicks, then the fault is in the wiring or motor.
- [ ] Starter relay faulty. Check it according to the procedure in Chapter 9.
- [ ] Starter switch not contacting. The contacts could be wet, corroded or dirty. Disassemble and clean the switch (Chapter 9).
- [ ] Wiring open or shorted. Check all wiring connections and harnesses to make sure that they are dry, tight and not corroded. Also check for broken or frayed wires that can cause a short to earth (see wiring diagram, Chapter 9).
- [ ] Engine kill switch defective. Check for wet, dirty or corroded contacts. Clean or renew the switch as necessary (Chapter 9).

Starter motor rotates but engine does not turn over

- [ ] Starter motor clutch defective. Inspect and repair or renew (Chapter 2).
- [ ] Damaged idler or starter gears. Inspect and renew the damaged parts (Chapter 2).

Starter works but engine won't turn over (seized)

- [ ] Seized engine caused by one or more internally damaged components. Failure due to wear, abuse or lack of lubrication. Damage can include seized valves, camshaft, piston, crankshaft, connecting rod bearings, or transmission gears or bearings. Refer to Chapter 2 for engine disassembly.

No fuel flow

- [ ] No fuel in tank.
- [ ] Fuel tank breather hose obstructed.
- [ ] Fuel tap filter clogged. Remove the tap and clean it and the filter (Chapter 4).
- [ ] Fuel line clogged. Pull the fuel line loose and carefully blow through it.
- [ ] Float needle valve clogged due to some foreign material entering the tank. Sometimes after a machine has been stored for many months without running, the fuel turns to a varnish-like liquid and forms deposits on the inlet needle valve and jet. The carburettor should be removed and overhauled if draining the float chamber doesn't solve the problem.

Engine flooded

- [ ] Float height too high. Check as described in Chapter 4.
- [ ] Float needle valve worn or stuck open. A piece of dirt, rust or other debris can cause the valve to seat improperly, causing excess fuel to be admitted to the float chamber. In this case, the float chamber should be cleaned and the needle valve and seat inspected. If the needle and seat are worn, then the leaking will persist and the parts should be renewed (Chapter 4).
- [ ] Starting technique incorrect.
  - a) *Under normal circumstances (i.e. the carburettor functions are sound) the machine should start with little or no throttle.*
  - b) *When the engine is cold, the choke should be operated and the engine started without opening the throttle.*
  - c) *When the engine is at operating temperature, only a very slight amount of throttle should be necessary. The 450/525 SX models have a hot start knob next to the choke which weakens the mixture for starting a hot engine.*
  - d) *If the engine is flooded, turn the fuel tap OFF, pull in the decompressor lever and hold the throttle open while cranking the engine. This will allow additional air to reach the cylinder. Remember to turn the fuel tap back ON after the engine starts.*

No spark or weak spark

- [ ] Spark plug dirty, defective or worn out. Locate reason for fouled plug using spark plug condition chart at the end of this manual and follow the plug maintenance procedures (Chapter 1).
- [ ] Spark plug cap or secondary (HT) wiring faulty. Check condition. Renew if cracks or deterioration are evident (Chapter 5).
- [ ] Spark plug cap not making good contact. Make sure that the plug cap fits snugly over the plug.
- [ ] CDI unit defective (Chapter 5).
- [ ] Pick-up coil or source coil defective. Check, referring to Chapter 5 for details.
- [ ] Ignition HT coil defective. Check the coil, referring to Chapter 5.
- [ ] Kill switch shorted. This is usually caused by water, corrosion, damage or excessive wear. The switch can be disassembled and cleaned with electrical contact cleaner. If cleaning does not help, renew the switches (Chapter 9).
- [ ] Wiring shorted or broken between:
  - a) *Engine kill switch and CDI unit*
  - b) *CDI unit and alternator*
  - c) *CDI unit and ignition HT coil*
  - d) *Ignition HT coil and spark plug*
  - e) *CDI unit and pick-up coil/source coil*
- [ ] Make sure that all wiring connections are clean, dry and tight. Look for chafed and broken wires (Chapters 5 and 9).

Compression low

- [ ] Spark plug loose. Remove the plug and inspect the threads. Reinstall and tighten securely.
- [ ] Cylinder head not sufficiently tightened down. If the cylinder head is suspected of being loose, then there's a chance that the gasket or head is damaged if the problem has persisted for any length of time. The head bolts should be tightened to the proper torque in the correct sequence (Chapter 2).
- [ ] Improper valve clearance. This means that the valve is not closing completely and compression pressure is leaking past the valve. Check and adjust the valve clearances (Chapter 1).
- [ ] Insufficient freeplay on decompressor. Check and adjust the decompressor cable (Chapter 1).
- [ ] Cylinder and/or piston worn. Excessive wear will cause compression pressure to leak past the rings. This is usually accompanied by worn rings as well. A top-end overhaul is necessary (Chapter 2).
- [ ] Piston rings worn, weak, broken, or sticking. Broken or sticking piston rings usually indicate a lubrication or carburation problem that causes excess carbon deposits or seizures to form on the pistons and rings. Top-end overhaul is necessary (Chapter 2).
- [ ] Cylinder head gasket damaged. If a head is allowed to become loose, or if excessive carbon build-up on the piston crown and combustion chamber causes extremely high compression, the head gasket may leak. Retorquing the head is not always sufficient to restore the seal, so gasket renewal is necessary (Chapter 2).
- [ ] Cylinder head warped. This is caused by overheating or improperly tightened head bolts. Machine shop resurfacing or head renewal is necessary (Chapter 2).
- [ ] Valve spring broken or weak. Caused by component failure or wear; the springs must be renewed (Chapter 2).
- [ ] Valve not seating properly. This is caused by a bent valve (from over-revving or improper valve adjustment), burned valve or seat (improper carburation) or an accumulation of carbon deposits on the seat (from carburation or lubrication problems). The valves must be cleaned and/or renewed and the seats serviced if possible (Chapter 2).

1 Engine doesn't start or is difficult to start (continued)

Stalls after starting

- [ ] Improper choke action. Make sure the choke plunger is getting a full stroke and staying in the OFF position (Chapter 4).
- [ ] Ignition malfunction. See Chapter 5.
- [ ] Carburettor malfunction. See Chapter 4.
- [ ] Fuel contaminated. The fuel can be contaminated with either dirt or water, or can change chemically if the machine is allowed to sit for several months or more. Drain the tank and float chamber (Chapter 4).
- [ ] Intake air leak. Check for loose carburettor-to-intake manifold connections or loose carburettor top (Chapter 4).
- [ ] Engine idle speed incorrect. Turn idle adjuster until the engine idles at the specified rpm (Chapter 1).

Rough idle

- [ ] Ignition malfunction. See Chapter 5.
- [ ] Idle speed incorrect. See Chapter 1.
- [ ] Carburettor malfunction. See Chapter 4.
- [ ] Fuel contaminated. The fuel can be contaminated with either dirt or water, or can change chemically if the machine is allowed to sit for several months or more. Drain the tank and float chamber (Chapter 4).
- [ ] Intake air leak. Check for loose carburettor-to-intake manifold connections or loose carburettor top (Chapter 4).
- [ ] Air filter clogged. Renew the air filter element (Chapter 1).

2 Poor running at low speeds

Spark weak

- [ ] Spark plug fouled, defective or worn out. Refer to Chapter 1 for spark plug maintenance.
- [ ] Spark plug cap or HT wiring defective. Refer to Chapter 5 for details on the ignition system.
- [ ] Spark plug cap not making contact.
- [ ] Incorrect spark plug. Wrong type, heat range or cap configuration. Check and install correct plug listed in Chapter 1.
- [ ] CDI unit defective. See Chapter 5.
- [ ] Pick-up coil or source coil defective. See Chapter 5.
- [ ] Ignition HT coil defective. See Chapter 5.

Fuel/air mixture incorrect

- [ ] Mixture screw out of adjustment (Chapter 4).
- [ ] Starter jet or air passage clogged. Remove and overhaul the carburettor (Chapter 4).
- [ ] Air bleed holes clogged. Remove carburettor and blow out all passages (Chapter 4).
- [ ] Air filter clogged, poorly sealed or missing (Chapter 1).
- [ ] Air filter housing poorly sealed. Look for cracks, holes or loose clamps and renew or repair defective parts.
- [ ] Fuel level too high or too low. Check the float height (Chapter 4).
- [ ] Fuel tank breather hose obstructed.
- [ ] Carburettor intake manifold loose. Check for cracks, breaks, splits or loose clamps. Renew the rubber intake manifold if split or perished.

Compression low

- [ ] Spark plug loose. Remove the plug and inspect the threads. Reinstall and tighten securely.
- [ ] Cylinder head not sufficiently tightened down. If the cylinder head is suspected of being loose, then there's a chance that the gasket and head are damaged if the problem has persisted for any length of time. The head bolts should be tightened to the proper torque in the correct sequence (Chapter 2).
- [ ] Improper valve clearance. This means that the valve is not closing completely and compression pressure is leaking past the valve. Check and adjust the valve clearances (Chapter 1).
- [ ] Insufficient freeplay on decompressor. Check and adjust the decompressor cable (Chapter 1).

- [ ] Cylinder and/or piston worn. Excessive wear will cause compression pressure to leak past the rings. This is usually accompanied by worn rings as well. A top-end overhaul is necessary (Chapter 2).
- [ ] Piston rings worn, weak, broken, or sticking. Broken or sticking piston rings usually indicate a lubrication or carburation problem that causes excess carbon deposits or seizures to form on the pistons and rings. Top-end overhaul is necessary (Chapter 2).
- [ ] Cylinder head gasket damaged. If a head is allowed to become loose, or if excessive carbon build-up on the piston crown and combustion chamber causes extremely high compression, the head gasket may leak. Retorquing the head is not always sufficient to restore the seal, so gasket renewal is necessary (Chapter 2).
- [ ] Cylinder head warped. This is caused by overheating or improperly tightened head bolts. Machine shop resurfacing or head renewal is necessary (Chapter 2).
- [ ] Valve spring broken or weak. Caused by component failure or wear; the springs must be renewed (Chapter 2).
- [ ] Valve not seating properly. This is caused by a bent valve (from over-revving or improper valve adjustment), burned valve or seat (improper carburation) or an accumulation of carbon deposits on the seat (from carburation, lubrication problems). The valves must be cleaned and/or renewed and the seats serviced if possible (Chapter 2).

Poor acceleration

- [ ] Carburettor leaking or dirty. Overhaul the carburettor (Chapter 4).
- [ ] Timing not advancing. The pick-up coil, CDI unit or, where fitted, the throttle position sensor may be defective. If so, they must be renewed, as they can't be repaired.
- [ ] Engine oil pump defective, blocked oil strainer gauze, filter or failed relief valve (Chapter 2).
- [ ] Engine oil viscosity too high. Using a heavier oil than that recommended in Chapter 1 can damage the oil pump or lubrication system and cause drag on the engine.
- [ ] Brakes dragging. Usually caused by debris which has entered the brake piston seals, or from a warped disc or bent axle. Repair as necessary (Chapter 7).

3 Poor running or no power at high speed

Firing incorrect

- [ ] Air filter restricted. Clean or renew filter (Chapter 1).
- [ ] Spark plug fouled, defective or worn out. See Chapter 1 for spark plug maintenance.
- [ ] Spark plug cap or HT wiring defective. See Chapter 5 for details of the ignition system.
- [ ] Spark plug cap not in good contact. See Chapter 5.
- [ ] Incorrect spark plug. Wrong type, heat range or cap configuration. Check and install correct plug listed in Chapter 1.
- [ ] CDI unit defective. See Chapter 5.
- [ ] Ignition HT coil defective. See Chapter 5.

Fuel/air mixture incorrect

- [ ] Main jet clogged. Dirt, water or other contaminants can clog the main jet. Clean the fuel tap filter, the float chamber area, and the jets and carburettor orifices (Chapter 4).
- [ ] Main jet wrong size. The standard jetting is for sea level atmospheric pressure and oxygen content.
- [ ] Air bleed holes clogged. Remove and overhaul carburettor (Chapter 4).
- [ ] Air filter clogged, poorly sealed, or missing (Chapter 1).
- [ ] Air filter housing poorly sealed. Look for cracks, holes or loose clamps, and renew defective parts.
- [ ] Fuel level too high or too low. Check the float height (Chapter 4).
- [ ] Fuel tank breather hose obstructed.
- [ ] Carburettor intake manifold clamps loose. Check for cracks, breaks, splits or loose clamps. Renew the rubber intake manifold if it is split or perished (Chapter 4).

Compression low

- [ ] Spark plug loose. Remove the plug and inspect the threads. Reinstall and tighten securely (Chapter 1).
- [ ] Cylinder head not sufficiently tightened down. If the cylinder head is suspected of being loose, then there's a chance that the gasket and head are damaged if the problem has persisted for any length of time. The head bolts should be tightened to the proper torque in the correct sequence (Chapter 2).
- [ ] Improper valve clearance. This means that the valve is not closing completely and compression pressure is leaking past the valve. Check and adjust the valve clearances (Chapter 1).
- [ ] Insufficient freeplay on decompressor. Check and adjust the decompressor cable (Chapter 1).
- [ ] Cylinder and/or piston worn. Excessive wear will cause compression pressure to leak past the rings. This is usually accompanied by worn rings as well. A top-end overhaul is necessary (Chapter 2).
- [ ] Piston rings worn, weak, broken, or sticking. Broken or sticking piston rings usually indicate a lubrication or carburation problem that causes excess carbon deposits or seizures to form on the pistons and rings. Top-end overhaul is necessary (Chapter 2).
- [ ] Cylinder head gasket damaged. If a head is allowed to become loose, or if excessive carbon build-up on the piston crown and combustion chamber causes extremely high compression, the head gasket may leak. Retorquing the head is not always sufficient to restore the seal, so gasket renewal is necessary (Chapter 2).
- [ ] Cylinder head warped. This is caused by overheating or improperly tightened head bolts. Machine shop resurfacing or head renewal is necessary (Chapter 2).
- [ ] Valve spring broken or weak. Caused by component failure or wear; the springs must be renewed (Chapter 2).
- [ ] Valve not seating properly. This is caused by a bent valve (from over-revving or improper valve adjustment), burned valve or seat (improper carburation) or an accumulation of carbon deposits on the seat (from carburation or lubrication problems). The valves must be cleaned and/or renewed and the seats serviced if possible (Chapter 2).

Knocking or pinking

- [ ] Carbon build-up in combustion chamber. Use of a fuel additive that will dissolve the adhesive bonding the carbon particles to the crown and chamber is the easiest way to remove the build-up. Otherwise, the cylinder head will have to be removed and decarbonised (Chapter 2).
- [ ] Incorrect or poor quality fuel. Old or improper grades of fuel can cause detonation. This causes the piston to rattle, thus the knocking or pinking sound. Drain old fuel and always use the recommended fuel grade.
- [ ] Spark plug heat range incorrect. Uncontrolled detonation indicates the plug heat range is too hot. The plug in effect becomes a glow plug, raising cylinder temperatures. Install the proper heat range plug (Chapter 1).
- [ ] Improper air/fuel mixture. This will cause the engine to run hot, which leads to detonation. Clogged jets or an air leak can cause this imbalance. See Chapter 4.

Miscellaneous causes

- [ ] Throttle valve doesn't open fully. Adjust the throttle twistgrip freeplay (Chapter 1).
- [ ] Clutch slipping. May be caused by loose or worn clutch components. Refer to Chapter 2 for clutch overhaul procedures.
- [ ] Timing not advancing. Check CDI unit and throttle position sensor (Chapter 5).
- [ ] Engine oil viscosity too high. Using a heavier oil than the one recommended in Chapter 1 can damage the oil pump or lubrication system and cause drag on the engine.
- [ ] Engine oil pump defective, blocked oil strainer gauze, filter or failed relief valve (Chapter 2).
- [ ] Brakes dragging. Usually caused by debris which has entered the brake piston seals, or from a warped disc or bent axle. Repair as necessary.

4 Overheating

Engine overheats

- ☐ Coolant level low. Check and add coolant (Pre-ride checks).
- ☐ Leak in cooling system. Check cooling system hoses and radiators for leaks and other damage. Repair or renew parts as necessary (Chapter 3).
- ☐ Thermostat sticking open or closed. Check as described in Chapter 3.
- ☐ Faulty radiator cap. Remove the cap and have it pressure-tested by a KTM dealer.
- ☐ Coolant passages clogged. Drain and flush the entire system, then refill with fresh coolant (Chapter 3).
- ☐ Water pump defective. Remove the pump and check the impeller (Chapter 3).
- ☐ Clogged radiator fins. Clean them by blowing compressed air through the fins from the rear side of each radiator.
- ☐ Cooling fan or fan switch fault, where fitted (Chapter 3). A cooling fan kit is available for EXC models not fitted with a fan as standard.

Firing incorrect

- ☐ Spark plug fouled, defective or worn out. See Chapter 1 for spark plug maintenance.
- ☐ Incorrect spark plug.
- ☐ CDI unit defective. See Chapter 5.
- ☐ Faulty ignition HT coil (Chapter 5).

Fuel/air mixture incorrect

- ☐ Main jet clogged. Dirt, water and other contaminants can clog the main jet. Clean the fuel tap filter, the float chamber area and the jets and carburettor orifices (Chapter 4).
- ☐ Main jet wrong size. The standard jetting is for sea level atmospheric pressure and oxygen content.
- ☐ Air filter clogged, poorly sealed or missing (Chapter 1).
- ☐ Air filter housing poorly sealed. Look for cracks, holes or loose clamps and renew or repair.
- ☐ Fuel level too low. Check float height (Chapter 4).
- ☐ Fuel tank breather hose obstructed.

- ☐ Carburettor intake manifold clamps loose. Check for cracks, breaks, splits or loose clamps. Renew the rubber intake manifold if split or perished.

Compression too high

- ☐ Carbon build-up in combustion chamber. Use of a fuel additive that will dissolve the adhesive bonding the carbon particles to the piston crown and chamber is the easiest way to remove the build-up. Otherwise, the cylinder head will have to be removed and decarbonised (Chapter 2).
- ☐ Improperly machined head surface or installation of incorrect gasket during engine assembly.

Engine load excessive

- ☐ Clutch slipping. Can be caused by damaged, loose or worn clutch components. Refer to Chapter 2 for overhaul procedures.
- ☐ Engine oil level too high. The addition of too much oil will cause pressurisation of the crankcase and inefficient engine operation. Check Specifications and drain to proper level (Chapter 1).
- ☐ Engine oil viscosity too high. Using a heavier oil than the one recommended in Chapter 1 can damage the oil pump or lubrication system as well as cause drag on the engine.
- ☐ Brakes dragging. Usually caused by debris which has entered the brake piston seals, or from a warped disc or bent axle. Repair as necessary.

Lubrication inadequate

- ☐ Engine oil level too low. Friction caused by intermittent lack of lubrication or from oil that is overworked can cause overheating. The oil provides a definite cooling function in the engine. Check the oil level (Pre-ride checks).
- ☐ Engine oil pump defective, blocked oil strainers, filters or failed relief valve (Chapter 2).
- ☐ Piston oil way and jet blocked (Chapter 2).
- ☐ Poor quality engine oil or incorrect viscosity or type. Oil is rated not only according to viscosity but also according to type. Some oils are not rated high enough for use in this engine. Refer to Chapter 1 Specifications and change to the correct oil.

5 Clutch problems

Clutch slipping

- ☐ Plates worn. Overhaul the clutch assembly (Chapter 2).
- ☐ Clutch springs broken or weak. Old or heat-damaged (from slipping clutch) springs should be renewed (Chapter 2).
- ☐ Clutch centre or housing unevenly worn. This causes improper engagement of the plates. Renew the damaged or worn parts (Chapter 2).

Clutch not disengaging completely

- ☐ Low clutch fluid level in master cylinder (see Pre-ride checks).
- ☐ Air in hydraulic line. Bleed as described in Chapter 2.
- ☐ Clutch plates warped. This will cause clutch drag, which in turn will cause the machine to creep. Overhaul the clutch assembly (Chapter 2).
- ☐ Clutch spring tension uneven. Usually caused by a sagged or broken spring. Check and renew the springs as a set (Chapter 2).
- ☐ Engine oil deteriorated. Old, thin, worn out oil will not provide

proper lubrication for the plates, causing the clutch to drag. Renew the oil and filter (Chapter 1).
- ☐ Engine oil viscosity too high. Using a heavier oil than recommended in Chapter 1 can cause the plates to stick together, putting a drag on the engine. Change to the correct weight oil (Chapter 1).
- ☐ Clutch bearing seized on input shaft. Lack of lubrication, severe wear or damage can cause the bearing to seize on the shaft. Overhaul of the clutch, and perhaps transmission, may be necessary to repair the damage (Chapter 2).
- ☐ Master cylinder or release cylinder seals failed or piston sticking. Overhaul (Chapter 2).
- ☐ Clutch lifter or pushrod defective (Chapter 2).
- ☐ Loose clutch centre nut (2003-on models). Causes housing and centre misalignment putting a drag on the engine. Engagement adjustment continually varies. Overhaul the clutch assembly (Chapter 2).

6 Gearchange problems

Doesn't go into gear or lever doesn't return

- [ ] Clutch not disengaging. See above.
- [ ] Gearchange shaft bent or seized. Often caused by dropping the machine or from lack of lubrication. Overhaul the transmission (Chapter 2).
- [ ] Gear(s) stuck on transmission shaft. Most often caused by a lack of lubrication or excessive wear in transmission bearings and bushes. Overhaul the transmission (Chapter 2).
- [ ] Selector drum binding. Caused by lubrication failure or excessive wear. Renew the drum and bearing (Chapter 2).
- [ ] Gearchange lever return spring weak or broken (Chapter 2).
- [ ] Gearchange lever broken. Splines stripped out of lever or shaft, caused by allowing the lever to get loose or from dropping the machine. Renew necessary parts (Chapter 2).
- [ ] Gearchange mechanism stopper arm broken or worn. Full engagement and rotary movement of selector drum results. Renew the arm (Chapter 2).

- [ ] Stopper arm spring broken. Allows arm to float, causing sporadic selector operation. Renew the spring (Chapter 2).
- [ ] Selector arm pawls worn or selector drum rotor pins worn (Chapter 2).

Jumps out of gear

- [ ] Selector fork(s) worn. Overhaul the transmission (Chapter 2).
- [ ] Gear groove(s) in selector drum worn. Overhaul the transmission (Chapter 2).
- [ ] Gear pinion dogs or dog slots worn or damaged. The gear pinions should be inspected and renewed. No attempt should be made to repair the worn parts.

Overselects

- [ ] Stopper arm spring weak or broken (Chapter 2).
- [ ] Gearchange shaft return spring post broken or distorted (Chapter 2).

7 Abnormal engine noise

Knocking or pinking

- [ ] Carbon build-up in combustion chamber. Use of a fuel additive that will dissolve the adhesive bonding the carbon particles to the piston crown and chamber is the easiest way to remove the build-up. Otherwise, the cylinder head will have to be removed and decarbonised (Chapter 2).
- [ ] Incorrect or poor quality fuel. Old or improper fuel can cause detonation. This causes the piston to rattle, thus the knocking or pinking sound. Drain the old fuel and always use the recommended grade fuel (Chapter 4).
- [ ] Spark plug heat range incorrect. Uncontrolled detonation indicates that the plug heat range is too hot. The plug in effect becomes a glow plug, raising cylinder temperatures. Install the proper heat range plug (Chapter 1).
- [ ] Improper air/fuel mixture. This will cause the engine to run hot and lead to detonation. Clogged jets, or an air leak or a maladjusted mixture screw setting can cause this imbalance. See Chapter 4.

Piston slap or rattling

- [ ] Cylinder-to-piston clearance excessive. Caused by improper assembly. Inspect and overhaul top-end parts (Chapter 2).
- [ ] Connecting rod bent. Caused by over-revving, trying to start a badly flooded engine or from ingesting a foreign object into the combustion chamber. Renew the damaged parts (Chapter 2).
- [ ] Piston pin or piston pin bore worn or seized from wear or lack of lubrication. Renew damaged parts (Chapter 2).
- [ ] Piston ring(s) worn, broken or sticking. Overhaul the top-end (Chapter 2).
- [ ] Piston seizure damage. Usually from lack of lubrication or overheating. Renew the piston and have the cylinder replated (Chapter 2). Check piston oil way and valve in crankcase.
- [ ] Connecting rod upper or lower end clearance excessive. Caused by excessive wear or lack of lubrication. Renew worn parts.

Valve noise

- [ ] Incorrect valve clearances. Adjust the clearances by referring to Chapter 1.
- [ ] Valve spring broken or weak. Check and renew weak valve springs (Chapter 2).
- [ ] Camshaft or cylinder head worn or damaged. Lack of lubrication at high rpm is usually the cause of damage. Insufficient oil or failure to change the oil at the recommended intervals are the chief causes. Since there are no replaceable bearings in the head, the head and camshaft cover will have to be renewed if there is excessive wear or damage (Chapter 2).

Other noise

- [ ] Cylinder head gasket leaking.
- [ ] Exhaust pipe leaking at cylinder head connection. Caused by improper fit of pipe or loose exhaust flange. Exhaust flange bolts and pipe securing springs should be checked. Weak or sprained springs will lead to a leak.
- [ ] Crankshaft runout excessive. Caused by a bent crankshaft (from over-revving) or damage from an upper cylinder component failure.
- [ ] Engine mounting bolts loose. Tighten all engine mounting bolts (Chapter 2).
- [ ] Crankshaft bearings worn (Chapter 2).
- [ ] Cam chain or cam chain adjuster worn or defective. Renew according to the procedure in Chapter 2.

8 Abnormal driveline noise

Clutch noise

☐ Clutch housing/friction plate clearance excessive (Chapter 2).
☐ Loose or damaged clutch pressure plate and/or bolts (Chapter 2).

Transmission noise

☐ Bearings worn. Also includes the possibility that the shafts are worn. Overhaul the transmission (Chapter 2).
☐ Gear pinions worn or chipped (Chapter 2).
☐ Metal chips jammed in gear teeth. Probably pieces from a broken clutch, gear or selector mechanism that were picked up by the gears. This will cause early bearing failure (Chapter 2).

☐ Engine oil level too low. Causes a howl from transmission. Also affects engine power and clutch operation (Pre-ride checks).
☐ Transmission oil pump defective, blocked oil strainer, filter or failed relief valve (Chapter 2).

Final drive noise

☐ Chain not adjusted properly or worn out (Chapter 1).
☐ Front or rear sprocket loose. Tighten fasteners (Chapter 7).
☐ Sprockets worn or warped. Renew both sprockets and chain as a set (Chapter 7).

9 Abnormal frame and suspension noise

Front end noise

☐ Low fluid level or improper viscosity oil in forks. This can sound like spurting and is usually accompanied by irregular fork action (Chapter 6). Bleed excessive air from fork legs and check condition of fork seals (Chapter 1).
☐ Spring weak or broken. Makes a clicking or scraping sound. Fork oil, when drained, will have a lot of metal particles in it (Chapter 6).
☐ Steering head bearings loose or damaged. Clicks when braking. Check and adjust or renew as necessary (Chapters 1 and 6).
☐ Fork yokes loose. Make sure all clamp bolts are tightened to the specified torques (Chapter 6).
☐ Fork leg bent. Good possibility if machine has been dropped. Check runout and renew as required (Chapter 6).
☐ Front axle nut or axle clamp bolts loose. Tighten them to the specified torques (Chapter 7).
☐ Worn wheel bearings. Check (Chapter 1) and renew (Chapter 7).

Shock absorber noise

☐ Fluid level incorrect. Indicates a leak caused by defective seal. Shock will be covered with oil. Renew shock or seek advice on repair from a suspension specialist (Chapter 6).
☐ Defective shock absorber with internal damage. This is in the body of the shock and can't be remedied. The shock must be rebuilt by a WP specialist (Chapter 6).

Brake noise

☐ Squeal caused by pad shim not installed or positioned correctly (where fitted) (Chapter 7).
☐ Squeal caused by dust on brake pads or other debris caught between pads and disc. Usually found in combination with glazed pads. Clean using brake cleaning solvent and renew the pads (Chapter 7).
☐ Contamination of brake pads. Fork oil or brake fluid causing brake to chatter or squeal. Renew pads (Chapter 7).
☐ Pads glazed. Caused by excessive heat from prolonged use or from contamination. Do not use sandpaper, emery cloth, carborundum cloth or any other abrasive to roughen the pad surfaces as abrasives will stay in the pad material and damage the disc. A very fine flat file can be used, but pad renewal is suggested as a cure (Chapter 7).
☐ Disc warped. Can cause a chattering, clicking or intermittent squeal. Usually accompanied by a pulsating lever and uneven braking. Renew the disc (Chapter 7).
☐ Worn wheel bearings. Check (Chapter 1) and renew (Chapter 7).

10 Excessive exhaust smoke

White smoke – oil burning

☐ Piston oil ring worn. The ring may be broken or damaged, causing oil from the crankcase to be pulled past the piston into the combustion chamber. Renew both rings as a set (Chapter 2).
☐ Cylinder worn, cracked, or scored. Caused by overheating or oil starvation. Replating is possible if the damage is not too great.
☐ Valve stem seal damaged or worn. Renew stem seals (Chapter 2).
☐ Valve guide worn. Have the guides renewed by an engineer (Chapter 2).
☐ Engine oil level too high, which causes the oil to be forced past the rings. Drain oil to the proper level (see *Pre-ride checks*).
☐ Head gasket broken between oil return and cylinder. Causes oil to be pulled into the combustion chamber. Renew the head gasket and check the head for warpage (Chapter 2).
☐ Abnormal crankcase pressurisation, which forces oil past the rings. A clogged crankcase breather hose is usually the cause.

Black smoke – air/fuel mixture too rich

☐ Air filter clogged. Clean or renew the element (Chapter 1).
☐ Main jet too large or loose. Compare the jet size to the Specifications (Chapter 4).

☐ Choke plunger stuck, causing fuel to be pulled through choke circuit (Chapter 4).
☐ Fuel level too high. Check and adjust the float height as necessary (Chapter 4).
☐ Float needle valve held off needle seat. Clean the float chamber and fuel line and renew the needle and seat if necessary (Chapter 4).

Brown smoke – air/fuel mixture too weak

☐ Main jet too small or clogged. Lean condition caused by wrong size main jet or by a restricted orifice. Clean float chamber and jet and compare jet size to Specifications (Chapter 4).
☐ Fuel flow insufficient. Float needle valve stuck closed due to chemical reaction with old fuel. Float height incorrect. Restricted fuel line. Clean line and float chamber and adjust float if necessary.
☐ Carburettor intake manifold clamps loose (Chapter 4).
☐ Air filter poorly sealed or not installed (Chapter 1).
☐ Accelerator pump fault. Check the pump diaphragm, gaskets and airways (Chapter 4).

11 Poor handling or stability

Handlebar hard to turn

☐ Steering head bearing adjuster nut too tight. Check adjustment as described in Chapter 1.

☐ Bearings damaged. Roughness can be felt as the bars are turned from side-to-side. Renew bearings (Chapter 6).

☐ Races dented or worn from a collision or hitting a pothole or from dropping the machine. Renew bearings (Chapter 6).

☐ Steering stem lubrication inadequate. Causes are grease getting hard from age or being washed out by jet washing. Disassemble steering head and repack bearings (Chapter 6).

☐ Steering stem bent. Caused by a collision, hitting a pothole or by dropping the machine. Renew damaged part. Don't try to straighten the steering stem (Chapter 6).

☐ Front tyre air pressure too low (Pre-ride checks).

Handlebar shakes or vibrates excessively

☐ Swingarm bearings worn. Renew worn bearings (Chapter 6).

☐ Wheel rim(s) warped or damaged. Inspect wheels for runout (Chapter 7).

☐ Wheel bearings worn. Worn front or rear wheel bearings can cause poor tracking. Worn front bearings will cause wobble (Chapters 1 and 7).

☐ Handlebar clamp bolts loose. Tighten them to the specified torque (Chapter 6).

☐ Fork yoke clamp bolts loose. Tighten them to the specified torque (Chapter 6).

☐ Engine mounting bolts loose. Will cause excessive vibration with increased engine rpm (Chapter 2).

Handlebar pulls to one side

☐ Frame bent. Definitely suspect this if the machine has been dropped. May or may not be accompanied by cracking near the bend. Renew the frame (Chapter 6).

☐ Wheels out of alignment. Caused by bent steering stem or frame (Chapter 6).

☐ Swingarm bent or twisted as the result of impact damage. Renew the swingarm (Chapter 6).

☐ Steering stem bent. Caused by impact damage or by dropping the motorcycle. Renew the steering stem (Chapter 6).

☐ Fork leg bent. Disassemble the forks and renew the damaged parts (Chapter 6).

☐ Fork oil level uneven. Check and add or drain as necessary (Chapter 6).

Poor shock absorbing qualities

☐ Too hard:
   a) Incorrect adjustment setting (Chapter 6).
   b) Excessive air pressure in front fork (Chapter 1).
   c) Front fork oil level excessive (Chapter 6).
   d) Front fork oil viscosity too high. Use a lighter oil (see the Specifications in Chapter 6).
   e) Front fork tube bent. Causes a harsh, sticking feeling (Chapter 6).
   f) Front fork internal damage (Chapter 6).
   g) Rear shock shaft or body bent or damaged (Chapter 6).
   h) Rear shock internal damage (Chapter 6).
   i) Tyre pressure too high (Chapter 1).

☐ Too soft:
   a) Incorrect adjustment setting (Chapter 6).
   b) Front fork oil level too low (Chapter 6).
   c) Front fork oil viscosity too light (Chapter 6).
   d) Front fork springs weak or broken (Chapter 6).
   e) Front fork or rear shock oil insufficient and/or leaking (Chapter 6).
   f) Rear shock internal damage (Chapter 6).

12 Braking problems

Brakes are spongy, don't hold

☐ Air in brake line. Caused by inattention to master cylinder fluid level or by leakage. Locate problem and bleed brakes (Chapter 7).

☐ Pads or disc worn (Chapters 1 and 7).

☐ Brake fluid leak. Locate problem and renew faulty component (Chapter 7).

☐ Contaminated pads. Caused by contamination with oil, grease, brake fluid, etc. Clean caliper and renew pads (Chapter 7).

☐ Brake fluid deteriorated. Fluid is old or contaminated. Drain system, replenish with new fluid and bleed the system (Chapter 7).

☐ Master cylinder internal seals worn or damaged causing fluid to bypass. Overhaul master cylinder (Chapter 7).

☐ Master cylinder bore scratched by foreign material or broken spring. Renew master cylinder (Chapter 7).

☐ Disc warped. Renew disc (Chapter 7).

Brake lever or pedal pulsates

☐ Disc warped. Renew disc (Chapter 7).

☐ Axle bent. Renew axle (Chapter 7).

☐ Brake caliper bolts loose (Chapter 7).

☐ Brake caliper sliders damaged or sticking, causing caliper to bind. Lubricate the sliders or renew them if they are corroded or bent (Chapter 7).

☐ Wheel warped or otherwise damaged (Chapter 7).

☐ Wheel bearings damaged or worn (Chapter 7).

Brakes drag

☐ Master cylinder piston seized. Caused by wear or damage to piston or cylinder bore (Chapter 7).

☐ Lever balky or stuck. Check pivot and lubricate (Chapter 7).

☐ Brake caliper binds. Caused by inadequate lubrication of caliper slider pins (Chapter 7).

☐ Brake caliper piston seized in bore. Caused by wear or ingestion of dirt past deteriorated seals (Chapter 7).

☐ Brake pad damaged. Pad material separated from backing plate. Usually caused by faulty manufacturing process or from contact with chemicals. Renew pads (Chapter 7).

13 Electrical problems

Battery dead or weak

☐ Battery faulty. If the battery doesn't hold a charge renew it (Chapter 9).
☐ Battery leads making poor contact. Clean off any corrosion. Smear battery terminal grease over terminals once they've been reconnected (Chapter 9).
☐ Load excessive. Caused by addition of high wattage lights.
☐ Regulator/rectifier defective (Chapter 9).
☐ Alternator stator coil open or shorted (Chapter 9).
☐ Wiring faulty. Wiring earthed or connections loose in ignition, charging or lighting circuits (Chapter 9).

Battery overcharged

☐ Regulator/rectifier defective. Overcharging is noticed when battery gets excessively warm (Chapter 9).
☐ Battery defective. Renew battery (Chapter 9).
☐ Battery amperage too low, wrong type or size. Install manufacturer's specified amp-hour battery to handle charging load (Chapter 9).

A

ABS (Anti-lock braking system) A system, usually electronically controlled, that senses incipient wheel lockup during braking and relieves hydraulic pressure at wheel which is about to skid.

Aftermarket Components suitable for the motorcycle, but not produced by the motorcycle manufacturer.

Allen key A hexagonal wrench which fits into a recessed hexagonal hole.

Alternating current (ac) Current produced by an alternator. Requires converting to direct current by a rectifier for charging purposes.

Alternator Converts mechanical energy from the engine into electrical energy to charge the battery and power the electrical system.

Ampere (amp) A unit of measurement for the flow of electrical current. Current = Volts ÷ Ohms.

Ampere-hour (Ah) Measure of battery capacity.

Angle-tightening A torque expressed in degrees. Often follows a conventional tightening torque for cylinder head or main bearing fasteners **(see illustration)**.

Angle-tightening cylinder head bolts

Antifreeze A substance (usually ethylene glycol) mixed with water, and added to the cooling system, to prevent freezing of the coolant in winter. Antifreeze also contains chemicals to inhibit corrosion and the formation of rust and other deposits that would tend to clog the radiator and coolant passages and reduce cooling efficiency.

Anti-dive System attached to the fork lower leg (slider) to prevent fork dive when braking hard.

Anti-seize compound A coating that reduces the risk of seizing on fasteners that are subjected to high temperatures, such as exhaust clamp bolts and nuts.

API American Petroleum Institute. A quality standard for 4-stroke motor oils.

Asbestos A natural fibrous mineral with great heat resistance, commonly used in the composition of brake friction materials. Asbestos is a health hazard and the dust created by brake systems should never be inhaled or ingested.

ATF Automatic Transmission Fluid. Often used in front forks.

ATU Automatic Timing Unit. Mechanical device for advancing the ignition timing on early engines.

ATV All Terrain Vehicle. Often called a Quad.

Axial play Side-to-side movement.

Axle A shaft on which a wheel revolves. Also known as a spindle.

B

Backlash The amount of movement between meshed components when one component is held still. Usually applies to gear teeth.

Ball bearing A bearing consisting of a hardened inner and outer race with hardened steel balls between the two races.

Bearings Used between two working surfaces to prevent wear of the components and a build-up of heat. Four types of bearing are commonly used on motorcycles: plain shell bearings, ball bearings, tapered roller bearings and needle roller bearings.

Bevel gears Used to turn the drive through 90°. Typical applications are shaft final drive and camshaft drive **(see illustration)**.

Bevel gears are used to turn the drive through 90°

BHP Brake Horsepower. The British measurement for engine power output. Power output is now usually expressed in kilowatts (kW).

Bias-belted tyre Similar construction to radial tyre, but with outer belt running at an angle to the wheel rim.

Big-end bearing The bearing in the end of the connecting rod that's attached to the crankshaft.

Bleeding The process of removing air from an hydraulic system via a bleed nipple or bleed screw.

Bottom-end A description of an engine's crankcase components and all components contained there-in.

BTDC Before Top Dead Centre in terms of piston position. Ignition timing is often expressed in terms of degrees or millimetres BTDC.

Bush A cylindrical metal or rubber component used between two moving parts.

Burr Rough edge left on a component after machining or as a result of excessive wear.

C

Cam chain The chain which takes drive from the crankshaft to the camshaft(s).

Canister The main component in an evaporative emission control system (California market only); contains activated charcoal granules to trap vapours from the fuel system rather than allowing them to vent to the atmosphere.

Castellated Resembling the parapets along the top of a castle wall. For example, a castellated wheel axle or spindle nut.

Catalytic converter A device in the exhaust system of some machines which converts certain pollutants in the exhaust gases into less harmful substances.

Charging system Description of the components which charge the battery, ie the alternator, rectifer and regulator.

Circlip A ring-shaped clip used to prevent endwise movement of cylindrical parts and shafts. An internal circlip is installed in a groove in a housing; an external circlip fits into a groove on the outside of a cylindrical piece such as a shaft. Also known as a snap-ring.

Clearance The amount of space between two parts. For example, between a piston and a cylinder, between a bearing and a journal, etc.

Coil spring A spiral of elastic steel found in various sizes throughout a vehicle, for example as a springing medium in the suspension and in the valve train.

Compression Reduction in volume, and increase in pressure and temperature, of a gas, caused by squeezing it into a smaller space.

Compression damping Controls the speed the suspension compresses when hitting a bump.

Compression ratio The relationship between cylinder volume when the piston is at top dead centre and cylinder volume when the piston is at bottom dead centre.

Continuity The uninterrupted path in the flow of electricity. Little or no measurable resistance.

Continuity tester Self-powered bleeper or test light which indicates continuity.

Cp Candlepower. Bulb rating commonly found on US motorcycles.

Crossply tyre Tyre plies arranged in a criss-cross pattern. Usually four or six plies used, hence 4PR or 6PR in tyre size codes.

Cush drive Rubber damper segments fitted between the rear wheel and final drive sprocket to absorb transmission shocks **(see illustration)**.

Cush drive rubbers dampen out transmission shocks

D

Degree disc Calibrated disc for measuring piston position. Expressed in degrees.

Dial gauge Clock-type gauge with adapters for measuring runout and piston position. Expressed in mm or inches.

Diaphragm The rubber membrane in a master cylinder or carburettor which seals the upper chamber.

Diaphragm spring A single sprung plate often used in clutches.

Direct current (dc) Current produced by a dc generator.

Decarbonisation The process of removing carbon deposits - typically from the combustion chamber, valves and exhaust port/system.

Detonation Destructive and damaging explosion of fuel/air mixture in combustion chamber instead of controlled burning.

Diode An electrical valve which only allows current to flow in one direction. Commonly used in rectifiers and starter interlock systems.

Disc valve (or rotary valve) A induction system used on some two-stroke engines.

Double-overhead camshaft (DOHC) An engine that uses two overhead camshafts, one for the intake valves and one for the exhaust valves.

Drivebelt A toothed belt used to transmit drive to the rear wheel on some motorcycles. A drivebelt has also been used to drive the camshafts. Drivebelts are usually made of Kevlar.

Driveshaft Any shaft used to transmit motion. Commonly used when referring to the final driveshaft on shaft drive motorcycles.

E

Earth return The return path of an electrical circuit, utilising the motorcycle's frame.

ECU (Electronic Control Unit) A computer which controls (for instance) an ignition system, or an anti-lock braking system.

EGO Exhaust Gas Oxygen sensor. Sometimes called a Lambda sensor.

Electrolyte The fluid in a lead-acid battery.

EMS (Engine Management System) A computer controlled system which manages the fuel injection and the ignition systems in an integrated fashion.

Endfloat The amount of lengthways movement between two parts. As applied to a crankshaft, the distance that the crankshaft can move side-to-side in the crankcase.

Endless chain A chain having no joining link. Common use for cam chains and final drive chains.

EP (Extreme Pressure) Oil type used in locations where high loads are applied, such as between gear tooth.

Evaporative emission control system Describes a charcoal filled canister which stores fuel vapours from the tank rather than allowing them to vent to the atmosphere. Usually only fitted to California models and referred to as an EVAP system.

Expansion chamber Section of two-stroke engine exhaust system so designed to improve engine efficiency and boost power.

F

Feeler blade or gauge A thin strip or blade of hardened steel, ground to an exact thickness, used to check or measure clearances between parts.

Final drive Description of the drive from the transmission to the rear wheel. Usually by chain or shaft, but sometimes by belt.

Firing order The order in which the engine cylinders fire, or deliver their power strokes, beginning with the number one cylinder.

Flooding Term used to describe a high fuel level in the carburettor float chambers, leading to fuel overflow. Also refers to excess fuel in the combustion chamber due to incorrect starting technique.

Free length The no-load state of a component when measured. Clutch, valve and fork spring lengths are measured at rest, without any preload.

Freeplay The amount of travel before any action takes place. The looseness in a linkage, or an assembly of parts, between the initial application of force and actual movement. For example, the distance the rear brake pedal moves before the rear brake is actuated.

Fuel injection The fuel/air mixture is metered electronically and directed into the engine intake ports (indirect injection) or into the cylinders (direct injection). Sensors supply information on engine speed and conditions.

Fuel/air mixture The charge of fuel and air going into the engine. See **Stoichiometric ratio**.

Fuse An electrical device which protects a circuit against accidental overload. The typical fuse contains a soft piece of metal which is calibrated to melt at a predetermined current flow (expressed as amps) and break the circuit.

G

Gap The distance the spark must travel in jumping from the centre electrode to the side electrode in a spark plug. Also refers to the distance between the ignition rotor and the pickup coil in an electronic ignition system.

Gasket Any thin, soft material - usually cork, cardboard, asbestos or soft metal - installed between two metal surfaces to ensure a good seal. For instance, the cylinder head gasket seals the joint between the block and the cylinder head.

Gauge An instrument panel display used to monitor engine conditions. A gauge with a movable pointer on a dial or a fixed scale is an analogue gauge. A gauge with a numerical readout is called a digital gauge.

Gear ratios The drive ratio of a pair of gears in a gearbox, calculated on their number of teeth.

Glaze-busting see **Honing**

Grinding Process for renovating the valve face and valve seat contact area in the cylinder head.

Gudgeon pin The shaft which connects the connecting rod small-end with the piston. Often called a piston pin or wrist pin.

H

Helical gears Gear teeth are slightly curved and produce less gear noise that straight-cut gears. Often used for primary drives.

Installing a Helicoil thread insert in a cylinder head

Helicoil A thread insert repair system. Commonly used as a repair for stripped spark plug threads **(see illustration)**.

Honing A process used to break down the glaze on a cylinder bore (also called glaze-busting). Can also be carried out to roughen a rebored cylinder to aid ring bedding-in.

HT (High Tension) Description of the electrical circuit from the secondary winding of the ignition coil to the spark plug.

Hydraulic A liquid filled system used to transmit pressure from one component to another. Common uses on motorcycles are brakes and clutches.

Hydrometer An instrument for measuring the specific gravity of a lead-acid battery.

Hygroscopic Water absorbing. In motorcycle applications, braking efficiency will be reduced if DOT 3 or 4 hydraulic fluid absorbs water from the air - care must be taken to keep new brake fluid in tightly sealed containers.

I

lbf ft Pounds-force feet. An imperial unit of torque. Sometimes written as ft-lbs.

lbf in Pound-force inch. An imperial unit of torque, applied to components where a very low torque is required. Sometimes written as in-lbs.

IC Abbreviation for Integrated Circuit.

Ignition advance Means of increasing the timing of the spark at higher engine speeds. Done by mechanical means (ATU) on early engines or electronically by the ignition control unit on later engines.

Ignition timing The moment at which the spark plug fires, expressed in the number of crankshaft degrees before the piston reaches the top of its stroke, or in the number of millimetres before the piston reaches the top of its stroke.

Infinity (∞) Description of an open-circuit electrical state, where no continuity exists.

Inverted forks (upside down forks) The sliders or lower legs are held in the yokes and the fork tubes or stanchions are connected to the wheel axle (spindle). Less unsprung weight and stiffer construction than conventional forks.

J

JASO Quality standard for 2-stroke oils.

Joule The unit of electrical energy.

Journal The bearing surface of a shaft.

K

Kickstart Mechanical means of turning the engine over for starting purposes. Only usually fitted to mopeds, small capacity motorcycles and off-road motorcycles.

Kill switch Handebar-mounted switch for emergency ignition cut-out. Cuts the ignition circuit on all models, and additionally prevent starter motor operation on others.

km Symbol for kilometre.

kmh Abbreviation for kilometres per hour.

L

Lambda (λ) sensor A sensor fitted in the exhaust system to measure the exhaust gas oxygen content (excess air factor).

Lapping see **Grinding**.
LCD Abbreviation for Liquid Crystal Display.
LED Abbreviation for Light Emitting Diode.
Liner A steel cylinder liner inserted in a aluminium alloy cylinder block.
Locknut A nut used to lock an adjustment nut, or other threaded component, in place.
Lockstops The lugs on the lower triple clamp (yoke) which abut those on the frame, preventing handlebar-to-fuel tank contact.
Lockwasher A form of washer designed to prevent an attaching nut from working loose.
LT Low Tension Description of the electrical circuit from the power supply to the primary winding of the ignition coil.

M

Main bearings The bearings between the crankshaft and crankcase.
Maintenance-free (MF) battery A sealed battery which cannot be topped up.
Manometer Mercury-filled calibrated tubes used to measure intake tract vacuum. Used to synchronise carburettors on multi-cylinder engines.
Micrometer A precision measuring instrument that measures component outside diameters **(see illustration)**.

Tappet shims are measured with a micrometer

MON (Motor Octane Number) A measure of a fuel's resistance to knock.
Monograde oil An oil with a single viscosity, eg SAE80W.
Monoshock A single suspension unit linking the swingarm or suspension linkage to the frame.
mph Abbreviation for miles per hour.
Multigrade oil Having a wide viscosity range (eg 10W40). The W stands for Winter, thus the viscosity ranges from SAE10 when cold to SAE40 when hot.
Multimeter An electrical test instrument with the capability to measure voltage, current and resistance. Some meters also incorporate a continuity tester and buzzer.

N

Needle roller bearing Inner race of caged needle rollers and hardened outer race. Examples of uncaged needle rollers can be found on some engines. Commonly used in rear suspension applications and in two-stroke engines.
Nm Newton metres.
NOx Oxides of Nitrogen. A common toxic pollutant emitted by petrol engines at higher temperatures.

O

Octane The measure of a fuel's resistance to knock.
OE (Original Equipment) Relates to components fitted to a motorcycle as standard or replacement parts supplied by the motorcycle manufacturer.
Ohm The unit of electrical resistance. Ohms = Volts ÷ Current.
Ohmmeter An instrument for measuring electrical resistance.
Oil cooler System for diverting engine oil outside of the engine to a radiator for cooling purposes.
Oil injection A system of two-stroke engine lubrication where oil is pump-fed to the engine in accordance with throttle position.
Open-circuit An electrical condition where there is a break in the flow of electricity - no continuity (high resistance).
O-ring A type of sealing ring made of a special rubber-like material; in use, the O-ring is compressed into a groove to provide the sealing action.
Oversize (OS) Term used for piston and ring size options fitted to a rebored cylinder.
Overhead cam (sohc) engine An engine with single camshaft located on top of the cylinder head.
Overhead valve (ohv) engine An engine with the valves located in the cylinder head, but with the camshaft located in the engine block or crankcase.
Oxygen sensor A device installed in the exhaust system which senses the oxygen content in the exhaust and converts this information into an electric current. Also called a Lambda sensor.

P

Plastigauge A thin strip of plastic thread, available in different sizes, used for measuring clearances. For example, a strip of Plastigauge is laid across a bearing journal. The parts are assembled and dismantled; the width of the crushed strip indicates the clearance between journal and bearing.
Polarity Either negative or positive earth (ground), determined by which battery lead is connected to the frame (earth return). Modern motorcycles are usually negative earth.
Pre-ignition A situation where the fuel/air mixture ignites before the spark plug fires. Often due to a hot spot in the combustion chamber caused by carbon build-up. Engine has a tendency to 'run-on'.
Pre-load (suspension) The amount a spring is compressed when in the unloaded state. Preload can be applied by gas, spacer or mechanical adjuster.
Premix The method of engine lubrication on older two-stroke engines. Engine oil is mixed with the petrol in the fuel tank in a specific ratio. The fuel/oil mix is sometimes referred to as "petroil".
Primary drive Description of the drive from the crankshaft to the clutch. Usually by gear or chain.
PS Pfedestärke - a German interpretation of BHP.
PSI Pounds-force per square inch. Imperial measurement of tyre pressure and cylinder pressure measurement.
PTFE Polytetrafluoroethylene. A low friction substance.

Pulse secondary air injection system A process of promoting the burning of excess fuel present in the exhaust gases by routing fresh air into the exhaust ports.

Q

Quartz halogen bulb Tungsten filament surrounded by a halogen gas. Typically used for the headlight **(see illustration)**.

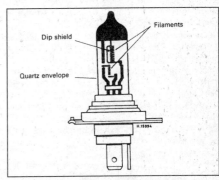

Quartz halogen headlight bulb construction

R

Rack-and-pinion A pinion gear on the end of a shaft that mates with a rack (think of a geared wheel opened up and laid flat). Sometimes used in clutch operating systems.
Radial play Up and down movement about a shaft.
Radial ply tyres Tyre plies run across the tyre (from bead to bead) and around the circumference of the tyre. Less resistant to tread distortion than other tyre types.
Radiator A liquid-to-air heat transfer device designed to reduce the temperature of the coolant in a liquid cooled engine.
Rake A feature of steering geometry - the angle of the steering head in relation to the vertical **(see illustration)**.

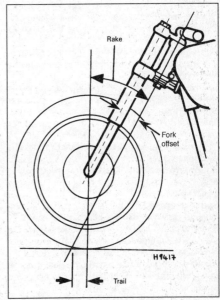

Steering geometry

Rebore Providing a new working surface to the cylinder bore by boring out the old surface. Necessitates the use of oversize piston and rings.

Rebound damping A means of controlling the oscillation of a suspension unit spring after it has been compressed. Resists the spring's natural tendency to bounce back after being compressed.

Rectifier Device for converting the ac output of an alternator into dc for battery charging.

Reed valve An induction system commonly used on two-stroke engines.

Regulator Device for maintaining the charging voltage from the generator or alternator within a specified range.

Relay A electrical device used to switch heavy current on and off by using a low current auxiliary circuit.

Resistance Measured in ohms. An electrical component's ability to pass electrical current.

RON (Research Octane Number) A measure of a fuel's resistance to knock.

rpm revolutions per minute.

Runout The amount of wobble (in-and-out movement) of a wheel or shaft as it's rotated. The amount a shaft rotates `out-of-true'. The out-of-round condition of a rotating part.

S

SAE (Society of Automotive Engineers) A standard for the viscosity of a fluid.

Sealant A liquid or paste used to prevent leakage at a joint. Sometimes used in conjunction with a gasket.

Service limit Term for the point where a component is no longer useable and must be renewed.

Shaft drive A method of transmitting drive from the transmission to the rear wheel.

Shell bearings Plain bearings consisting of two shell halves. Most often used as big-end and main bearings in a four-stroke engine. Often called bearing inserts.

Shim Thin spacer, commonly used to adjust the clearance or relative positions between two parts. For example, shims inserted into or under tappets or followers to control valve clearances. Clearance is adjusted by changing the thickness of the shim.

Short-circuit An electrical condition where current shorts to earth (ground) bypassing the circuit components.

Skimming Process to correct warpage or repair a damaged surface, eg on brake discs or drums.

Slide-hammer A special puller that screws into or hooks onto a component such as a shaft or bearing; a heavy sliding handle on the shaft bottoms against the end of the shaft to knock the component free.

Small-end bearing The bearing in the upper end of the connecting rod at its joint with the gudgeon pin.

Spalling Damage to camshaft lobes or bearing journals shown as pitting of the working surface.

Specific gravity (SG) The state of charge of the electrolyte in a lead-acid battery. A measure of the electrolyte's density compared with water.

Straight-cut gears Common type gear used on gearbox shafts and for oil pump and water pump drives.

Stanchion The inner sliding part of the front forks, held by the yokes. Often called a fork tube.

Stoichiometric ratio The optimum chemical air/fuel ratio for a petrol engine, said to be 14.7 parts of air to 1 part of fuel.

Sulphuric acid The liquid (electrolyte) used in a lead-acid battery. Poisonous and extremely corrosive.

Surface grinding (lapping) Process to correct a warped gasket face, commonly used on cylinder heads.

T

Tapered-roller bearing Tapered inner race of caged needle rollers and separate tapered outer race. Examples of taper roller bearings can be found on steering heads.

Tappet A cylindrical component which transmits motion from the cam to the valve stem, either directly or via a pushrod and rocker arm. Also called a cam follower.

TCS Traction Control System. An electronically-controlled system which senses wheel spin and reduces engine speed accordingly.

TDC Top Dead Centre denotes that the piston is at its highest point in the cylinder.

Thread-locking compound Solution applied to fastener threads to prevent slackening. Select type to suit application.

Thrust washer A washer positioned between two moving components on a shaft. For example, between gear pinions on gearshaft.

Timing chain See **Cam Chain.**

Timing light Stroboscopic lamp for carrying out ignition timing checks with the engine running.

Top-end A description of an engine's cylinder block, head and valve gear components.

Torque Turning or twisting force about a shaft.

Torque setting A prescribed tightness specified by the motorcycle manufacturer to ensure that the bolt or nut is secured correctly. Undertightening can result in the bolt or nut coming loose or a surface not being sealed. Overtightening can result in stripped threads, distortion or damage to the component being retained.

Torx key A six-point wrench.

Tracer A stripe of a second colour applied to a wire insulator to distinguish that wire from another one with the same colour insulator. For example, Br/W is often used to denote a brown insulator with a white tracer.

Trail A feature of steering geometry. Distance from the steering head axis to the tyre's central contact point.

Triple clamps The cast components which extend from the steering head and support the fork stanchions or tubes. Often called fork yokes.

Turbocharger A centrifugal device, driven by exhaust gases, that pressurises the intake air. Normally used to increase the power output from a given engine displacement.

TWI Abbreviation for Tyre Wear Indicator. Indicates the location of the tread depth indicator bars on tyres.

U

Universal joint or U-joint (UJ) A double-pivoted connection for transmitting power from a driving to a driven shaft through an angle. Typically found in shaft drive assemblies.

Unsprung weight Anything not supported by the bike's suspension (ie the wheel, tyres, brakes, final drive and bottom (moving) part of the suspension).

V

Vacuum gauges Clock-type gauges for measuring intake tract vacuum. Used for carburettor synchronisation on multi-cylinder engines.

Valve A device through which the flow of liquid, gas or vacuum may be stopped, started or regulated by a moveable part that opens, shuts or partially obstructs one or more ports or passageways. The intake and exhaust valves in the cylinder head are of the poppet type.

Valve clearance The clearance between the valve tip (the end of the valve stem) and the rocker arm or tappet/follower. The valve clearance is measured when the valve is closed. The correct clearance is important - if too small the valve won't close fully and will burn out, whereas if too large noisy operation will result.

Valve lift The amount a valve is lifted off its seat by the camshaft lobe.

Valve timing The exact setting for the opening and closing of the valves in relation to piston position.

Vernier caliper A precision measuring instrument that measures inside and outside dimensions. Not quite as accurate as a micrometer, but more convenient.

VIN Vehicle Identification Number. Term for the bike's engine and frame numbers.

Viscosity The thickness of a liquid or its resistance to flow.

Volt A unit for expressing electrical "pressure" in a circuit. Volts = current x ohms.

W

Water pump A mechanically-driven device for moving coolant around the engine.

Watt A unit for expressing electrical power. Watts = volts x current.

Wear limit see **Service limit**

Wet liner A liquid-cooled engine design where the pistons run in liners which are directly surrounded by coolant **(see illustration).**

Wet liner arrangement

Wheelbase Distance from the centre of the front wheel to the centre of the rear wheel.

Wiring harness or loom Describes the electrical wires running the length of the motorcycle and enclosed in tape or plastic sheathing. Wiring coming off the main harness is usually referred to as a sub harness.

Woodruff key A key of semi-circular or square section used to locate a gear to a shaft. Often used to locate the alternator rotor on the crankshaft.

Wrist pin Another name for gudgeon or piston pin.

Note: *References throughout this index are in the form - "Chapter number" • "Page number"*

Haynes Motorcycle Manuals – The Complete List

Title	Book No
APRILIA RS50 (99 - 06) & RS125 (93 - 06)	4298
Aprilia RSV1000 Mille (98 - 03)	♦ 4255
BMW 2-valve Twins (70 - 96)	♦ 0249
BMW K100 & 75 2-valve Models (83 - 96)	♦ 1373
BMW R850, 1100 & 1150 4-valve Twins (93 - 04)	♦ 3466
BMW R1200 (04 - 06)	♦ 4598
BSA Bantam (48 - 71)	0117
BSA Unit Singles (58 - 72)	0127
BSA Pre-unit Singles (54 - 61)	0326
BSA A7 & A10 Twins (47 - 62)	0121
BSA A50 & A65 Twins (62 - 73)	0155
BSA Rocket 3 (see Triumph Trident)	0136
DUCATI 600, 620, 750 and 900 2-valve V-Twins (91 - 05) ♦	3290
Ducati MK III & Desmo Singles (69 - 76)	◊ 0445
Ducati 748, 916 & 996 4-valve V-Twins (94 - 01)	♦ 3756
GILERA Runner, DNA, Ice & SKP/Stalker (97 - 04)	4163
HARLEY-DAVIDSON Sportsters (70 - 03)	♦ 2534
Harley-Davidson Shovelhead and Evolution Big Twins (70 - 99)	2536
Harley-Davidson Twin Cam 88 (99 - 03)	♦ 2478
HONDA NB, ND, NP & NS50 Melody (81 - 85)	◊ 0622
Honda NE/NB50 Vision & SA50 Vision Met-in (85 - 95)	◊ 1278
Honda MB, MBX, MT & MTX50 (80 - 93)	0731
Honda C50, C70 & C90 (67 - 03)	0324
Honda XR80/100R & CRF80/100F (85 - 04)	2218
Honda XL/XR 80, 100, 125, 185 & 200 2-valve Models (78 - 87)	0566
Honda H100 & H100S Singles (80 - 92)	◊ 0734
Honda CB/CD125T & CM125C Twins (77 - 88)	◊ 0571
Honda CBR125R (04 - 07)	4620
Honda CG125 (76 - 05)	◊ 0433
Honda NS125 (86 - 93)	◊ 3056
Honda MBX/MTX125 & MTX200 (83 - 93)	◊ 1132
Honda CD/CM185 200T & CM250C 2-valve Twins (77 - 85)	0572
Honda XL/XR 250 & 500 (78 - 84)	0567
Honda XR250L, XR250R & XR400R (86 - 03)	2219
Honda CB250 & CB400N Super Dreams (78 - 84)	◊ 0540
Honda CR Motocross Bikes (86 - 01)	2222
Honda CRF250 & CRF450 (02 - 06)	2630
Honda CBR400RR Fours (88 - 99)	◊ ♦ 3552
Honda VFR400 (NC30) & RVF400 (NC35) V-Fours (89 - 98)	◊ ♦ 3496
Honda CB500 (93 - 01)	◊ ♦ 3753
Honda CB400 & CB550 Fours (73 - 77)	0262
Honda CX/GL500 & 650 V-Twins (78 - 86)	0442
Honda CBX550 Four (82 - 86)	◊ 0940
Honda XL600R & XR600R (83 - 00)	2183
Honda XL600/650V Transalp & XRV750 Africa Twin (87 - 02)	♦ 3919
Honda CBR600F1 (87 - 90) & 1000F Fours (87 - 96)	♦ 1730
Honda CBR600F2 & F3 Fours (91 - 98)	♦ 2070
Honda CBR600F4 (99 - 06)	♦ 3911
Honda CB600F Hornet & CBF600 (98 - 06)	◊ ♦ 3915
Honda CBR600RR (03 - 06)	♦ 4590
Honda CB650 sohc Fours (78 - 84)	0665
Honda NTV600 Revere, NTV650 and NT650V Deauville (88 - 05)	◊ ♦ 3243
Honda Shadow VT600 & 750 (USA) (88 - 03)	2312
Honda CB750 sohc Four (69 - 79)	0131
Honda V45/65 Sabre & Magna (82 - 88)	0820
Honda VFR750 & 700 V-Fours (86 - 97)	♦ 2101
Honda VFR800 V-Fours (97 - 01)	♦ 3703
Honda VFR800 V-Tec V-Fours (02 - 05)	♦ 4196
Honda CB750 & CB900 dohc Fours (78 - 84)	0535
Honda VTR1000 (FireStorm, Super Hawk) & XL1000V (Varadero) (97 - 00)	♦ 3744
Honda CBR900RR FireBlade (92 - 99)	♦ 2161
Honda CBR900RR FireBlade (00 - 03)	♦ 4060
Honda CBR1000RR Fireblade (04 - 06)	♦ 4604
Honda CBR1100XX Super Blackbird (97 - 02)	♦ 3901
Honda ST1100 Pan European V-Fours (90 - 02)	♦ 3384

Title	Book No
Honda Shadow VT1100 (USA) (85 - 98)	2313
Honda GL1000 Gold Wing (75 - 79)	0309
Honda GL1100 Gold Wing (79 - 81)	0669
Honda Gold Wing 1200 (USA) (84 - 87)	2199
Honda Gold Wing 1500 (USA) (88 - 00)	2225
KAWASAKI AE/AR 50 & 80 (81 - 95)	1007
Kawasaki KC, KE & KH100 (75 - 99)	1371
Kawasaki KMX125 & 200 (86 - 02)	◊ 3046
Kawasaki 250, 350 & 400 Triples (72 - 79)	0134
Kawasaki 400 & 440 Twins (74 - 81)	0281
Kawasaki 400, 500 & 550 Fours (79 - 91)	0910
Kawasaki EN450 & 500 Twins (Ltd/Vulcan) (85 - 04)	2053
Kawasaki EX500 (GPZ500S) & ER500 (ER-5) (87 - 05)	♦ 2052
Kawasaki ZX600 (ZZ-R600 & Ninja ZX-6) (90 - 06)	♦ 2146
Kawasaki ZX-6R Ninja Fours (95 - 02)	♦ 3541
Kawasaki ZX600 (GPZ600R, GPX600R, Ninja 600R & RX) & ZX750 (GPX750R, Ninja 750R)	♦ 1780
Kawasaki 650 Four (76 - 78)	0373
Kawasaki Vulcan 700/750 & 800 (85 - 04)	♦ 2457
Kawasaki 750 Air-cooled Fours (80 - 91)	0574
Kawasaki ZR550 & 750 Zephyr Fours (90 - 97)	♦ 3382
Kawasaki ZX750 (Ninja ZX-7 & ZXR750) Fours (89 - 96)	♦ 2054
Kawasaki Ninja ZX-7R & ZX-9R (94 - 04)	♦ 3721
Kawasaki 900 & 1000 Fours (73 - 77)	0222
Kawasaki ZX900, 1000 & 1100 Liquid-cooled Fours (83 - 97) ♦	1681
MOTO GUZZI 750, 850 & 1000 V-Twins (74 - 78)	0339
MZ ETZ Models (81 - 95)	◊ 1680
NORTON 500, 600, 650 & 750 Twins (57 - 70)	0187
Norton Commando (68 - 77)	0125
PEUGEOT Speedfight, Trekker & Vivacity Scooters (96 - 05) ◊	3920
PIAGGIO (Vespa) Scooters (91 - 06)	◊ 3492
SUZUKI GT, ZR & TS50 (77 - 90)	◊ 0799
Suzuki TS50X (84 - 00)	◊ 1599
Suzuki 100, 125, 185 & 250 Air-cooled Trail bikes (79 - 89)	0797
Suzuki GP100 & 125 Singles (78 - 93)	◊ 0576
Suzuki GS, GN, GZ & DR125 Singles (82 - 05)	◊ 0888
Suzuki 250 & 350 Twins (68 - 78)	0120
Suzuki GT250X7, GT200X5 & SB200 Twins (78 - 83)	◊ 0469
Suzuki GS/GSX250, 400 & 450 Twins (79 - 85)	0736
Suzuki GS500 Twin (89 - 06)	♦ 3238
Suzuki GS550 (77 - 82) & GS750 Fours (76 - 79)	0363
Suzuki GS/GSX550 4-valve Fours (83 - 88)	1133
Suzuki SV650 & SV650S (99 - 05)	♦ 3912
Suzuki GSX-R600 & 750 (96 - 00)	♦ 3553
Suzuki GSX-R600 (01 - 03), GSX-R750 (00 - 03) & GSX-R1000 (01 - 02)	♦ 3986
Suzuki GSX-R600/750 (04-05) & GSX-R1000 (03-06)	♦ 4382
Suzuki GSF600, 650 & 1200 Bandit Fours (95 - 06)	♦ 3367
Suzuki Intruder, Marauder, Volusia & Boulevard (85 - 06)	♦ 2618
Suzuki GS850 Fours (78 - 88)	0536
Suzuki GS1000 Four (77 - 78)	0484
Suzuki GSX-R750, GSX-R1100 (85 - 92), GSX600F, GSX750F, GSX1100F (Katana) Fours	♦ 2055
Suzuki GSX600/750F & GSX750 (98 - 02)	♦ 3987
Suzuki GS/GSX1000, 1100 & 1150 4-valve Fours (79 - 88)	0737
Suzuki TL1000S/R & DL1000 V-Strom (97 - 04)	♦ 4083
Suzuki GSX1300R Hayabusa (99 - 04)	♦ 4184
TRIUMPH Tiger Cub & Terrier (52 - 68)	0414
Triumph 350 & 500 Unit Twins (58 - 73)	0137
Triumph Pre-Unit Twins (47 - 62)	0251
Triumph 650 & 750 2-valve Unit Twins (63 - 83)	0122
Triumph Trident & BSA Rocket 3 (69 - 75)	0136
Triumph Bonneville (01 - 05)	♦ 4364
Triumph Daytona, Speed Triple, Sprint & Tiger (97 - 05)	♦ 3755
Triumph Triples and Fours (carburettor engines) (99-04)	♦ 2162
VESPA ET2 & ET4 (see Piaggio Scooters)	3492
Vespa P/PX125, 150 & 200 Scooters (78 - 06)	0707
Vespa Scooters (59 - 78)	0126

Title	Book No
YAMAHA DT50 & 80 Trail Bikes (78 - 95)	◊ 0800
Yamaha T50 & 80 Townmate (83 - 95)	◊ 1247
Yamaha YB100 Singles (73 - 91)	◊ 0474
Yamaha RS/RXS100 & 125 Singles (74 - 95)	0331
Yamaha RD & DT125LC (82 - 87)	◊ 0887
Yamaha TZR125 (87 - 93) & DT125R (88 - 02)	◊ 1655
Yamaha TY50, 80, 125 & 175 (74 - 84)	◊ 0464
Yamaha XT & SR125 (82 - 02)	◊ 1021
Yamaha Trail Bikes (81 - 00)	2350
Yamaha 250 & 350 Twins (70 - 79)	0040
Yamaha XS250, 360 & 400 sohc Twins (75 - 84)	0378
Yamaha RD250 & 350LC Twins (80 - 82)	0803
Yamaha RD350 YPVS Twins (83 - 95)	1158
Yamaha RD400 Twin (75 - 79)	0333
Yamaha XT, TT & SR500 Singles (75 - 83)	0342
Yamaha XZ550 Vision V-Twins (82 - 85)	0821
Yamaha FJ, FZ, XJ & YX600 Radian (84 - 92)	2100
Yamaha XJ600S (Diversion, Seca II) & XJ600N Fours (92 - 03)	♦ 2145
Yamaha YZF600R Thundercat & FZS600 Fazer (96 - 03)	♦ 3702
Yamaha YZF-R6 (99 - 02)	♦ 3900
Yamaha YZF-R6 (03 - 05)	♦ 4601
Yamaha 650 Twins (70 - 83)	0341
Yamaha XJ650 & 750 Fours (80 - 84)	0738
Yamaha XS750 & 850 Triples (76 - 85)	0340
Yamaha TDM850, TRX850 & XTZ750 (89 - 99)	◊ ♦ 3540
Yamaha YZF750R & YZF1000R Thunderace (93 - 00)	♦ 3720
Yamaha FZR600, 750 & 1000 Fours (87 - 96)	♦ 2056
Yamaha XV (Virago) V-Twins (81 - 03)	♦ 0802
Yamaha XVS650 & 1100 Drag Star/V-Star (97 - 05)	♦ 4195
Yamaha XJ900F Fours (83 - 94)	♦ 3239
Yamaha XJ900S Diversion (94 - 01)	♦ 3739
Yamaha YZF-R1 (98 - 03)	♦ 3754
Yamaha YZF-R1 (04 - 06)	♦ 4605
Yamaha FZS1000 Fazer (01 - 05)	♦ 4287
Yamaha FJ1100 & 1200 Fours (84 - 96)	♦ 2057
Yamaha XJR1200 & 1300 (95 - 03)	♦ 3981
Yamaha V-Max (85 - 03)	♦ 4072

ATVs

Title	Book No
Honda ATC70, 90, 110, 185 & 200 (71 - 85)	0565
Honda Rancher, Recon & TRX250EX ATVs	2553
Honda TRX300 Shaft Drive ATVs (88 - 00)	2125
Honda TRX300EX, TRX400EX & TRX450R/ER ATVs (93 - 06)	2318
Honda Foreman 400 and 450 ATVs (95 - 02)	2465
Kawasaki Bayou 220/250/300 & Prairie 300 ATVs (86 - 03)	2351
Polaris ATVs (85 - 97)	2302
Polaris ATVs (98 - 06)	2508
Yamaha YFS200 Blaster ATV (88 - 02)	2317
Yamaha YFB250 Timberwolf ATVs (92 - 00)	2217
Yamaha YFM350 & YFM400 (ER and Big Bear) ATVs (87 - 03)	2126
Yamaha Banshee and Warrior ATVs (87 - 03)	2314
Yamaha Kodiak and Grizzly ATVs (93 - 05)	2567

TECHBOOK SERIES

Title	Book No
ATV Basics	10450
Twist and Go (automatic transmission) Scooters Service and Repair Manual	4082
Motorcycle Basics TechBook (2nd Edition)	3515
Motorcycle Electrical TechBook (3rd Edition)	3471
Motorcycle Fuel Systems TechBook	3514
Motorcycle Maintenance TechBook	4071
Motorcycle Modifying	4272
Motorcycle Workshop Practice TechBook (2nd Edition)	3470

◊ = not available in the USA   ♦ = Superbike

The manuals on this page are available through good motorcycle dealers and accessory shops.
In case of difficulty, contact: **Haynes Publishing**
(UK) +44 1963 442030   (USA) +1 805 498 6703
(SV) +46 18 124016
(Australia/New Zealand) +61 3 9763 8100

MCL22.4/07

Preserving Our Motoring Heritage

< The Model J Duesenberg Derham Tourster. Only eight of these magnificent cars were ever built – this is the only example to be found outside the United States of America

Almost every car you've ever loved, loathed or desired is gathered under one roof at the Haynes Motor Museum. Over 300 immaculately presented cars and motorbikes represent every aspect of our motoring heritage, from elegant reminders of bygone days, such as the superb Model J Duesenberg to curiosities like the bug-eyed BMW Isetta. There are also many old friends and flames. Perhaps you remember the 1959 Ford Popular that you did your courting in? The magnificent 'Red Collection' is a spectacle of classic sports cars including AC, Alfa Romeo, Austin Healey, Ferrari, Lamborghini, Maserati, MG, Riley, Porsche and Triumph.

A Perfect Day Out

Each and every vehicle at the Haynes Motor Museum has played its part in the history and culture of Motoring. Today, they make a wonderful spectacle and a great day out for all the family. Bring the kids, bring Mum and Dad, but above all bring your camera to capture those golden memories for ever. You will also find an impressive array of motoring memorabilia, a comfortable 70 seat video cinema and one of the most extensive transport book shops in Britain. The Pit Stop Cafe serves everything from a cup of tea to wholesome, home-made meals or, if you prefer, you can enjoy the large picnic area nestled in the beautiful rural surroundings of Somerset.

> John Haynes O.B.E., Founder and Chairman of the museum at the wheel of a Haynes Light 12.

< The 1936 490cc sohc-engined International Norton – well known for its racing success

The Museum is situated on the A359 Yeovil to Frome road at Sparkford, just off the A303 in Somerset. It is about 40 miles south of Bristol, and 25 minutes drive from the M5 intersection at Taunton.
Open 9.30am - 5.30pm (10.00am - 4.00pm Winter) 7 days a week, *except Christmas Day, Boxing Day and New Years Day*
Special rates available for schools, coach parties and outings Charitable Trust No. 292048